Q

f

to Customer Satisfaction

Bo Bergman

Professor in Quality Technology
Linköping University, Sweden

Bengt Klefsjö

Professor in Quality Technology
Luleå University, Sweden

McGRAW-HILL BOOK COMPANY

London · New York · St Louis · San Francisco · Auckland
Bogotá · Caracas · Lisbon · Madrid · Mexico · Milan
Montreal · New Delhi · Panama · Paris · San Juan
São Paulo · Singapore · Sydney · Tokoyo · Toronto

British Library Cataloguing-in-Publication Data
A catalogue record for this book is available from the British Library

Library of Congress Cataloging-in-Publication Data
Bergman, Bo.
  [Quality. English]
  Quality: from customer needs to customer satisfaction / Bo Bergman,
  Bengt Klefsjö.
  p.   cm.
  Includes bibliographical references and index.
  ISBN 0-07-709016-0
  1. Customer service – Quality control.   2. Consumer satisfaction.
I. Klefsjö, Bengt. II. Title.
HF5415.5.B45713 1994
658.8'12--dc20   94-7346
                                                         CIP

All rights reserved. No part of this publication may be reproduced or transmitted
in any form or by any means, electronic or mechanical, including photocopying,
recording, or any information storage and retrieval system, without permission in
writing from the publisher.

© Bo Bergman, Bengt Klefsjö and Studentlitteratur, Lund, Sweden 1994

Published in Sweden, Finland, Norway, Denmark & Iceland by
Studentlitteratur Lund, Sweden.

Published elsewhere by
McGRAW-HILL Book Company Europe
Shoppenhangers Road, Maidenhead, Berkshire, SL6 2QL, England
Telephone 0628 23432
Fax 0628 770224

ISBN 0-07-709016-0

Printed in Sweden
Studentlitteratur, Lund
Third printing

Contents

Part I Quality for Survival

Part II Design for Quality

Part IV Quality for Customer Satisfaction

Part V Leadership for Quality

Appendix

Contents

Foreword

Quality has become a more and more important means of competition. A strategy based on management commitment for continuous improvement has therefore to be used more generally and systematically by any organization if it is to keep its position on the market. In addition to a strong commitment from upper management the customers must be placed in focus, decisions must be based on facts and everybody in the organisation must be involved in a continuous effort for process improvements. These are briefly the elements of what nowadays is called Total Quality Management (TQM).

The book is aimed at teaching TQM in Industry, Universities, Business Schools and Engineering Schools. The purpose is to show how the quality improvement process can be used during all steps of a product life cycle, i.e. from customer needs to customer satisfaction, as well as in support processes of the organisation. It is hoped that the book will also be of use for the COMETT programme and the new European Masters Programme in TQM.

Our aim is to describe philosophies as well as methods and techniques, the history as well as the future, the planning and development phase as well as the manufacturing phase and quality for goods as well as for services. Also quality in supply processes of the organisation and in leadership is treated. This means that much of the material is discussed rather briefly. Therefore we have made a serious effort to include a lot of references for further studies. The book is to a large extent based on a translation of a Swedish edition, which has been used extensively both at university level and in industry.

We have had a lot of help and comments from many colleagues and friends both at universities and in industry when writing both the Swedish edition and this English version.

We are very grateful to Roland Andersson, a graduate from the Division of Quality Technology in Linköping, for his kind permission to use a part of his Licenciate Thesis as inspiration for Chapter 19, the Seven Management Tools and Professor Yoshio Kondo, Kyoto University, for his valuable comments on Chapter 16. We also want to thank many of our colleagues at the Division of Quality Technology in Linköping and the Division of Quality Technology & Statistics in Luleå for reading and commenting on the English version.

Of those working in industry we particularly want to thank Johnny Lindström, the Swedish Institute for Quality, Torsten Olsson, IBM, Göthe Wallin, ABB and Sture Ögren, Ericsson AB, for their help.

We are also very grateful to Gunnar Nyström and Stefan Lundgren who helped us with the translation of the Swedish version and to Alan McLean who has helped us with a lot of linguistic improvements. Many thanks also to Jan Ahnelöf, who has helped us by drawing most of the figures. Bonnie Ohlsson and Ronnie Andersson at Studentlitteratur, Lund, Sweden, and Fiona Sperry and her colleagues at McGraw-Hill, England, have also provided valuable support during the production of the book.

Linköping and Luleå, December 1993

Part I

Quality for Survival

The quality of a product is "its ability to satisfy the needs and expectations of the customers". In this first part of the book we discuss the quality concept, quality strategies and the close relations between the questions of quality and productivity and survival of the company. We also make some historical reviews.

1 The Quality Concept

Quality has become an increasingly important means of competition on the world market. A strategy based on management commitment to continuous quality improvement has therefore to be applied more generally and systematically in any organization to enable it to keep its position on the market. Otherwise, large shares of the market will be lost to those competitors who are more aware of the importance of quality.

An important reason for the great successes of many Japanese companies is the strategic role quality has played for Japanese top managers. At an early stage they realized that a definition of the term quality had to emanate from the needs and expectations of the customers. They have long realized that the costs of poor quality related to design changes, scrappings, reworking and delays were substantial, as was the cost of keeping large buffer stocks. It has proven possible to reduce these costs dramatically by a systematical use of simple statistical methods in order to identify and eliminate sources of variation.

After the Second World War, when the Japanese were trying to get their industry going they had great difficulties with regard to quality. However, they were very susceptible to ideas from the West dealing with quality control and quality improvement. Two Americans, W. Edwards Deming and Joseph M. Juran have played an important role in quality development in Japan, a development which in many respects has brought Japan to a leading position on the world market.

1.1 Quality

The word "quality" is derived from the latin "qualitas" meaning "of what". Cicero and other ancient writers seem to have used the word in the sense of "nature". There are many definitions of the quality concept. A good, but not always complete, definition of the quality of a product, where by products we mean goods or services or a combination thereof, is the following:

> *The quality of a product (article or service) is its ability to satisfy the needs and expectations of the customers*

A similar, but less clear definition, can be found in the International Standard ISO 8402 Quality Vocabulary and also in the ISO 9000 series: "Quality is the totality of features and characteristics of a product or service that bear on its ability to satisfy stated or implied needs".

Figure 1.1   The Japanese signs for the concept of quality. The first sign is pronounced "hin" and roughly means "product". The second sign is pronounced "shitsu" and roughly means "quality". Originally this second sign illustrated two axes on top of a mussel and could be interpreted as "a promise of money or the value of money". Nowadays, the combination of the signs denotes the concept of "quality" and not only "product quality".

The above definition has similarities to the one which is credited to the American Joseph Juran: "fitness for use". Another, often too narrow and sometimes deceptive definition, is "conformance to requirements" (see for instance Crosby, 1979). A more progressive definition is presented in Figure 1.2.

Quality is what makes it possible for a customer to have a love affair with your product or service. Telling lies, decreasing the price or adding features can create a temporary infatuation. It takes quality to sustain a love affair.

Love is always fickle. Therefore, it is necessary to remain close to the person whose loyalty you wish to retain. You must be ever on the alert to understand what pleases the customer, for only customers define what constitutes quality. The wooing of the customer is never done.

Figure 1.2   A definition worth considering of the term quality was introduced by Myron Tribus in ASQC Statistics Division Newsletter, 1990, Number 3, page 2.

The definition in Figure 1.2 indicates that it is not always sufficient to fulfil the expectations of the customers as described in our basic definition. Sometimes the expectations even have to be exceeded. The customer should be delighted. Kano (1984) emphasizes this point and talks about *basic needs* and *exciting experiences.*

The Japanese engineer Genichi Taguchi (see Taguchi & Wu, 1979) defines quality, or rather non-quality, as "the losses of society caused by the product after its delivery". Even if Taguchi uses his definition for goods, the interpretation might just as well be used for quality of services. In practice, Taguchi interprets non-quality either as a deviation from the set target values of the product function or as a harmful side effect in connection with product usage.

One can look upon the term quality from many angles. In the following presentation we will discuss some different aspects, which might be of special interest.

The term *product quality* has many dimensions. For goods some of them are:

- *performance,* suited to the customers on the intended market segment

- *reliability,* which is a measure of how often trouble occurs and how serious these problems are

- *maintainability,* which summarizes how easy or hard it is to detect, localize and take care of the problem

- *safety.*

These and some further dimensions are illustrated in Figure 1.3.

Quality dimensions of an article

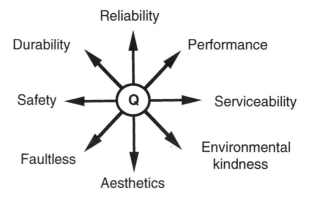

Figure 1.3 *Some quality dimensions of an article.*

Sometimes we also assign extravagance and aesthetic aspects to product quality. There can be motivation for this when laying out a competitive strategy with the aspect of quality in focus. Then we also have to take into consideration the fact that experienced quality is affected not only by the above mentioned dimensions, but also by such things as marketing and whatever "prejudices" the customer might have. In the future, different types of environmental aspects will also become important quality dimensions. A discussion of quality dimensions is given in Garvin (1988).

The quality of a service also has many dimensions. Some are:

- *tangibles,* which is the physical environment in which the service is presented

- *reliability,* which is the consistency of performance and dependability

- *responsiveness,* which is the willingness to help the customer

- *courtesy,* which refers to the supplier's behaviour, e.g. politeness and kindness

- *communication,* which is the ability of talking in a way which is understandable to the customer.

In summary, many of these dimensions are related to the customers' confidence in those providing the service. See also Figure 1.4. A discussion of service quality is given in Chapter 15.

It should be noted that a generic list of quality dimensions can only give a first set of ideas needed for product planning. Each product, article or service, has to meet its own special set of customer requirements. As we shall see later, these wishes and needs have to be thoroughly investigated and they should have a major impact on the planning of the work to be performed.

Quality dimensions of a service

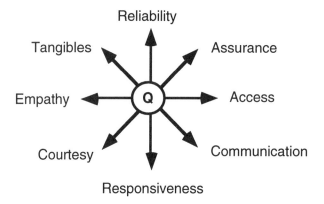

Figure 1.4   Some quality dimensions of a service.

So far we have mainly discussed *external customers* and their quality concept, but within the company every employee has *internal customers,* with their needs, expectations and requirements which are necessary for them to do a good job, satisfying their customers. Too often internal customers are forgotten, which in the end creates unsatisfied external customers.

Sometimes separate quality concepts are referred to, indicating when in the product life cycle the main activities affecting quality take place. Such concepts are for example (see Gummesson, 1988):

- design quality
- production quality
- delivery quality
- relational quality.

Design quality indicates that the product or service is designed or planned to satisfy the demands of the customer. Quality affects the external customer's experience of quality when it comes down to usage, reliability in operation and user friendliness. Good design quality is in other words necessary, but not sufficient, to make a good product.

Production quality indicates that the product or service fulfills the specifications that were set during design or planning. Production quality has by tradition been paid the most attention.

Delivery quality means that the agreed product is delivered at the agreed time. *Delivery safety* is another term with the same meaning.

Relational quality is affected by everybody who has contact with the customer, both internal and external. It is a sort of service quality which is to a large extent dependent on how contacts are handled by, for instance, marketing people and service staff. It is of course of great importance how the internal customer is treated by management and personnel officers. This quality concept is becoming increasingly important. See also Figure 16.3.

The division of the quality concept just described should however be used very carefully. In many cases the design process is very important for the manufacturing process in order to obtain high quality.

In big international groups like Philips, Motorola, Xerox, IBM, ABB, Electrolux and Ericsson, the group executive boards frequently talk about quality and the importance of top management commitment to quality. Such involvement is the basis of what today is called *Total Quality Management, TQM*. This means that "you continuously endeavour to fulfil or exceed the demands and expectations of the customers at lower and lower costs in all processes which continuously are being improved and to which everybody is committed. Here external as well as internal customers are to be considered."

1.2 Elements of a TQM Strategy

A quality strategy in a company must be built on continuous and consistent commitment from top management regarding questions of quality. Top management has to include quality aspects in the company vision, and support activities regarding quality financially, morally and with management resources. Top management must also actively take part in the improvement process. If the management do not show by their actions that quality is as important as, say, direct costs and delivery times the rest of the staff in the company will not make such a valuation.

One example of the importance of top management commitment with respect to quality is described in Karatsu (1988). Nowadays General Motors and Toyota co-operate at a factory in Freemont, California. Before this co-operation existed, GM had serious problems with its activities. The new management that were appointed after the co-operation agreement concentrated their work on training for quality improvements for all their employees. Today productivity and product quality at the factory in Freemont are as good as those at the factories belonging to Toyota in Japan. Earlier the workers were blamed for the bad quality of American cars. In reality, a lack of commitment and inadequate knowledge within top management were the reasons for their problems.

A quality strategy must be based on top management commitment in order to be successful. With this commitment as a basis the strategy should include the following important elements:

- focus on customers
- base decisions on facts
- focus on processes
- improve continuously
- let everybody be committed.

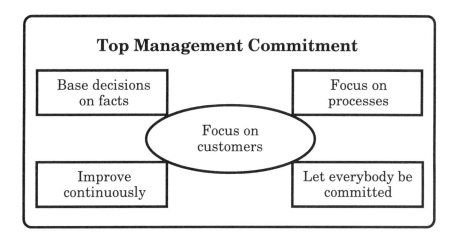

Figure 1.5 Important elements in a successful quality strategy.

1.2.1 Focus on Customers

In today's view of quality we have to focus on the customers. Quality has to be valued by the customers, and it has to be put in relation to their needs and expectations.

This means that quality is a relative term, which to a large extent is set by the competition on the market. The quality of products, both goods and services, can be experienced as having deteriorated significantly if a competitive alternative with better properties turns up on the market. The crisis of the American car industry a few years ago is a good example of this. In addition, the connection between the needs of the customer and the function and the price of the product means a lot for the valuation of the product quality.

To focus on the customers implies finding out what the customers want and need. This must be done by conducting market research and then trying to fulfil the market expectations while systematically developing and manufacturing the product.

To focus on the customers does not mean that the customers are always right. However, we have to understand the customers and understand why they have the stated opinions and expectations. We are the experts on our products. If we can see through our customers' stated opinions and understand the background we have the opportunity of supplying our customers with products that fill them with surprise and delight.

Focusing on the customers does not only apply to the *external customers,* the buyers and final users. Every employee has customers within the company, *internal customers.* Their needs, in order to do a good job, also have to be satisfied. In order to be able to satisfy the external customers (high *external quality*) we also have to satisfy our internal customers (high *internal quality*). Low internal quality means disturbances in the form of redesigns, re-processing, scrapping and delays with losses of productivity and high costs as a consequence. Trying to reach high external quality with low internal quality is bound to be unsuccessful in the long run.

Customers

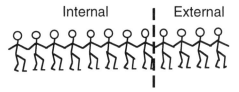

Figure 1.6   *We have to satisfy both the internal customers within the company and the external customers outside the company.*

1.2.2   Base Decisions on Facts

An important element in modern quality philosophy is to make decisions based on facts which are well-founded, and not to allow random factors be of decisive importance. International surveys show that between 20 % and 95% of all product development projects commenced are failures from a business point of view. A possible explanation is that there has not been a thorough examination of what the customers actually want and how much they are prepared to pay for it. Decisions have not been based on facts about market elements. These facts could have been obtained through well performed market analyses.

Another cause of failure might be that the company had insufficient knowledge about the product before it was marketed, they had missed crucial facts. Designed experiments are often neglected in connection with product and process development. Such experiments can act as a basis for a process design which results in better quality at a lower price.

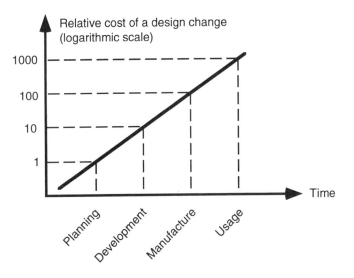

Figure 1.7   The costs for design changes increase rapidly as a function of time during the planning and production process.

It is becoming more and more important to create conditions for high quality during the development of products. Facts have to be considered early in the product life cycle and should not come as a surprise later on. One reason is illustrated in Figure 1.7. A change at an early stage of product development is much less expensive than changing a product which has already been produced or, even worse, a product which is already on the market. Figure 1.8 illustrates what the change process can look like in Japanese and American companies. There is hardly any reason to believe that other Western companies would be better than American ones in this respect.

Another strong factor in favour of early activities regarding quality is the fact that the life cycles of products are getting shorter and shorter. The shortness of life cycles is the reason why it is impossible to make successive improvements and in this way test the product on the market. The product has to be completely developed when introduced on the market in order to yield a profit right from the sales growth; see Figure 1.9.

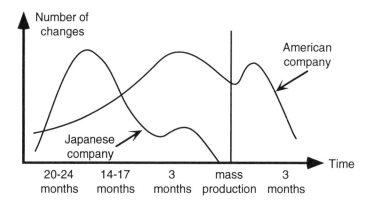

Figure 1.8   Illustration of the design change frequencies in a Japanese and an American company. (From Sullivan, 1986. © American Society for Quality Control. Reprinted with Permission)

It is also important to have a strategy for making decisions based on facts in connection with manufacturing. Earlier, a lot of facts have been collected and a lot of measurements have been made. It rarely occurs that the most important conclusions about the manufacturing process have been drawn from these data. Measurements have been made to evaluate single units and not to evaluate and improve the manufacturing process in which the units have been produced. Collected data have been stored in files, later on tapes or discs, without ever being used. Simple statistical methods have not been used to process and analyse the data. Such an analysis could have served as an excellent basis for variation reduction of the manufacturing process and thus for achieving improved quality.

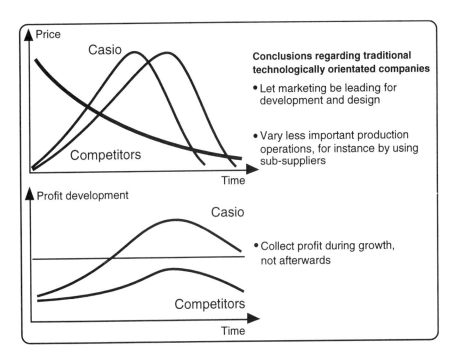

Figure 1.9   *Competition strategy at the Japanese company Casio, whose products include watches and calculators. Casio uses its flexibility to accelerate and shorten the product life cycles. By being in close contact with the market and by analysing the wants and needs of the customers it is possible for the company to transform these into technical solutions. By quickly reaching a production volume it is possible to take a large share of the market. When the competitors have achieved a large volume prices can be lowered, still at a profit. The competitors, however, are not able to cover their costs. (From Ohmae, 1985.)*

Data also have to be collected for support processes, i.e. processes which support the main processes of the company, for instance various administrative processes. This should be done in order to continuously improve these processes too, see Chapter 18.

1.2.3 Focus on Processes

Nearly every organized activity can be looked upon as a process, whose aim it is to deliver products which satisfy its customers. This process is supported by an organization consisting of people and their relations, resources and tools.

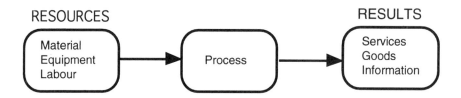

Figure 1.10 *A process transforms certain resources into results that should satisfy the customers of the process by using as small amounts of resources as possible.*

The process transforms certain input like, say, information and material into certain output in the form of various kinds of goods or services. The process links history with future. From the process, data are generated. These data, including measurements of the results, indicate how well the process satisfies the needs of the customers.

Using statistics from the histories of the processes it is possible to draw conclusions regarding their future results. Also, and more importantly, it is possible to obtain the information needed to improve the process. The process view means not looking upon every single piece of data, for instance a measurement result or a complaint from a customer, as something unique. Instead it should be looked upon as a part of the statistics which can give information about how well the process is working and how it can be improved. The process view is further discussed in Chapter 18.

1.2.4 Improve Continuously

The third element in a successful quality strategy is working towards *continuous quality improvements*. The external demands for quality are continuously being increased. Therefore, continuous quality improvement of goods and services produced by the company is necessary. Competitive advantages can thereby be achieved. Market shares will not be lost to companies which better live up to the quality demands of the market.

Even without any external pressure a continuous improvement of quality is well justified from a cost point of view. Measured costs due to defects and other non-quality contributions are large today. It is not unusual for them to amount to between 5% and 20% of the sales price. In most cases defects also cause other costs. If a high rate of disturbances has been accepted this has to be compensated for by many products in work and big buffer stocks. The corresponding capital costs are not usually registered as costs due to poor quality. Their contributions can however amount to a considerable part of the costs that have to be paid due to the fact that far too low a quality level has been accepted and in fact organised for.

In the Western world one often speaks about production growth curves, by which it is understood that the production costs per produced unit are reduced by, say, a factor of 0.80 when the production volume is doubled. In Japan they strive for the factor 2/3, see for instance Schonberger (1984).

Important tools in the continuous drive for better quality are simple statistical methods such as "the seven QC-tools"; see Figure 1.11. Here QC stands for Quality Control. These tools are discussed in more detail in Chapter 11.

The basic rule of quality improvements is:

> *It is always possible to improve quality
> and at the same time reduce costs*

This simple basic rule is surprisingly often applicable. In many cases very simple steps can bring about dramatic effects in terms of improved quality and reduced total costs.

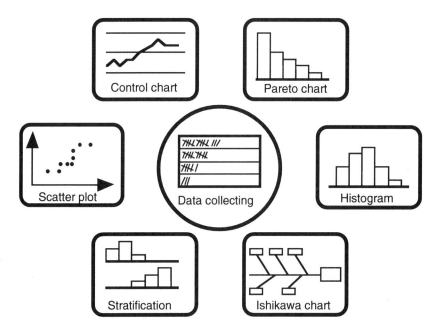

Figure 1.11   The seven QC-tools.

Some experts on quality have earlier talked about "optimal" quality. They believed that there would be an upper level of quality, indicating that work in order to improve the product above this level would not be profitable, see Figure 1.12. It has not been realized that there are an infinite number of possibilities to improve quality without increasing the costs by using knowledge gained.

Moreover, the term "percentage defective" is often unsuitable as a quality measure. Even if this percentage is zero that is not always good enough. There may still be room for a large potential of quality improvements by reducing the variation or by finding completely different solutions that better satisfy the wants and needs of the customers and at a lower cost. Systematic ways to fulfil the wishes and needs of the customers will be discussed further in Chapter 4. The problem of reducing variation will be dealt with further in Chapter 8.

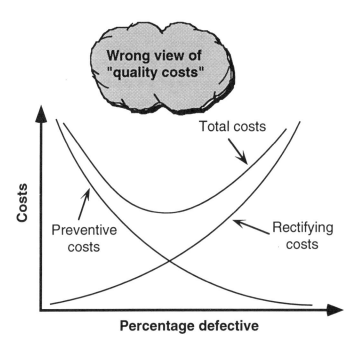

Figure 1.12   The old view regarding "quality costs".

Let us finally comment on the popular slogan "Do it right the first time". This slogan must be interpreted carefully. In order to delight our customers we have to change in order to improve. Therefore, we have to dare to make some mistakes in the improvement process. However, it is a deadly sin not to learn from these mistakes.

1.2.5 Let Everybody be Committed

In order to ensure that the quality strategy is successful everybody has to be committed to customer satisfaction and to continuous quality improvement. Both the internal customer, the next part in the process of product development and manufacturing or in other supporting processes, and the external customer, the final user, have to be satisfied. The fourth element in the quality strategy of a company is therefore to make everybody committed to the improvement process.

Jan Carlzon (1987), formerly President of Scandinavian Airlines Systems (SAS), tells a story about two stone-masons who make granite blocks square. When asked what they were doing one of them answered tiredly that he was making the granite blocks square, while the other one enthusiastically answered that he was building a cathedral. The employees must have the chance to feel commitment, professional pride and responsibility to be able to do a good job.

As a matter of fact this fourth element could also be interpreted as a consequence of the other elements rather than a condition. Those who have been given a chance to do a good job and to feel professional pride, and who are recognized when they have done a good job, will also be committed to their job. This leads to improved product quality.

Not only everybody within the company, but also all the suppliers of material, have to be involved in the quality work. An obvious trend today is that large companies drastically reduce the number of suppliers. These companies choose to tie down a small number of suppliers even if these do not offer the lowest prices. The aim of big companies is to increase the commitment, responsibility and quality awareness of the suppliers. The employee who is making a screw for a seat in a car probably does not feel that he is building a car. However, the supplier who is responsible for the whole seat probably does.

Once more we want to emphasize the fact that a basic condition for a company to succeed in its overall efforts to improve quality and to lower costs is that management show a strong commitment to questions regarding quality. Only then can a quality strategy focusing on the customers and built upon the four elements described above be successful. The quality strategy has to involve all the activities in the company, not only those which are directly involved in the manufacturing of the product.

1.3   Product Life Cycle

Quality improvements are necessary in all the stages of a product's life cycle, from idea to scrapping; see Figure 1.13. Product quality is affected in different ways at the different stages.

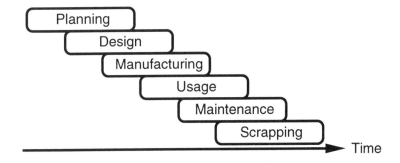

Figure 1.13   *Different stages in the life cycle of a product. During all these stages there must be active work on quality improvements.*

Planning a product means that we have to understand the needs and wants of the customers and the demands of the market. Market research and competitor analyses are important tools here. Customer needs and wants have then to be translated into product requirements. We will discuss this in Chapter 4.

33

Customer needs and wants and product requirements should be translated into product concepts and product specifications and drawings. This is done during the design stage, which may be divided into three phases:

- *system design,* which is the most creative phase when technical solutions for the product concept are produced

- *parameter design,* when design parameters are decided upon for the chosen technical solution

- *tolerance design,* when tolerances, based on costs due to variation, on process abilities and on measurements, are set.

Quality activities during the design stage are discussed further in Chapters 5-9.

Manufacturing quality is to a very great extent set by the design of the manufacturing processes. The same quality aspects that apply to product development should also apply to the development of manufacturing processes.

When starting manufacturing a substantial effort has usually to be made to improve quality and effectiveness in the manufacturing stage. Here Statistical Process Control (SPC) is an important tool to find sources of variation and to supervise the process so that new sources of variation are not introduced. SPC and other tools for controlling and improving manufacturing processes are discussed in Chapters 10-14. The ideas in these chapters are important not only for manufacturing processes but also in all other processes in the company.

Usage of a product, as well as scrapping, can sometimes cause environmental pollution. To many customers it has also become increasingly important that the manufacturing processes do not cause severe pollution and thus add to the already existing environmental problems of our society. The environmental problems are further emphasized when we realize that we should include future generations among our customers. Environmental aspects are very close to the quality issues and they will certainly, to a large extent, keep us busy in the future. It is important that the side-effects that may arise when a product is used and scrapped are examined along with the other quality issues during product planning, product development and development of manufacturing processes. Sometimes the Life Cycle Cost (LCC) concept is useful for summarizing all costs during the product life cycle, see Chapter 5.

Product quality is an important sales argument. It is important that marketing is based on facts so that the customer will not be disappointed due to false promises. Otherwise a reputation for bad quality may be gained, which can be very hard to repair. Also remember that it is much cheaper to retain a satisfied customer than to get a new one.

In order to achieve customer satisfaction and customer delight we have to consider quality aspects during all the periods of the product life cycle when planning a new product.

1.4 Notes and References

Quality has become a strategic weapon in the fight for market shares and improved profitability. After having discussed the term quality and its development and importance in this part of the book, we will in subsequent parts discuss methods and techniques that are being used for modern quality control.

Garvin (1988) gives further aspects of the terms quality, quality control and quality management. This book is based on the observations Garvin made when he examined the quality of air conditioning equipment. He found great differences between different manufacturers, regarding both internal and external quality. A comparison between Japanese and American producers gives a clear picture of the differences between Japanese and American quality.

Received material in American companies had a defective percentage of between 0.8% and 16% while the corresponding figure for Japanese companies was between 0% and 0.3%. When assembling, American companies showed between 8 and 165 defects per 100 produced units whereas the Japanese companies showed between 0.15 and 3 defects per 100 units. Furthermore, the American companies showed more than 20 times as many cases of warranty claims as the Japanese companies. Similar comparisons have been made within the car industry; see for example "The Machine That Changed the World" by Womack et al. (1990) and more generally in "Made in America" by Dertouzos et al. (1989).

Other books well worth reading about the term quality in general and the importance of management when concentrating successfully on quality are Deming (1986, 1993), Juran (1988, 1992) and Oakland (1991).

2 Quality and Prosperity

Improved quality affects the company's success in many ways. Some of these are:

- a better market position
- shorter lead times
- reduced costs due to waste and rework
- higher productivity.

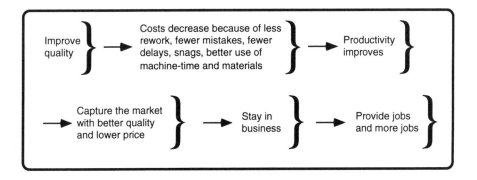

Figure 2.1 The importance of quality for the development of companies. (From Deming, 1986.)

The implications are illustrated in Figure 2.2 and are further commented on in this chapter. The many ways in which improved quality can result in improved profitability can lead to remarkable kinds of leverage. Improved profitability can be used to make the quality gap even wider in relation to competitors. This positive "quality spiral" is also illustrated in Figure 2.9.

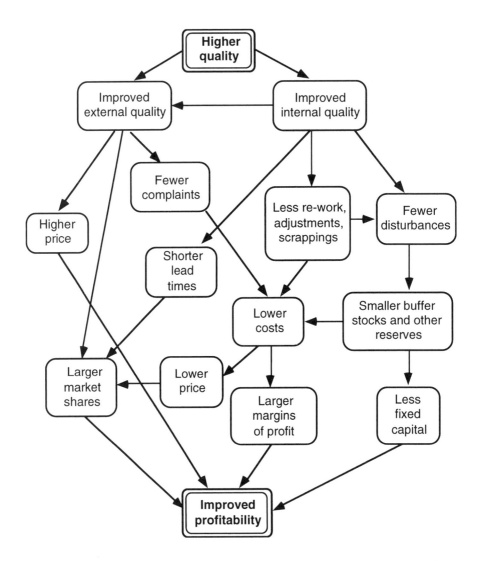

Figure 2.2   Relations between improved quality and increased profitability.

Top management views regarding the connection between quality and prosperity have been expressed through the foundation of EFQM (European Foundation for Quality Management). A McKinsey report, which was presented at the EFQM conference "Quality Management Forum" in 1989, showed that 90% of the top managers of leading companies in Europe look upon quality as a decisive factor as far as the success of the company is concerned. According to the report, 87% responded that research and training within the quality area are decisive when focusing on quality for the company.

2.1 Quality and the Market

On a competitive market, product quality is of great importance. On the markets for industrial products this is especially obvious. Feigenbaum (1987) refers to a survey which shows that customers, as far as both consumption goods and industrial products are concerned, state that quality is playing a more important part. In a survey carried out in 1979 only four customers out of ten valued quality as much as the price, while in 1987 eight customers out of ten valued quality at least as much as the price.

The PIMS (Profit Impact of Market Strategy) database was created during the 1970s when General Electric wanted to get hold of key factors regarding profitability as guidance when reconstructing the company. Different key factors were collected from a great number of business fields. Quality was one of these factors. In PIMS the term *relative quality* is used. Relative quality is defined as the market share of the competitors whose quality is lower, minus the market share of competitors whose quality is higher than that of the company studied. The database has gradually been expanded and after having been run by Harvard Business School it is now run by an independent company. The database supports the statement that customers are prepared to pay more for a product of higher quality than the costs of achieving this higher quality. See Figure 2.3.

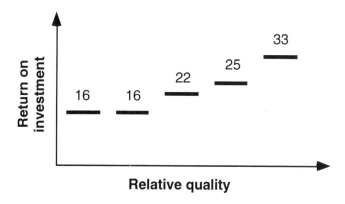

Figure 2.3   *Return on investment of business units with products of different relative quality. (From Buzzell & Gale, 1987.)*

2.2 Quality and Productivity

Every kind of adjustment, rework or scrapping leads to a reduction of productivity. Earlier, productivity and quality were looked upon as being in opposition to each other. It was believed that higher quality could only be achieved at the expense of productivity. This would be true if the quality improving activities were only of one type, say increased inspection. In a modern quality approach, however, such a way of working is avoided. Improvements have to be made in the production process and during product design. There are an infinite number of ways in which it is possible to improve quality. See also Figures 2.4, 2.5 and 2.6.

Focusing on quality often implies other positive effects of importance for productivity. Examples of these are decreased staff turnover and smaller numbers of staff on sick leave; see Figure 2.6.

In the long run it is perhaps not the profitability aspect which will be most important. When competition regarding quality gets tougher company survival comes into focus. High quality at a low price becomes a necessity to stay in business. As Deming states, "survi-

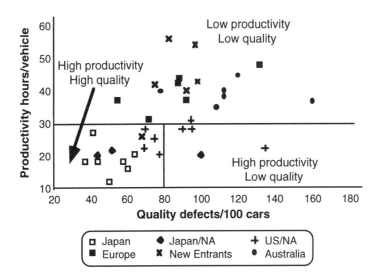

Figure 2.4   *An illustration from the car industry regarding the connection between high quality and high productivity. (From Krafcik & MacDuffie, 1989.)*

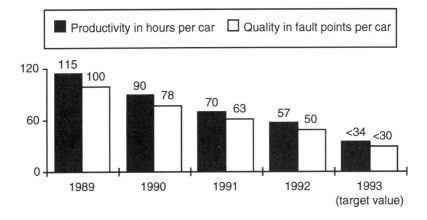

Figure 2.5   *That productivity is a consequence of quality is here illustrated by results obtained at Saab Automobile in Sweden. During the last few years quality has improved considerably on the cars in the Saab 9000 series and at the same time productivity has followed the same trend.*

41

val is not compulsory". When he paid a visit to Japan as early as the 1950s he impressed the issues of quality on the Japanese managers who took part in his seminars. Figure 2.1 was presented at those seminars. Today we should not only talk about having plenty of job opportunities but also about the fact that these should give meaningful, stimulating and responsible tasks. Joy-in-work is an important goal as well as an important means to achieve high quality.

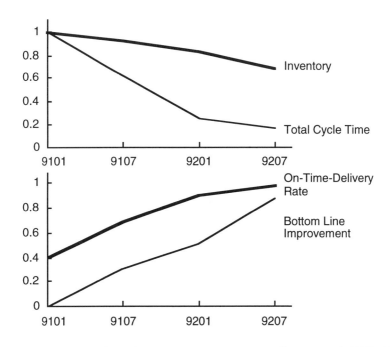

Figur 2.6   *Examples of improvements at one division of ABB (Asea Brown Boveri) in Sweden, as a result of the T50 quality improvement program, which is described in more detail in Section 20.6.*

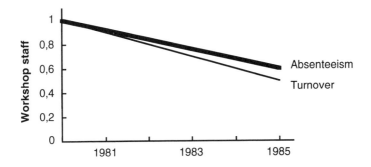

Figure 2.7 *Focusing on quality within the company results in a positive effect on staff turnover and absence due to illness. The figure illustrates the development at Alfa-Laval, Sweden, a company producing agricultural machines. Note that the results are from a business boom period.*

What is productivity?

Above all else, productivity is an attitude of mind

- It is the mentality of progress, of the constant improvement of that which exists.
- It is the certainty of being able to do better today than yesterday, and less well than tomorrow.
- It is the will to improve on the present situation, no matter how good it may seem, no matter how good it may really be.
- It is the constant adaptation of economic and social life to changing conditions.
- It is the continual efforts to apply new techniques and new methods.
- It is the faith in human progress.

Figure 2.8 *Japan Productivity Center has for more than 30 years used the above definition of productivity, a definition that looks very Japanese. In fact, the definition was formulated by the European Productivity Agency at a congress in Rome in 1958. The definition clearly indicates the close relation between productivity and quality. (After Helling, 1991.)*

2.3 Quality and Logistics

Poor internal quality necessitates large stores and reserves in order to avoid quality problems within one workshop area from resulting in serious consequences for other links of the production chain. By increasing internal quality it is possible to drastically decrease the need for intermediate stocks and other reserves. The ideal situation can be approached with JIT-production (JIT = Just In Time). High internal quality is a prerequisite for the Just-In-Time philosophy. A company which works hard with its logistics must therefore work hard with its internal quality and the quality of its suppliers too. Focusing on quality in a company opens up substantial opportunities for a far-reaching capital release.

On the other hand it is possible to use a reduction of buffer stocks and other reserves to bring quality problems into the light. When these are eliminated further storage reductions can be carried out. This will in turn lead to further quality improvements since new problems are forced to come up to the surface and can then be eliminated. Today, most problems are concealed, we are not aware of their existence but they cause large costs.

We also want to emphasize that in the development and design process, too, a considerable amount of resources are bound up owing to the fact that companies organize for coping with poor quality. An example of this is provided by the resources tied up in the design change process.

2.4 Quality Investments

As mentioned earlier, quality has been thought of as opposed to productivity. There has been a lot of talk about "quality costs". Efforts have been made to find the optimal balance between costs for poor quality and "preventive quality costs"; see Figure 1.12.

This is, however, a myopic point of view. Remember the basic rule regarding quality improvements. By not wasting knowledge and experience we can achieve a better result at a lower cost. Costs due to poor quality might however work well as indicators. The aim for quality work can be formulated in terms of these costs.

Furthermore, the word "quality cost" is very unsuitable. Quality does not cost, but non-quality does. Costs arise when defective units are manufactured or services are performed in such a way that rework in different forms is necessary or when process quality is so uncertain that special inspection has to be performed. Instead of "quality cost" the term "poor-quality costs" should be used.

The term "preventive quality costs" is also deceptive. The most essential work regarding quality has to be performed as an integrated part of the company processes. Therefore the corresponding costs cannot be identified in an organization which works with quality of goods and services in a proper way.

The connection between "lower price" and "improved profitability" through "larger market shares" in Figure 2.2 should also be commented on. Of course it is possible to achieve short-term improvements of profitability by offering a lower price and thus probably getting increased market shares. Generally this is not a long-term solution. Resources that are set free must in this case be invested in production capacity instead of in a quality advantage over the competitors.

The Japanese way has been to invest in the further development of new products and in further quality improvements by increased margins of profit. In this way a number one position is created. It must be very hard and costly for the competitors to compensate for this. See also Figure 2.9, which illustrates this positive quality spiral.

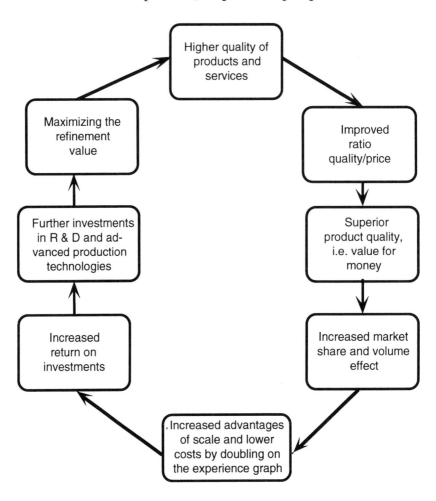

Figure 2.9   A *new interpretation of the quality spiral illustrating a long-term maximization of the refinement value instead of a short-term maximization of the profit. (Ahlmann, 1989.)*

2.5   The Win-Win Strategy

A leading theme in Total Quality Management which has not yet been made obvious is the insight that in most cases everyone can be made a winner. The importance of the win-win strategy is emphasized by Edwards Deming. Very often people try to play win-lose games in the business world. In the long run these will all turn out to be lose-lose games. Those cultures which can foster the win-win players will be the winners in the long run.

There is an obvious objection to the above discussion: "people are not trustworthy". However, the late Dr Kaoru Ishikawa was quite sure that we make people untrustwothy by not having faith in them. We create a self-fulfilling prophecy. If we base cooperation on trust it is possible to base businesses not on the conditions of minimax strategies but on strategies optimizing the total gain of both parties in a win-win strategy. Turning earlier vicious circles into good ones creates these possibilities, see Figure 2.10.

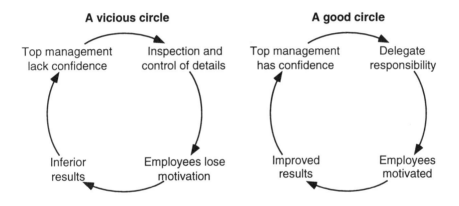

Figure 2.10   A vicious circle and a good one.

In Figure 2.11 a list of employee answers to the question "what is in it for me" has been compiled by Hans Fries, a now retired president of Unilever Company, Sweden.

- More time for real work
- We can do a better job
- We think we can work more effectively
- More satisfaction
    - easier to have an influence
    - results are visible
    - new challenges
    - greater responsibility
- Greater openness in the company
- Better understanding of the whole
- Invites own initiatives
- More cross-functional contacts
- Reduced number of errors and failures
- Takes away stress
- Less overtime
- Simpler routines
- Better sense for their own success and development
- Pride in work

Figure 2.11   Spontaneous comments from the employees to Hans Fries, former president of Unilever Company, Sweden, of the question "what is in it for me".

2.6   Notes and References

In his book "Managing Quality", Garvin (1988) discusses the connection between quality and profitability. The PIMS data base and conclusions regarding the connection between quality and profitability are discussed in Buzzel & Gale (1987).

The book "The Machine That Changed the World" is a description of "the International Motor Vehicle Program" (IMVP). In this program a thorough study of the development of the car industry is provided. The study was performed over five years at a cost of five million dollars at Massachusetts Institute of Technology, MIT. In this book, which is well worth reading, Henry Ford's mass production is compared to the Japanese "lean production", which consumes much less resources. The leading theme of the book is the superiority of lean production.

In Bowles & Hammond (1991), with the title "Beyond Quality", is the past, present and future of the quality concept are discussed. Interpretations, results and improvement programs, with emphasis on American companies, are discussed and analysed.

3 The Development of Quality Philosophy

From time immemorial man has worried about mistakes and their consequences. The Babylonian king Hammurabi (about 1700 BC) heralded today's notion of product liability. This is illustrated in Figure 3.1.

> *If a building falls into pieces and the owner because of this gets killed the builder also shall be killed. If one of the owner's children is killed, one of the builder's children also shall...*

Figure 3.1   Codex Hammurabi (about 1700 BC).

Building pyramids called for exact measurements. In an Egyptian work of art from that time a picture of an inspector is to be seen. This picture has become the logotype for the Juran Institute, one of the major consulting companies dealing with quality issues in the USA, see Figure 3.2.

The Roman aqueduct Pont du Gard in the Gard Valley in France has lasted more than 2000 years. Pont du Gard (see Figure 3.3), which reaches across the river Gardon, is 275 metres long and 50 metres high and is probably the first bridge built by the Romans.

Figure 3.2   Egyptian inspector supervising the making of building blocks intended for a pyramid. (From Juran & Gryna, 1980.)

Figure 3.3   Pont du Gard, the Roman aqueduct in Southern France, is 275 metres long and 50 metres high. It was built by the Romans more than 2000 years ago and will withstand wind-forces of about 215 km/h, which is roughly twice as much as the top wind-forces that have been measured in the area. (From "Illustrerad Vetenskap", a Swedish journal).

Pont du Gard was built on the basis of more than 200 years of experience from Norman arches and the design is probably the result of assiduous improvement work which has led to more and more reliable solutions. The wind-force would have to reach 215 km/h before the columns on the second floor would lift. The strongest gales in the area reach forces of about 100 km/h.

Acceptance sampling has probably taken place at the Royal Mint in Great Britain since the middle of the 12th century. This has been done in the form of a ceremony with the name "the trial of the Pyx". For every 15th gold coin produced one coin was put in a box named "the Pyx" (after the Greek word "pyx" meaning box). This box was kept in Westminster Abbey for later inspection. The inspection was performed at intervals of one to four years by an independent jury. The object of the procedure was to make sure that the Royal Mint, which was independent of the Crown, had not been cheating when manufacturing the coins. If for instance the total amount of gold was below the set standard by a certain amount the Master of the Mint was charged a fee to serve as punishment.

Probably the best known Master of the Mint was Isaac Newton (1642-1727). There is much that indicates that he might have been able to use his knowledge of the variation of mean values for his own purposes. However, there are no suspicions that he used his knowledge for his own gain. On the contrary, he seems to have been very anxious about the reputation of the Mint and he is believed to have taken pains to keep the variation in coin manufacturing down. More information about "the trial of the Pyx" is to be found in Stiegler (1977).

However, it was not until after the breakthrough of industrialism and in conjunction with mass production that systematic methods of control quality were used. In the 1920s some Germans (see Daeves, 1924, and Becker, Plaut & Runge, 1927) realized that variations in a production process can be described by using statistical methods.

Walter A. Shewhart, the predecessor of modern quality control, suggested at the same time the use of control charts and wrote the book "Economic Control of Manufactured Product" (Shewhart, 1931). This book is still well worth reading.

3.1 Walter A. Shewhart

Walter A. Shewhart was employed at the Western Electric Company in 1918, just after having taken his doctor's degree in physics at the University of California, Berkeley. Later he worked at Bell Laboratories (nowadays AT&T, American Telephone and Telegraph). At that time statistical models of explanation had begun to be used in science. For Shewhart, who was well acquainted with the mathematical statistics of the time, it was natural to apply a statistical view to the production process too. As early as 1924 he suggested in an internal memorandum what has later come to be called a "control chart". Shewhart's view of quality issues is best highlighted with the following quotation from Shewhart (1931), page 54:

> *"Looked at broadly there are at a given time certain human wants to be fulfilled through the fabrication of raw materials into finished products of different kinds. These wants are statistical in nature in that the quality of a finished product in terms of the physical characteristics wanted by one individual are not the same for all individuals.*
>
> *The first step of the engineer in trying to satisfy these wants is therefore that of translating as nearly as possible these wants into the physical characteristics of the thing manufactured to satisfy these wants. In taking this step intuition and judgement play an important role as well as the broad knowledge of the human element involved in the wants of individuals.*

The second step of the engineer is to set up ways and means of obtaining a product which will differ from the arbitrarily set standards for these quality characteristics by no more than may be left to chance."

Focusing on the customer was in other words already very important to Shewhart. But the central topic in Shewhart's publications is how to take care of data and draw conclusions from them in order to supervise and reduce the variation in the production process, i.e. what is called "the second step" in the quotation above.

Shewhart has had a profound influence on the modern view of quality control. If one single individual could be called the father of modern quality philosophy that person would probably be Walter A. Shewhart.

Figure 3.4   Walter A. Shewhart (1891-1967), left, and W. Edwards Deming (1900–1993), right, are two people who have been very important for the development of quality philosophy.

3.2   The Second World War

Quality questions came into the forefront during the Second World War, especially in the USA. Above all, methods for statistical acceptance sampling were developed at that time. This development had already been initiated by Harold F. Dodge (1893-1976) in the 1920s and also later by Harry G. Romig (1900-1989); see Dodge & Romig (1941). Both were working at Bell Laboratories. Epoch-making contributions for a "Sequential Probability Ratio Test" were made by Abraham Wald (1902-1950). His results were considered so important that they were kept secret until the end of the Second World War. Much of the material that today is part of various standards of acceptance sampling was produced at this time.

3.3 W. Edwards Deming and Joseph M. Juran

W. Edwards Deming (see Figure 3.4) and Joseph M. Juran (see Figure 3.6) share Shewhart's statistical point of view regarding the production process. Deming, in particular, heavily stresses the statistical point of view. Deming worked together with Shewhart at Western Electric and was influenced by his statistical philosophy. In addition, both Deming and Juran emphasize the top management role very strongly. Only if top management commit themselves body and soul to the quality issues is it possible to achieve continuous quality improvement. Deming's philosophy is available in a condensed form in his famous 14-point management list, see Deming (1982, 1986). The 14 points are presented in Figure 3.5 and they are commented on in Chapter 22.

Juran (1964) stresses in his book "Managerial Breakthrough" the importance of continuously working on quality improvements. This was a breakthrough as regards the view both of the managerial task and of achieving improvement. With his definition of quality, "fitness for use", Juran also adopts an attitude which is close to the customer.

Deming's 14 points

1. Create constancy of purpose for improvement of product and service.
2. Adopt the new philosophy.
3. Cease dependence on inspection to acheive quality.
4. End the practice of awarding business on the basis of price tag alone. Instead, minimize total cost by working with a single supplier.
5. Improve constantly and forever every process for planning, production and service.
6. Institute training on the job.
7. Adopt and institute leadership.
8. Drive out fear.
9. Break down barriers between staff areas.
10. Eliminate slogans, exhortations and targets for the work force.
11. Eliminate numerical quotas for the work force and numerical goals for the management.
12. Remove barriers that rob people of pride of workmanship. Eliminate the annual rating or merit system.
13. Institute a vigorous program of education and self-improvement for everyone.
14. Put everybody in the company to work to accomplish the transformation.

Figure 3.5   Deming's list of 14 points. (From Deming, 1986.)

Both Deming and Juran have been ascribed great importance for Japan's successes within the field of quality. Ichiro Ishikawa, president of JUSE (Union of Japanese Scientists and Engineers) in 1950 invited Deming to Japan, where he had the opportunity of talking to several of Japan's leading manufacturers. He told them that they, the management, were the problem and that nothing would be better until they took personal responsibility for the change. He also told them that if they would use statistical analysis to build quality into their products, they could overcome their reputation for shoddy quality within five years. His efforts on this and subsequent visits to Japan when he gave courses on statistical methodology for Japanese industry led to the creation of the Deming Prize by JUSE in 1951, a very prestigious prize awarded to companies which have succeeded particularly well in the application of their quality philosophy. The Deming Prize, and some other quality awards, will be discussed further in Chapter 21. In 1954 Juran was also invited to Japan by JUSE. He had already at that time a good reputation after having written the book "Quality Control Handbook", first published in 1951. In its latest edition from 1988, this book still gives a good picture of the extent of the field of quality. In his book "What is Total Quality Control? The Japanese Way", Kaoru Ishikawa (1985) describes what happened when Juran visited Japan in 1954:

> *"...The Juran visit created an atmosphere in which QC was to be regarded as a tool of management, thus creating an opening for the establishment of total quality control as we know it today."*

Figure 3.6   *Joseph M. Juran (born 1904), left, and Kaoru Ishikawa (1915-1989), right, have both had a decisive influence on the development of quality philosophy.*

Dr Joseph M. Juran has decided to retire and is giving his last tour as a quality expert across the US continent during 1993 and 1994. Dr W. Edwards Deming died at his home December 20, 1993, at the age of 93 and he remained active to the very end of his life, see e.g. Deming (1993). Japanese successes within the field of quality have made people and companies take more interest than ever in Juran's and Deming's philosophies and methods. Their philosophies will certainly have a great influence on quality work for many years, maybe forever.

3.4　The Development of Reliability

An important dimension of quality is reliability. Reliability engineering deals with the problems of investigating a system with respect to its resistance against future failures and its ability to survive failures that have already occurred. Reliability is discussed in Chapters 5 and 6.

Figure 3.7　　*Waloddi Weibull (1887-1979), left, and Benjamin Epstein (born 1918), right, who have made crucial contributions to the development of reliability. The photo of Weibull was taken by Sam C Saunders, who has also made important contributions to reliability theory.*

Early studies regarding reliability initially dealt with endurance limits and the reliability of components. The Swede Waloddi Weibull (1887-1979), see Figure 3.7, made essential contributions to the understanding of the statistical properties of fatigue life lengths. Such studies were in fact initiated as early as in the nineteenth century, for instance by August Wöhler (1819-1914), see Wöhler (1860).

Weibull was Professor of Mechanical Engineering at the Royal Institute of Technology (KTH) in Stockholm after having worked at the Coastal Artillery and "Nordiska Kullager AB" in Gothenburg. He suggested a life distribution, which later was to be given the name "Weibull distribution" (see Weibull, 1951). The exponential distribution, which is another important distribution within reliability, was thoroughly scrutinized by Benjamin Epstein (born 1918), see Figure 3.7, in the early 1950s (see Epstein & Sobel, 1953).

With the exception of a discussion regarding the safety of single-engined and multi-engined aircraft in the 1920s, systematic methods for analysis of system reliability were not used until the 1950s. The increased usage of electronic tubes led to this development accelerating. A theory regarding the description of the reliability of complex systems was suggested by Birnbaum, Esary & Saunders (1961). This theory was later refined and further developed, for instance by Barlow & Proschan (1965, 1981).

A useful method for analysis of system reliability and system safety is *Fault Tree Analysis (FTA)*, which was developed by Bell Laboratories and Boeing when studying the reliability of the Minuteman missiles in the early 1960s. This technique has later been used quite frequently when analysing the reliability of many different kinds of systems. The same thing applies to another quality tool which is used when working with reliability, namely *Failure Mode and Effects Analysis (FMEA)*. These methods are described further in Chapter 6.

3.5 The Japanese Miracle

In the 1950s Japanese quality had a reputation which was consistently bad. A deliberate and concentrated effort was made to get rid of this reputation. Part of this effort was the visits paid by Deming and Juran mentioned earlier. At the same time Dr Kaoru Ishikawa (1915-1989) started a campaign aimed at teaching all foremen simple statistical methods which were useful as tools for quality improvements. This is how "the seven QC-tools" were created, see Figure 1.11 and Chapter 11.

Besides Ishikawa, Taiichi Ohno (born 1912) is one the Japanese who has had greatest impact on the development of production and quality philosophies in Japan. He developed the famous Toyota production system and created the concept of Just-in-Time. His production techniques are the basis of what is now called "lean production". After a visit to Ford's plant in Detroit with mass production in 1950 he grouped workers at Toyota together in teams with responsibility for quality-checking. He also set aside time for the workers to meet with the industrial engineers to discuss how to improve the process, an embryo to the QC-circles. Furthermore, he was the one who installed a cord above every work station and instructed all workers to stop the line immediately if they spotted a problem (Bowles & Hammond, 1991).

With the intention of ensuring the commitment of all a company's employees in the improvement process, Ishikawa suggested the establishment of QC-circles. But the efforts were made not only on the shop-floor. The commitment of management was emphasized, and so it still is, and furthermore the ideas of quality control had to permeate the whole company. It is referred to as *CWQC (Company Wide Quality Control)* or *TQC (Total Quality Control)* using a term which was coined by Feigenbaum (1951). This has however been interpreted in Japan in a different way than was meant by Feigenbaum. According to Ishikawa, TQC implies "a system for integrating quality technologies in various functional departments" while CWQC implies "provision of good and low cost products dividing the benefits among customers, employees and stockholders while improving the quality of people's lives".

During the 1970s new simple tools in the forms of charts and matrices have been put together in order to systematize and facilitate management. These are often named "the seven management tools" or sometimes "the seven new QC-tools" and will be discussed in Chapter 19. One of these tools has been developed into Quality Function Deployment, QFD, a very useful technique for product and process planning. Quality Function Deployment is described further in Chapter 4.

3.6 Design of Experiments

In the 1920s the British scientist Sir Ronald A. Fisher (1890-1962) developed statistical design of experiments for the handling of agricultural tests. The industrial applications of Fisher's work were soon realized, for instance by Leonard H.C. Tippet (1902-1985). In Duncan's classic book "Quality Control and Industrial Statistics" from 1951 (the latest edition was published in 1986), considerable space is devoted to design of experiments. A modern survey of the classic design of experiments intended for industrial usage is to be found in Box, Hunter & Hunter (1978).

A weakness in the classic design of experiments is the fact that above all it describes expected results and not their variations. On the contrary, it is assumed that the variation is equal (or with the help of some transformation can be made equal) in all experimental conditions. This flaw was noticed by the Japanese Genichi Taguchi (born 1924), who in the 1950s and onwards has developed a variation of the statistical design of experiments where indeed the variation is the very central consideration.

The main issue in Taguchi's philosophy is how to achieve a design such that the properties of the product vary as little as possible in spite of the influence of disturbing factors, i.e. to achieve a *robust design.* This main issue was earlier highligthed by Shewhart (see Shewhart, 1931, pages 31 and 259). Taguchi has however pointed to a systematic way of answering it. Unfortunately, he has not always used the modern developments within the field of statistical design of experiments; see for instance Box et al. (1988).

Figure 3.8 *Sir Ronald Aylmer Fisher (1890-1962), left, and George E.P. Box (born 1919), right, both of great importance to the development of design of experiments, which is an important area within modern quality methodology.*

3.7 The On-going Development

The development during the last few decades has led to quality being paid more and more attention during the early development and production processes.

Shortly after the Second World War quality work was dominated by inspection activities. Finished products were checked and sorted out and defective units were reworked. This defensive technique has been abandoned in favour of controlling the production process. The underlying belief was that it is in the interest of companies to look for signs in the production process that indicate that there will be something wrong with the units produced. Development is now very clearly heading towards increasing quality efforts even before the process is started. By systematically determining the wishes and demands of the customers, by performing well planned experiments and by making robust designs it is possible to prevent bad and unprofitable products from being produced. Figure 3.9 illustrates the development process.

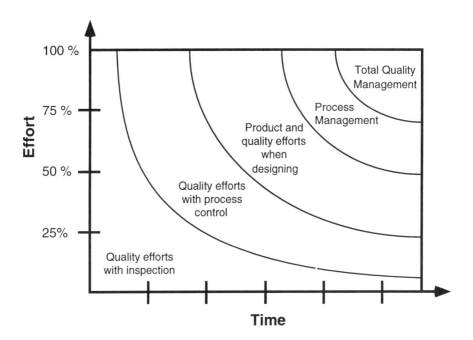

Figure 3.9　*The development of quality methodology during the last few decades has moved from inspection activities towards process control and other preventive activities at earlier and earlier stages of the development of the product. Today some companies are putting a lot of emphasis on design of the development and other processes in the company. This planning, control and improvement of company processes including business processes is called Process Management. The most advanced companies are also putting a lot of effort into the quality of the management process as such. Different countries and different companies have of course reached different stages on this scale.*

Even if Taguchi, through his ideas of robust design, touches on methods in one of the most modern fields in quality methodology it is still not the most important element that has recently emerged as regards the development of quality issues. The most important element is without doubt the change in the way of thinking that has taken place with regard to management strategies. This changed view regarding quality issues which has now started to spread within the management of companies and organisations will undoubtedly have far-reaching consequences for future quality development.

The introduction of different quality awards in order to stimulate a systematic and preventive quality improvement process is part of this on-going development. One example of this is the Malcolm Baldrige National Quality Award, which is awarded annually to companies which have been successful within the quality field. The award is presented by the President of the USA. In 1992 the European Foundation for Quality Management, EFQM, instituted the European Quality Award. Several countries have also instituted national quality awards. A discussion about quality awards will be presented in Chapter 21.

In the future we hope for an even more progressive development where societal organizations and structures are involved in a progressive cultural change towards customer focusing and continuous improvement of life. Otherwise the survival of human society on Earth may be at stake.

It is our hope that the methods and ideas which later on will be introduced in this book will be of benefit in this development.

3.8 Notes and References

Shewhart's importance for the development of quality methodology cannot be strongly enough emphasized and his book from 1931 is warmly recommended. A special issue of Industrial Quality

Control, August 1967, in honour of Walter Shewhart also provides a lot of interesting reading.

Some interesting articles about the development of quality philosophy are to be found in the journal Quality Progress, which is published by ASQC, the American Society for Quality Control. For instance, in 1986 a series with a few short descriptions of ASQC's honorary members were introduced. Among these are Shewhart, Deming, Juran, Feigenbaum and Ishikawa. An introduction to Fisher is to be found in the magazine Chance, 1990:1, pages 22-32. Bowles & Hammond (1991) also give an interesting description of the influence of Juran and Deming on the quality development in Japan.

We have chosen not to make this summary too detailed and that is the reason why we have not discussed the philosophies of such people as Armand V Feigenbaum and Philip Crosby. Feigenbaum introduced the concept "Total Quality Control" in his book of the same name, first published in 1951 (a third edition was published in 1983). Crosby introduced the concept "Quality is Free" in his book of the same name published in 1979. His publications also include Crosby (1984) and (1986). Crosby also created the concept "zero defects" during the 1960s when working at the Martin Company which was building Pershing Missiles for the US Army. An article in the magazine "Quality" by Lowe & Mazzeo (1986) deals with similarities and differencies between the strategies of quality as far as Deming, Juran and Crosby are concerned.

It is possible to read more about the development of reliability technology in an article written by Barlow (1984). Also Henley & Kumamoto (1981) and Villemeur (1992) discuss the development of reliability.

Many books attempt to explain the Japanese miracle. The books written by Ishikawa (1982) and Karatsu (1988) give good descriptions of this. Bowles & Hammond (1991) discusses the influence of Deming, Juran, Ishikawa and others on quality development in

Japan. Sullivan (1986) has tried to compare the interpretation of TQC made in the Western World with the Japanese point of view. Ishikawa (1989) also discusses a comparison between Japanese and Western quality development. To provide a link towards the JIT (Just-In-Time) concept, Schonberger (1984) can be recommended.

Another line of development starts from observations of the insuffiency of the current economic information system in the company, see Johnson & Caplan (1987). The principles for *Activity Based Costing* have been developed from this awareness. A further development of these ideas, close to ideas in Total Quality Management, is called *Activity Based Management,* see e.g. Brimson (1991). Similar ideas based on reducing company lead times have developed into *Time Based Management.*

An excellent treatise of the QC-circle phenomenon in Japan is presented in Lillrank & Kano (1989).

We would also like to mention that there are nowadays quite a number of periodicals dealing with quality. Some of these are: Continuous Journey, European Quality, International Journal of Quality and Reliability Management, Journal of Quality Technology, Managing Service Quality, Quality, Quality Progress, Quality Forum, Quality Engineering, Quality and Reliability Engineering International, Quality Management Journal, Qualität und Zuverlässigkeit, Total Quality Management and the TQM Magazine.

Part II

Design for Quality

Quality has to be planned for very early in the product life cycle in order to reduce costs and increase prosperity. In this part of the book we will study some methods useful for product planning and product development. We will discuss Quality Function Deployment, a tool for translating customer wishes and needs into product and process properties. Reliability engineering and data analysis will also be discussed. Additionally, Design of Experiments, Robust Design, and the contributions by Genichi Taguchi will be studied. Finally a short discussion on software quality is included.

4 Quality Function Deployment

The modern view of the quality concept focuses on customer needs and customer expectations. Few systematic methods for transferring these wants and needs into product and process characteristics have been suggested. One such method is, however, *Quality Function Deployment, QFD*.

With customer wants and needs as a basis and with due regard to competitors, this technique gives a possibility of systematically deriving product quality demands and parameter designs as well as production process demands. The technique was developed in Japan during the late 1960s by Shigeru Mizuno (1910-1989) and Yoji Akao (born 1928).

Quality Function Deployment is also an excellent tool for communication. It requires cross-functional groups to meet and to work out common concepts and it provides a common basis necessary for *Integrated Product Development* or variants such as *Simultaneous Engineering* or *Concurrent Engineering*.

The work involved in Quality Function Deployment can be divided into the following four parts:

(1) market analysis to find out about the needs and expectations of the customers

(2) examination of the competitors to find out about their ability to satisfy the needs and wants of the customers

(3) identification of key factors for the success of the company's product on the market with steps (1) and (2) as a basis

(4) translation of these key factors into product and process characteristics in connection with design, development and production.

As far as market analyses are concerned there are a number of different methods. One of them is *Conjoint Analysis*. This method is built on statistical design of experiments with the use of simple factorial designs, see Chapter 7. Potential customers are asked to place in order a number of product concepts, where important factors are chosen according to a factorial design with two levels.

Also simpler methods can be efficient. It is said that Toyota, at car exhibitions, collect opinions of the customers regarding their views on quality and functional properties. Then these opinions are analysed and transferred to the development and production stages using methods from quality function deployment. It is also said that Toyota halved their design costs and reduced product development time by a third after starting to use Quality Function Deployment.

Analysis of the competitors has to go on continuously. Properties that are to be analysed should be controlled by the results of marketing research as far as the needs and expectations of the customers are concerned. One way of always having the quality situation of the competitors in mind is to let their products undergo the same scrutiny as the company's products.

In this chapter we will briefly describe Quality Function Deployment, QFD. For a more thorough discussion we refer to sources such as King (1987) and Akao (1990).

Figure 4.1   In Japanese, Quality Function Deployment is "hinshitsu
             kino tenkai" and is written as shown above. The first two
             symbols ("hin shitsu") mean "quality" (see Figure 1.1), the
             next two ("ki no"), mean "function, mechanization" and the
             last two ("ten kai") mean "deployment, development, evolu-
             tion".

4.1 The Four Steps

The aim of QFD is to transfer the wants and needs of the customers into product and process characteristics by systematically letting the wishes be reflected at every level of the product development process. Without a systematical method it is hardly possible

to break down the wishes of the customers completely as far as parts of the product and elements in the production process are concerned. Essentially, the quality function deployment method can be divided into four steps; see Figure 4.2.

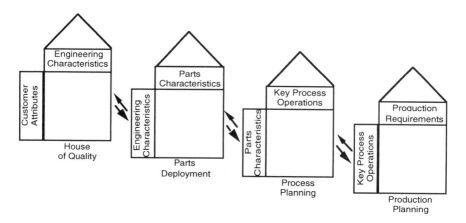

Figure 4.2   *The four planning documents consist of different kinds of matrices, where wishes or demands from a higher level are transferred to a lower level. See also Figures 4.4. and 4.5.*

Below, we give a short description of these steps.

(1) *Product planning.* The wishes of the customer are transferred to properties of the product. At the same time a valuation of these wishes is made, using analyses of the competitors as one source. The final result is an identification of important product properties which will be transferred to the next step of the QFD work.

(2) *Product design.* The design concept is chosen that best fulfils the given target values. Parts and components that will be critical for the product are identified and then the part properties are set in a way corresponding to the product properties in the previous step. Part properties that will be critical are also identified in order to find out where there is

a need for further development and research in order to meet the demands of the market.

(3) *Process design.* The critical detail properties are transferred to production operations and their critical parameters are identified. Methods for process control and process improvement are set.

(4) *Production design.* Production instructions are designed. The operator needs exact descriptions of the parts that have to be measured and the measurements that have to be observed. Also instructions must be developed regarding how many units should be measured, how often this should be done and what tools should be used.

All over the world QFD has been utilized to improve product planning and product and process development. From Japan, it has been reported that very substantial effects have been achieved especially with respect to the running-in costs. Quite a few successes have also been reported from the USA. Some Swedish experiences are also described in Figure 4.3. With a strict product and process development, which is set by the customer, it is possible to avoid nearly all the changes that often must be made due to misunderstandings in connection with a development which is run internally rather than by the customers on the market.

In the QFD work a form of matrix is used, sometimes called the Quality House. In Figure 4.4 an example of a completely filled matrix can be found illustrating the design of a wrench. In Figure 4.5 the concepts in the different parts of the "Quality House" is illustrated.

The method is spreading

Philips use QFD on trial when a new micro-wave is designed. Interviews showed that customers valued much more than expected the fact that the food was clearly visible from the outside. Something that must be given priority by the technicians. On top of that the customers wanted a rotating plate in the micro-wave. "It is of no use and makes production harder. But if the customers want it that way we have of course to make sure that the food can rotate" says Christer Åkerlund at Philips.

Saab Automobile have used the matrix on trial when further developing a glove compartment. The designers were fully convinced that the customers wanted to have a glove compartment large enough to hold an A4 file and a system camera. But it turned out they were wrong. Much more important was that the glove compartment was easily accessible. "Everybody on the QFD-team was very happy about the increased co-operation between the different departments", says Jan Därnemyr at Saab Automobile.

Electrolux use the QFD-method when designing a new refrigerator. In order to find out how the customer wants the new refrigerator, market analyses have been studied more carefully than usual.

Volvo had quite a few complaints regarding a leaking water pump. The basis of a QFD-project was to improve it. The result was that the production of the pump now takes place in one place, not in many as was earlier the case. Thus one person got a general view of the production and the responsibility as well. Furthermore a decision has been made to reduce the pressure in the cooling system, which reduces the risk of a leak.

Figure 4.3   *Translation of an article from the Swedish economic journal "Veckans Affärer", 1990:5 written by Helena Ahlbom, in which it is discussed to what extent QFD is being used in Swedish industry.*

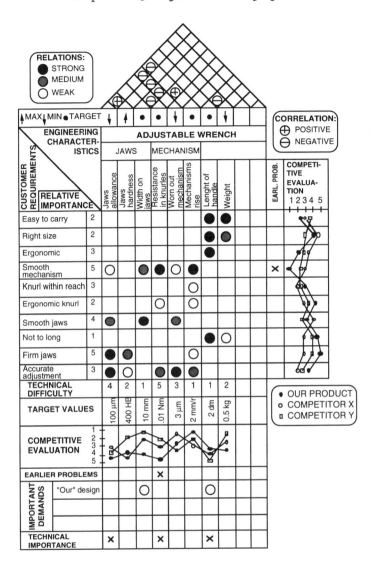

Figure 4.4   *A completely filled matrix. The example deals with the design of a wrench. If a row in the matrix lacks symbols, that customer requirement is not fulfilled. If a column lacks symbols, that engineering characteristic is of no influence on the customer requirements and can be chosen in the most economic way. The correlation matrix at the top of the Quality House is designed from the customer point of view. (From Roland Andersson.)*

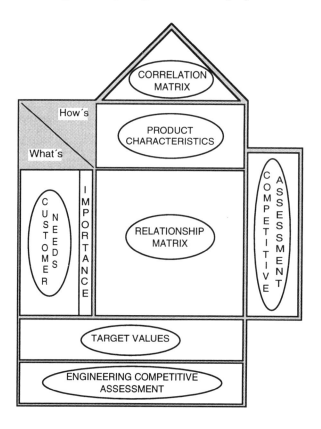

Figur 4.5   The concepts in the different parts of the "The Quality House".

4.2   Notes and References

Quality Function Deployment and its connection to other progressive methods regarding quality control are described in King (1987), Akao (1990), Bossert (1991) and Day (1993).

Research and applications within the QFD field have been reported by Akao and others in a series of twelve articles in a magazine published by the Japanese Standardization Board. These articles have been translated into English and published by G.O.A.L. In

Japan, QFD has also been successfully used in connection with the design of software. Yoshizawa et al. (1993) have described the use of QFD in software development; see also Chapter 9. Other recent applications of the QFD technique are presented in Akao & Ono (1993) concerning deployment of costs and in Yoshizawa (1993) concerning deployment of company strategies.

In QFD, a kind of matrix is used for formalizing coincidences between concepts at different system levels. This kind of matrix is part of "the seven management tools" or "the seven new QC-tools". These are introduced in Chapter 19.

The ways in which Conjoint Analysis can be used in connection with market analyses are described by Luce & Tukey (1964), Green & Rao (1971) and Green & Srinivasan (1978). Gustafsson (1993) discusses the use of Conjoint Analysis for the identification of customer expectations if QFD.

Books discussing Simultaneous Engineering or Concurrent Engineering include Andreasen & Hein (1987), Hubka (1987) and Carter & Baker (1992). Furthermore, the March/April issue of the magazine Manufacturing Breakthrough is devoted to Simultaneous Engineering. Among the articles in that issue is Milburn (1992).

5 Reliability

Reliability is a very important quality dimension. Therefore reliability engineering is a very important tool for quality improvement. Its aim is:

- to find the causes of failures and try to eliminate them, i.e. to increase the failure resistance of the product

- to find the consequences of failures and if possible reduce or eliminate their effects, i.e. increase the tolerance of the product to failures.

A general means of obtaining reliable products is to use robust design methodology, which will be discussed in Chapter 8. To provide a basis for the improvement work, the reliability of the product also has to be evaluted and measured. Information feedback therefore is a very important part of the reliability activity.

Basic reliability concepts and measures will be discussed in Sections 5.1 and 5.2. In Section 5.3 we will deal with causes of failures and how these can sometimes be eliminated. In the following paragraph a few ways of increasing failure tolerance will be dealt with. Thereafter we will make an overall study of repairable systems, reliability growth and product liability. In the next chapter we will mention some important methods regarding reliability analysis of non-repairable as well as repairable systems.

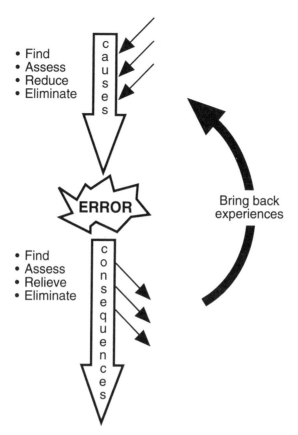

Figure 5.1   The aim of reliability engineering.

5.1   Dependability

An important property of a product is its *dependability,* which can
be defined as

> *the property of a unit to be able to perform given
> achievement under given conditions with consideration
> taken to reduction of performance due to failures and
> maintenance.*

The dependability of a unit is determined by its

- *reliability,* which is the ability of the unit to work without failures

- *maintainability,* which is a measure of how easy it is to detect, localize and remedy failures

- *maintenance support,* which is the ability of the maintenance organisation to mobilise maintenance resources when needed.

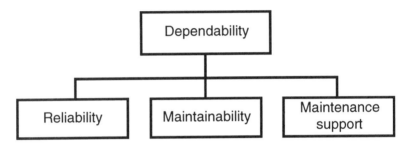

Figure 5.2   *Factors affecting system dependability.*

The first two properties mentioned are thus tied to the product, while maintenance support is a measure of the efficiency of the maintenance organization. Exact definitions of the above mentioned concepts can be found in IEC 50(191) "International Electrotechnical Vocabulary".

Often the concept "reliability" is used also in a general sense covering a number of characteristics and terms. When something is expressed quantitatively or when a certain property is referred to, this should be specified by using the appropriate concept. Examples of this could be the terms "reliability function" or "maintenance support". Correspondingly, the specific terms should not be used for a comprehensive designation of the associated characteristics. Usage is however not consistent and readers and listeners should be observant of this.

The properties "maintainability" and "maintenance support" will not be discussed in this book. In this chapter we will deal mainly with reliability and measures of reliability.

5.2 Basic Concepts

To be able to speak of the reliability of a product we need a good definition of the failure concept and the failure consequences. We also have to be able to describe how frequently failures occur and what the risk is a failure occurring. Defining the concept of failure can be hard and as a rule it has to be defined separately, depending on the product and the problem. Generally speaking, a failure is a deviation of the product from the demands made on it.

As a rule it is impossible to predict when a failure will occur. Therefore, we experience the time to failure as a random variable and have to use the probability concept to describe reliability. Some probability concepts are dealt with in Appendix A. In this paragraph we will study some measures of reliability.

5.2.1 Reliability Function

Let us study a unit, randomly chosen from a manufactured batch. The probability that this unit still works after the operating time t is called the *survival probability* at time t. This probability regarded as a function of t is called the *reliability function (survival function)* and is written R(t). If R(1000) = 0.90 this implies that about 90% of the units of a big batch will survive 1000 operating hours. This also means that the failure probability at the time t = 1000 hours is 0.10, i.e. about 10% of the units have failed after an operating time of 1000 hours. The probability of a failure before t is usually denoted F(t). Thus it follows that F(t) = 1 − R(t). The function F(t) is denoted *life distribution* (or *distribution function*) for the time to failure.

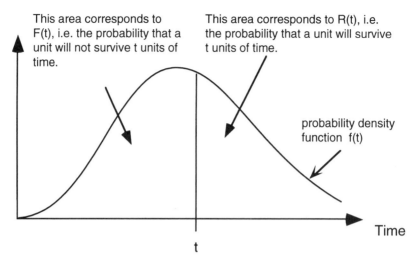

Figure 5.3   *The connection between the probability density function*
f(t), the life distribution F(t) and the survival function R(t).

5.2.2 Failure Rate

The risk that a unit, which has survived the time t, has failed at
the time t+h can be expressed as the *failure rate* z(t) multiplied by
h, when h is small. The failure rate is, in other words, a measure of
how likely it is that a unit that has survived the time t will fail in a
"very near future". If for instance z(t) = 0.01 at t = 1000 (i.e. the
failure rate after 1000 operating hours is 0.01) this can be interpreted as the probability for a unit, which works after 1000 hours
operating time, to fail during the next following hour is roughly
0.01. Thus about 1% of the units that have survived 1000 hours
will fail during the next hour.

Formally the failure rate is defined as the ratio between the probability density function f(t) for the time to failure and the corresponding survival function R(t), i.e.

$$z(t) = \frac{f(t)}{R(t)}$$

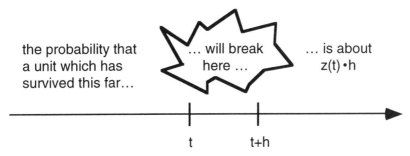

Figure 5.4   *The probability that a unit which has survived until time t will fail before the time t+h is roughly z(t)h.*

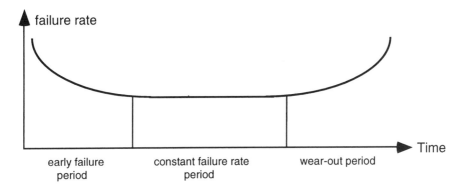

Figure 5.5   *Typical shape of the failure rate of a non-repairable unit, the so-called bath-tub curve.*

Figure 5.5 illustrates how the failure rate often varies with time. Owing to its characteristic appearance it is often called the *bath-tub curve*. Variations of manufacturing and material give certain units bad reliability. These units will then break down first and the population will improve as time passes. This first period is called the *early failure period*. It is followed by the *constant failure rate period* where the failure rate is nearly constant. The failures that occur can arise from temporary overloading. This period is sometimes called the *best period*. Finally increased wear and ageing make the failure rate grow during the *wear-out period*.

Today, many reliability engineers want to modify the bath-tub curve to what sometimes is called a *"roller-coaster"* curve, see Figure 5.6. The reason for this is that even if a subpopulation of components is weak it may take some time to develop a failure. This explains the initial increase in failure rate before the weak part of the population is screened out.

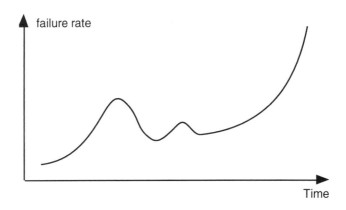

Figure 5.6   *The "roller-coaster" curve, which sometimes better than the bath-tub curve describes the failure rate of a population of components.*

For non-repairable units it is sometimes assumed that the failure rate is constant, i.e. independent of the age of the unit. It is said that the units do not age. Then the probability of failure in a certain time interval, given that the unit is functioning at the start of the interval, depends only on the interval length and not on the age of the unit. In this case the age of the unit does not give us any information about its remaining length of life. This can be interpreted as implying that a unit fails due to factors that are independent of the earlier operating time of the unit, for instance a temporary overload. It should also be observed that, in most cases, we understand the concept of time as meaning operating time.

If the failure rate is constant, say λ, the reliability function can be written $R(t) = \exp(-\lambda t)$, $t > 0$. Then the time to failure is said to be *exponentially distributed;* see Appendix A.

Another common life distribution is the *Weibull distribution,* whose reliability function can be written $R(t) = \exp(-(t/\alpha)^\beta)$, $t \geq 0$. Here $\beta > 1$ corresponds to increasing failure rate and $\beta < 1$ corresponds to decreasing failure rate. When $\beta = 1$ the failure rate is constant, which means that the time to failure is exponentially distributed, see Figure 5.7.

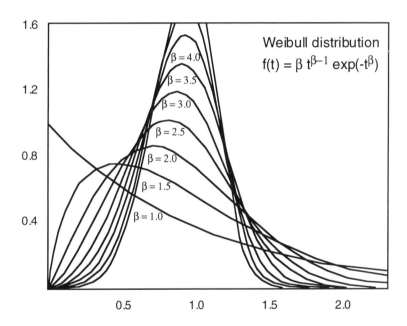

Figure 5.7   *Probability densities of Weibull distributions with some different values of the shape parameter β. When $\beta = 1$ the exponential distribution is achieved.*

If, for instance, two subpopulations of units, with constant but different failure rates, are mixed, the population gets a decreasing failure rate. This kind of mixture can for example arise in production under different conditions; see Figure 5.8. This phenomenon is

85

one main reason for the decreasing failure rate at the beginning of the bath-tub curve.

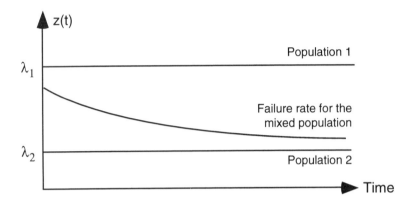

Figure 5.8   *A population consists of two kinds of units with the constant failure rates λ_1 and λ_2, respectively. The proportions are p_1 and $p_2 = 1 - p_1$. With increasing age more and more units from population 1 will fail and the reliability of the population is successively improved.*

5.2.3   Mean Time to Failure

Mean Time to Failure, MTTF, is another measure of the reliability of a non-repairable unit. If we were to note the times to failure for many units of the same kind that operate under the same environmental conditions the arithmetic mean of these times to failure would be close to MTTF. For a given expression of the reliability function we can calculate MTTF as

$$MTTF = \int_0^\infty R(t)dt \; ;$$

here R(t) is the probability that the unit has passed t units of time without failure. In other words MTTF is equal to the area below the curve of the reliability function.

The measures defined above have to be interpreted as measures of properties of a population of units and not as properties of each individual unit. It is for instance completely possible to produce a decreasing failure rate even if the failure mechanism of every unit is due to wear. The condition is that there is a mixture of wear mechanisms that make certain units wear out tremendously fast, whereas others wear out slowly.

5.3 Stress-Strength Analysis

Most failures arise because a weak point of a design is exposed to a stress that is too great. This stress can arise due to the external or internal environment. An illustration is given in Figure 5.9, which also illustrates that the environment can have two different effects on the component, a slow weakening one and a more catastrophic one.

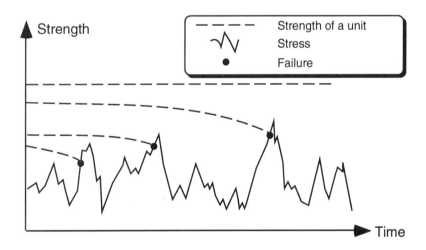

Figure 5.9 *Illustration of the strength of a number of units against failure and the stress the units are exposed to. The concept "strength" should here be interpreted in a very broad sense, i.e. not only as the ability of the unit to withstand mechanical stress but also for instance thermal or electric stress.*

The slow weakening can be caused by fatigue, corrosion, deterioration or diffusion. The catastrophic effect is as a rule an immediate overload, for instance in the form of mechanical, thermal or electric stress.

Observe that in many cases the failure resistance differs from unit to unit and that there is also a variation in applied stress. An illustration of this is to be found in Figure 5.10.

From Figures 5.10 and 5.11 we draw the conclusion that the load and resistance distributions should be kept separate. In particular it is the "tails" that should be kept apart as well as possible.

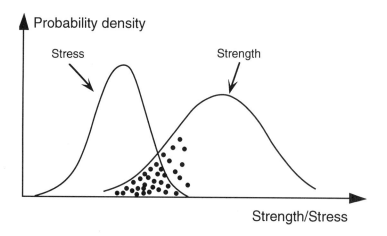

Figure 5.10   *Probability densities regarding instantaneous stress and strength, respectively. The risk of failure is illustrated by the fact that the two probability densities overlap. As it frequently is possible to regard the loads in various stress cycles as independent it will probably turn out, after a great number of stress cycles, that all the components which have strength within the critical area will be defective, i.e. the part indicated by the shaded area. (We have then disregarded the fact that a slow weakening can take place.)*

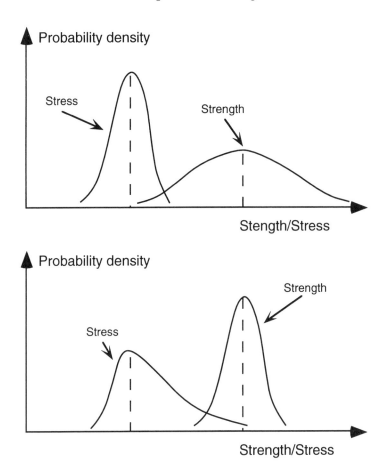

Figure 5.11 *Illustration of two different cases with the same difference between average strength and average stress. However, different appearances of the tails of the two distributions result in completely different effects regarding reliability. In (a) the variation of strength is large whereas case (b) illustrates the situation where the variation of strength is well limited while the variation of stress is large.*

Also observe that it is not certain that a reliable product is at hand merely because there is a great difference between average strength and average stress. This difference, which is often called a *safety margin,* gives little information about safety against failure. It is the interaction between the right "tail" in the stress distribution and the left tail in the strength distribution that is important. A long right tail in the stress distribution can cause a disastrous effect on a large number of the total population of units. Usually, the same unit is exposed to many independent loads. The size of the largest of these is to a high degree set by the right tail of the stress distribution. If, on the other hand, the stress distribution is fairly limited such dramatic effects are not encountered. Only the weak units are in trouble. See Figure 5.11.

If it is possible to limit the environmental influence, above all regarding extreme stress, positive effects regarding reliability are often achieved. These are as a rule far larger than it is possible to achieve by downward limiting the strength of the design.

Burn-in means that a unit (component, apparatus or equipment) is exposed to a fairly large stress during a certain time before usage. This can be looked upon as an efficient way to reduce the left "tail" of the strength distribution. The weakest components fail during the burn-in and stronger, more reliable, components are left in the products when they start being used, see Figure 5.12.

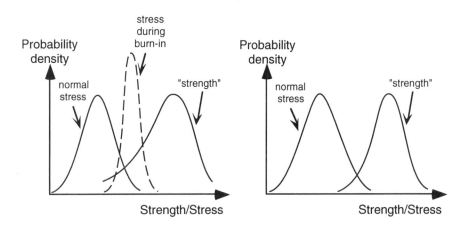

Figure 5.12   *Illustration of the effect of burn-in on the strength distribution of the components. Observe that here and in many other places in this chapter we use the concept of strength in a very broad sense.*

Even for mechanical products it sometimes is possible to achieve similar effects. For products that are manufactured from new materials, for instance composites, so called *proof-testing* has been suggested. By this is meant that the product is proof stressed with a stress larger than it will be subjected to during usage.

So far we only have discussed situations which have been independent of time, i.e. situations when the strength of the units does not deteriorate with time. The strength distribution of the population can however change with time, either because of the ongoing sorting out of weaker units or because of ageing. This, more complex, situation will not be studied here.

Finally, we want to point out that systems with many components also have many chances to fail. Because of this the design of single components has to be done with large safety margins, larger than might seem reasonable when studying only the component level.

5.4 Fault Tolerance

When *fault tolerance* is to be achieved, i.e. resistance against consequences when faults occur, it is necessary to distinguish between two different kinds of faults:

- faults influencing functions that are used occasionally

- faults influencing functions that are frequently used.

In order to prevent the first kind of fault it is possible to introduce supervision or testing. By this means it is possible to efficiently avoid serious damage from faults that occur between periods of usage cause serious consequences.

In order to increase resistance against those faults that arise in constant usage another view has to be applied. One way is to make the design in such a way that one single defective component will not affect the intended function. Other components take over the function of the defective component. This way of increasing fault tolerance is called *redundancy.*

Another way is to prevent faults from developing in such a way that they are allowed to cause non-acceptable damage. How easy it is to take these measures is strongly dependent on the current fault mechanisms. It is sometimes called *graceful degradation.*

Here we will only deal with design utilizing redundancies. Ways of finding design solutions that minimize the influence of variation from various disturbing sources are discussed in Chapter 8.

5.4.1 Redundancy

Redundancies can be classified according to many different criteria. A *redundancy* can for instance be

- parallel or functional
- complete or partial
- active or stand-by
- load-carrying or non-load-carrying.

Parallel redundancy exists when two or more units are installed instead of one. Instead of one emergency cooling pump in a nuclear power plant there are several. When spare functions that can replace the regular function are created, we speak of *functional redundancy.* The spare function rarely has the same power as the regular function but it satisfies certain minimum demands which often originate from aspects of safety. An example of this is the weaker spare tyres in certain cars. Not uncommonly a functional redundancy also implies a *technical redundancy,* by which is meant that a completely different technical solution is used for the spare function. This, it is hoped, will make it insensitive to disturbances that can knock out the main function.

When there is a *complete redundancy* the functional level is kept even after a fault whereas it is lowered in the case of a *partial redundancy.*

In an *active redundancy* all the units or functions are loaded in the same way during regular operation. The bolts of a car wheel are examples of redundancy of this kind. In a *stand-by redundancy* only one unit or function at a time is loaded. Spare units regarding electricity supply at hospitals and the spare tyre in a car can illustrate this kind of redundancy.

A *load-carrying redundancy* is active and the load on the remaining units increases after faults occur. This is the case with many structural elements in mechanical systems.

Redundancies are not always efficient and sometimes they also bring negative side-effects. Before redundancy is introduced into a design the following arguments against the use of redundancies should be considered.

Even if the tolerance of certain kinds of faults has increased with the help of redundancy, the tolerance of other kinds of faults might have decreased. One example of this is redundancy with relays. Relays connected in series give increased resistance against faults like short circuits while on the other hand the resistance against interruption has decreased. Another example regarding redundancy is provided by the use of electro-explosive devices in life-saving equipment. By doubling the devices the risk that the equipment will not work when needed is reduced but at the same time the risk of accidental triggering is increased.

Redundancy has good efficiency only if faults are detected and remedied. Otherwise the life increase is usually fairly modest. Furthermore, redundancy implies increased complexity in the system not only because of the duplication of a unit but also often because of the introduction of extra test devices or adjustment functions. This increased complexity brings an increased occurrence of failures which have to be taken care of by preventive maintenance. This results in higher maintenance costs and sometimes lower availability. The increased complexity makes the system structure less clear and there is an increased risk of failure modes against which no precautions have been taken.

As far as load-carrying redundancies are concerned it has to be taken into consideration that when there is a failure of a unit in a redundancy the load on the remaining unit may become twice as heavy as it was before the failure. The risk of a failure is therefore strongly increased after the first failure.

The efficiency of a redundancy depends very much on the degree of dependency between the fault mechanisms of the different units in the redundancy. Assume for instance that two units of a redundancy both come from a batch with the same defective material. If the units are exposed to the same load it is very likely that if one of them fails because of overload the other unit will do the same. No major effect is achieved by the redundancy owing to the dependence between the units. Failure dependency between units can for instance be caused by the units

- having the same design
- originating from the same batch
- operating under the same environmental conditions
- getting the same maintenance
- having the same energy supply.

This defect will then hit all the units in the redundancy. In the manufacturing process an operation might be forgotten or wrongly performed in the whole batch. The batch might furthermore be manufactured from the same raw material, and destructive environmental shocks might occur at the same time for different units. A maintenance mistake which is made on one unit will probably also be made on the other units in the redundancy. Examples of these kinds of faults are the closed valves of the emergency cooling pumps in the nuclear power accident at Three Mile Island in 1979 and the incorrect oil change of all the engines of a four-engined passenger airliner outside Hamburg in Germany some years ago.

The above-mentioned negative aspects imply that redundancy should not be introduced too quickly and too frequently. Instead, supervision of the environment or conditioning monitoring should be introduced, where possible.

5.5 Repairable Systems

The failure risk when studying repairable systems is often described using the concept of failure intensity. The *failure intensity* $\lambda(t)$ of a repairable unit can be interpreted as the risk of failure per unit of time. The probability that a unit which works at time t will fail before time t+h is roughly equal $\lambda(t)h$, i.e. the failure intensity multiplied by the length of the interval, if h is small.

The concept of failure intensity for a repairable unit should not be confused with the concept of failure rate for a population of non-repairable units, which is a conditional measure.

A decreasing failure intensity implies that defects which are in the system from the beginning are eliminated in connection with failures and thus reliability increases. A constant failure intensity means that the system does not show any symptoms of ageing. Possible failures occur randomly independently of age. An increasing failure intensity indicates that the system somehow is ageing, for instance owing to fatigue or wear. Often these three effects appear during different periods of the life of the system. At the beginning the failure intensity is decreasing, then it is constant and finally it is increasing. As a result we get the *bath-tub curve,* which often quite well describes the failure intensity of a repairable system; see Figure 5.13.

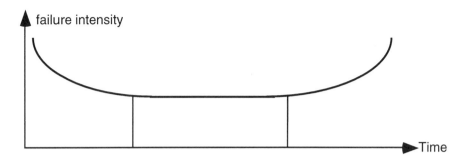

*Figure 5.13   The failure intensity function of a repairable system typi-
cally has the form of a bath-tub curve.*

As far as repairable units are concerned the concept of *MTBF,
(Mean Time Between Failures)* is frequently used. This is however
not always a well defined quantity. The statistical properties of the
times between failures change character when the unit gets older.
Most frequently, a description of times between failures during the
best period is referred to.

For a unit that has broken down and is in need of repair there are
various possible results of the repair. We will briefly comment on
two such models.

- The repair is so complete that the unit will afterwards be
  practically new. This can be compared to the unit being replaced by a new identical unit. This means that the unit is
  "as-good-as-new" after the repair. The model is therefore
  often called a *renewal model.* Sometimes it is referred to as a
  maximum repair.

- The repair is fairly superficial and reinstates the unit to
  about the same condition as it was before it broke down. The
  unit is then assumed to have the same failure rate after the
  repair as it had just before the failure occurred. This model is
  normally called *minimal repair.* Sometimes the expression
  "as-bad-as-old" is used for this model.

When analysing data from a repairable system, the assumption is often made that the system is repaired to "as-good-as-new" state, i.e. maximum repair is at hand. This assumption means that all the times between failures are observations from the same life distribution. It is then possible to use methods regarding analysis of failure data of non-repairable units. We will discuss some techniques in Chapter 6.

Generally an assumption about maximum repair is unrealistic and incorrect. If for instance you repair a tyre or a water pump on your car, you do not get a new car. Many times it probably is the other way round, i.e. minimal repair is closer at hand. Then the times between failures are neither independent nor from the same distribution. If the data analysis supports the fact that there is a dependency or a trend in the material the same methods as for non-repairable units cannot be used. We will return to this problem in Chapter 6.

5.6 Dependability Measures

Dependability and quality are connected in at least two ways. First of all, dependability is an important quality parameter of a system or a product. Secondly, dependability in a production plant influences the process quality as regards not only efficiency but also capability, as defined in Chapter 13. Today we often talk about *Total Productive Maintenance, TPM;* see Nakajima (1988). This philosophy is based on activities to maximize equipment effectiveness, autonomous maintenance by operators, and company-led small group activities. In Japan there has been a PM Award since 1964, founded by JIPM (Japan Institute of Plant Maintenance). Only two companies outside Japan have received that reward (October 1993), namely Nachi Industries in Singapore and Volvo Cars in Belgium.

Product dependability depend not only on the product's reliability, but also on its maintainability and maintenance support. If a product has high maintainability, this implies that it can quickly and cheaply be maintained provided that adequate resources in the form of personnel, spare parts and tools are available. Maintenance support is, as we have seen, a measure of the effectiveness of the maintenance organization. In many cases it is up to the user to choose the right level of this. Reliability of a system is, to a great extent, determined already during the development of the system. The same applies for maintainability.

In order to achieve the intended product dependability, right from the design stage, we have to devote our attention to maintainability. We have to take into consideration the requirements that components must be easy to reach, that proper and clear marking must prevail, that wear is indicated and that maintenance staff will suffer no risk of being injured.

5.6.1 Availability

As a comprehensive measure of product dependability, i.e. its ability to function in the intended manner despite the disturbances that may occur, the concept of *availability A(t)* is used. According to IEC 50(191) "International Electrotechnical Vocabulary" *availability* is:

> *the ability of an item to be in a state to perform a required function under given conditions at at given instant of time, assuming that the required external resources are provided.*

Several different availability measures are used depending on, for example, what state of preparedness or what state of functioning is intended. For instance, *material availability, constructive availability* and *operational availability* are used, depending on the extent to which maintenance should influence the measure.

The probability A(t) is in most cases hard to calculate. Therefore the limit of A(t) when t increases, called the *asymptotical availability* A, is often used. It is possible to show that A is the fraction of "current" time during which the product is "available" (depending on, among other things, state of preparedness and of functioning). For instance, the *operational availability* A_0 is defined as

$$A_0 = \frac{MTBM}{MTBM + MDT}$$

here *MBTM (Mean Time Between Maintenance)* is the mean time between function-interrupting maintenance (rectifying or preventive) and *MDT (Mean Down Time)*, the mean length of time when the system does not function, i.e. including time spent on waiting for maintenance personnel together with the time spent on maintenance itself. This availability measure takes into consideration not only maintenance ability, but also maintenance support.

Example 5.1

A machine with MTBM = 150 h and MDT = 30 h has the operational availability

$$A_0 = \frac{150}{150 + 30} = 0.83$$

The problem of testing and evaluating availability, in a guarantee situation for example, is studied by Rise (1979) among others.

5.6.2 Life Cycle Costs

The sum of all costs during the life cycle of a project is usually denoted as the *Life Cycle Cost, LCC*. For a productive system it is common to sum up all proceeds of the system and subtract the life cycle costs. We then get what is called *Life Cycle Profit, LCP*. In the following we will only treat the LCC-concept, since the LCP-concept can be treated similarly.

The heaviest costs are those regarding research and development, manufacturing and sales, together with running and maintenance. Methods of estimating LCC at an early stage have been developed by the military industry, but are becoming more frequently used in civilian industry as well. Two such quantitative methods are the *parameter method* and the *factor summation method*.

The parameter method implies that life cycle costs of future systems are estimated through statistics from earlier similar systems and systems in operation. Since earlier systems are not identical to the one being studied, parametric models are built to explain how the total life cycle cost depends on different types of parameters. The factor summation method implies that the costs of the project are broken down in a hierarchical form to factors at the lowest possible level. Based on these costings, decisions are then made. The parameter method is best suited at early stages, whereas the factor summation method is better suited at later stages. At very early stages, when there is still not enough knowledge of future system solutions, quantitative methods are useless.

Of course, it can be difficult to achieve a realistic cost model taking into account the essential costs of the system. A cost model can be simple or extremely complex depending on the situation. An example of a very simple cost model for LCC-analysis, not including discounting of future costs, is

$$LCC = I + N \cdot (D+U+S) - R,$$

where

I = Initial costs
N = Life cycle factor in years
D = Running costs per annum
U = Maintenance costs per annum, direct costs
S = Standstill costs, proceeds losses
R = Residual value

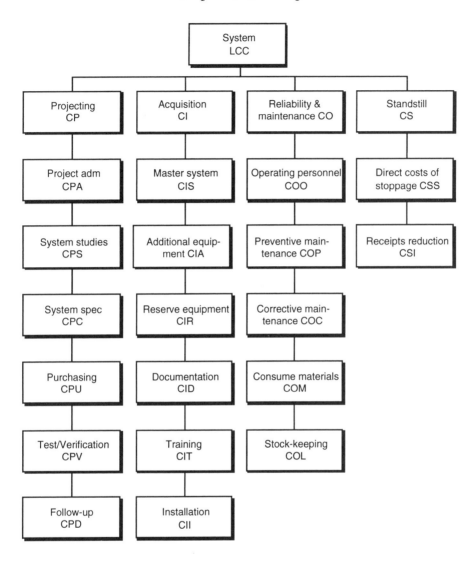

Figure 5.14 *An illustration of hierarchical breaking down of LCC into cost elements. The breaking down is done in such a way that the model will indicate what department is responsible for the different costs and what cost element is concerned. COP, for example, refers to "Cost, Operational Preventive Maintenance". (After Mekanresultat 84216.)*

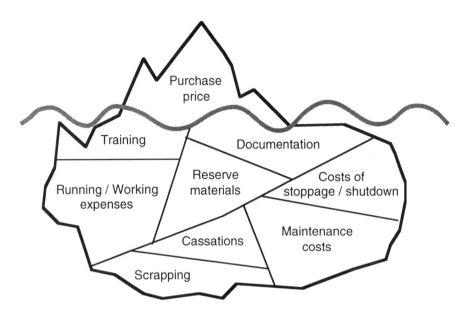

Figure 5.15   *The so called "iceberg" which illustrates that Life Cycle Cost, LCC, of a system comprises all costs during the system's life cycle, not only the purchase price, which is the immediate cost visible above the water surface.*

The result of Life Cycle Cost analyses is appropriate, among other things, for the valuation of various design solutions and for the assessment of different kinds of maintenance design. Life Cycle Cost should always be put in relation to the use or efficiency that can be obtained from the product in the form of technical achievement, dependability and availability.

5.7 Reliability Growth

Taking advantage of experience from older designs is extremely important for the design of reliable products. It is also very important that the designers are promptly informed about faults regarding new products in use. Otherwise it is not possible to take measures quickly to increase reliability. Therefore a systematic feedback of reliability information from usage and tests is important for the designer. By considering this information and interpreting it correctly it is possible for the designer to make changes in the design to increase reliability. Also with respect to reliability the PDSA-cycle for continuous improvement has to be in active use.

There are many different models for describing reliability growth during, for instance, reliability testing. However, here we only want to stress the general principle that the design process should be organized in such a way that from a reliability aspect it can be looked upon as an automatic control system. From a general point of view every activity should be built in such a way that resources are set aside for improvement work. Test results and results from usage have to be taken care of efficiently so that well considered changes of design are performed as soon as enough information is available. The efficiency of feedback from testing and usage to design sets the level of reliability growth.

Adopting a somewhat broader approach, the design process should be seen as an evolution. Design solutions that have turned out to fullfil the demands of the users when confronted with reality, must be taken advantage of when designing new products, while solutions that have caused problems in connection with usage should be abandoned or modified.

Generally speaking, a certain conservatism is sound from a reliability point of view. Completely new design solutions often have weak points which, if they are not spotted at the latest during test, might cause the manufacturer and the user serious problems. However, certain caution also has to be observed when using old design solutions in new products. If the conditions of usage and environment are not similar there might be problems.

It is always important to identify potential problem fields when analysing environment and usage at early stages of product definition in order to prevent expensive surprises during testing.

5.8 Product Liability

Every manufacturer has a responsibility for damage and injuries that the product causes to people and property. It is said that the manufacturer has *product liability*. This liability means that the manufacturer may have to pay damages to those who have been affected. Sometimes it might also lead to other legal consequences. The importer has sometimes taken over the liability of the manufacturer. *Product safety* is thus one important characteristic of the product. In connection with cases regarding product liability it is important to be able to show that the product has been systematically and carefully scrutinised in respect of possible damage that it can cause. Thus documentation of various reliability activities performed during product development is important. In order to offer insurance, the insurance companies as a rule demand various kinds of documentation.

In the USA the number of product liability lawsuits is huge and the damages awarded are often very high. This depends partly on the fact that US lawyers get part of the damages the court decides upon. If they lose the case they get no fees.

A common European legislation within the field of product liability was initiated in 1985 by the Common Market. A description of the development in the Common Market and EFTA is described in a publication by ORGALIME (1989). ORGALIME is an association of mechanical industries in Europe.

The bill has now been made permanent as national laws of product liability in most countries within the Common Market and EFTA. The new act means that *strict liability* is introduced instead of the earlier fault liability. Earlier, those affected had to prove that the damage had been caused by negligence on behalf of the manufacturer or the distributor. Strict liability means that the burden of proof is up to the manufacturer. This means that great demands will be made on the manufacturer. He has to have systems of quality assurance which are carefully adhered to, well documented and contain activities which in a number of ways take product safety into consideration.

Finally it should be noted that the product liability laws so far only deal with goods and not services. Thoughts of creating a common act within the Common Market regarding services that have been incorrectly performed have however been initiated.

5.9   Notes and References

Classical books on reliability theory, even though they partly are quite advanced, are Barlow & Proschan (1965, 1981), Mann, Shafer & Singpurwalla (1974), Nelson (1982) and Bain (1991). Another more practically oriented and highly recommended book is O'Conner (1991).

A general article regarding reliability with many references is Bergman (1985). The history of reliability is discussed in Barlow (1984).

Repairable systems and different models of maintenance are discussed in the book by Ascher & Feingold (1984) which is well worth considering.

Among the models of reliability growth, those by Duane, see Duane (1964), and Crow, for instance Crow (1972), have been paid most attention. Several applications of these models and their variations have been introduced at the "Annual Reliability and Maintainability Symposium", a conference about reliability and maintenance held every year in January in the USA. Proceedings from these conferences can be bought from ASQC, American Society for Quality Control.

Books which deal with product liability are ORGALIME (1989) and Roche (1989). A journal published once a month is Product Liability International, Lloyd's of London Press Ltd.

The concept of Life Cycle Cost is discussed in Blanchard (1978) and Isaacson (1990).

An introductory book discussing Total Productivity Maintenance is Nakajima (1988). Other book discussing Total Productivity Maintenance are Tajiri & Gotoh (1992) and Suzuki (1992).

We would also like to mention that there are a number of periodicals within the field of reliability. Some of them are Quality and Reliability Engineering International, IEEE Transactions on Reliability, International Journal of Reliability, Quality and Safety Engineering, Microelectronics and Reliability, and Reliability Engineering and System Safety.

6 Reliability Analysis

Within the field of reliability engineering a great number of techniques for system analyses have been developed. We will briefly deal with some of the most important ones, namely graphical methods for analysis of failure data, system reliability analysis, reliability prediction, Failure Mode and Effects Analysis (FMEA) and Fault Tree Analysis (FTA).

6.1 Graphical Methods

Feedback from faults experienced in tests and usage is of primarily importance in reliability work. We will here deal with some simple graphical methods regarding analysis of failure data of non-repairable units, namely *probability plotting* and *TTT-plotting*. We will also study analysis of failure data from repairable systems on log-log paper.

6.1.1 Probability Plotting

The scale of a probability plotting paper is designed in such a way that the distribution of the time to failure corresponds to a line. With the help of failure data an estimation of this distribution is made on the probability paper. If the estimated distribution fits fairly well to a line this indicates that the distributional assumption may be reasonable.

There are probability papers for most common life distributions. We will here only briefly describe the *Weibull Probability Paper* or more briefly *Weibull Paper*. In Appendix A a short description of a probability paper for the normal distribution is given.

Assume that n units have been tested until they have failed. Furthermore, assume that the times to failure have been rearranged in size order, so we have the observations $t_1 < t_2 < ... < t_n$. Then t_j is plotted on one of the scales (in general the horizontal one) against an estimator of $F(t_j)$, i.e. the probability to fail before the time t_j, on the other one. This estimator can be made in different ways. Here we choose to use *mean ranges* by which is meant that t_j is plotted against $j/(n+1)$.

Example 6.1

Assume that we have tested nine units and got the ordered times to failure: 1.36, 2.00, 3.20, 3.80, 5.00, 5.90, 7.00, 9.00 and 11.20.

Then we plot $t_1 = 1.36$ against the mean range 0.10, $t_2 = 2.00$ against the mean range 0.20, ..., $t_9 = 11.20$ against 0.90. The result is illustrated in Figure 6.2. As the plotted points fit well to a line there is no indication that the assumption that the observations are from a Weibull distribution is incorrect.

With the help of the probability paper it is possible to estimate the parameters α and β in the Weibull distribution function $F(t) = 1 - \exp(-(t/\alpha)^\beta)$, $t \geq 0$. It is also possible to estimate different measures of time to failure such as L_{50}, L_{10} and MTTF (see Appendix A for a description of L_{50} and L_{10}). How this is done is illustrated in Figures 6.1 and 6.2.

If the failure data are incomplete, for instance if the test has been interrupted before all the units have failed, the plotting has to be done according to a slightly different technique (see e.g. Nelson, 1982).

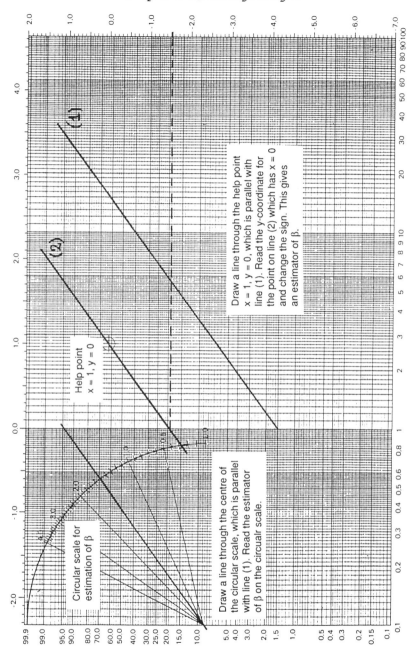

Figure 6.1   Illustration of a Weibull paper and how it is used for plot-ting and estimation of parameters.

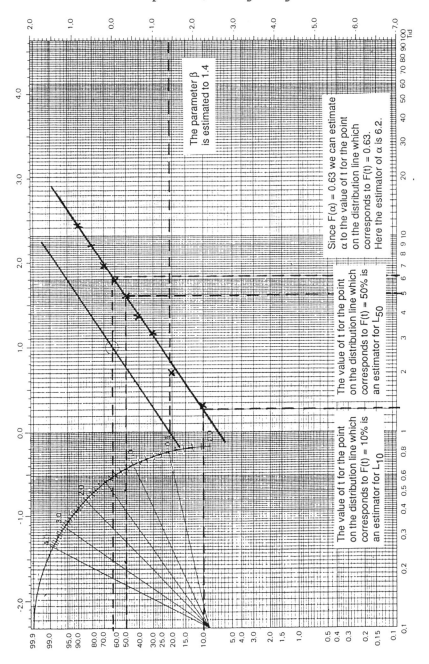

The parameter β is estimated to 1.4

Since $F(\alpha) = 0.63$ we can estimate α to the value of t for the point on the distribution line which corresponds to $F(t) = 0.63$. Here the estimator of α is 6.2.

The value of t for the point on the distribution line which corresponds to $F(t) = 50\%$ is an estimator for L_{50}

The value of t for the point on the distribution line which corresponds to $F(t) = 10\%$ is an estimator for L_{10}

Figure 6.2   A Weibull paper illustrating the material and the corresponding estimation procedures in Example 6.1.

6.1.2 TTT-plotting

TTT-plotting, where TTT is short for "Total Time on Test" is a completely different technique from plotting on a probability paper. The so called *TTT-plot* gives a picture of the failure data which is independent of the scale and is situated completely within the unit square with corners in (0,0), (0,1), (1,0) and (1,1). The deviation of the plot from the diagonal gives, among other things, information about the deviation of the life distribution from the exponential distribution.

The TTT-plot of an ordered sample $0 = t_0 < t_1 < t_2 < ... < t_n$ of times to failure is obtained by plotting, for $j = 0, 1, ..., n$, the points $(j/n, S_j/S_n)$, where $S_0 = 0$ and

$$S_j = nt_1 + (n-1)(t_2-t_1) + ... + (n-j+1)(t_j-t_{j-1}) \quad \text{for } j = 1, 2, ..., n$$

and then connecting these points with line segments. As $0 \le j/n \le 1$ and $0 \le S_j/S_n \le 1$ the TTT-plot starts at (0,0) and ends at (1,1) and is situated completely within the unit square; see Figure 6.3.

Example 6.2

Assume that we have tested n = 9 units and have obtained the following times to failure (see Example 6.1):

1.36	2.00	3.20	3.86	5.00	5.90	7.00	9.00	11.20
t_1	t_2	t_3	t_4	t_5	t_6	t_7	t_8	t_9

This gives the following values of the total time on test:

$S_1 = 9 \cdot 1.36 = 12.24$ $S_2 = S_1 + 8(2.00-1.36) = 17.36$
$S_3 = S_2 + 7(3.20-2.00) = 25.76$ $S_4 = S_3 + 6(3.86-3.20) = 29.72$
$S_5 = S_4 + 5(5.00-3.86) = 35.42$ $S_6 = S_5 + 4(5.90-5.00) = 39.02$
$S_7 = S_6 + 3(7.00-5.90) = 42.32$ $S_8 = S_7 + 2(9.00-7.00) = 46.32$
$S_9 = S_8 + 1(11.20-9.00) = 48.52$

In order to draw the TTT-plot of the material we calculate

$S_0/S_9 = 0$ $S_1/S_9 = 0.25$

$S_2/S_9 = 0.36$ $S_3/S_9 = 0.53$

$S_4/S_9 = 0.61$ $S_5/S9 = 0.73$

$S_6/S_9 = 0.80$ $S_7/S_9 = 0.87$

$S_8/S_9 = 0.95$ $S_9/S_9 = 1.00$

If in a unit square we plot the ten points $(0,0)$, $(1/9,0.25)$, $(2/9,0.36)$, $(3/9,0.53)$, $(4/9,0.61)$, $(5/9,0.73)$, $(6/9,0.80)$, $(7/9,0.87)$, $(8/9,0.95)$ and $(9/9,1.00)$ and connect them with line segments we get the TTT-plot in Figure 6.3.

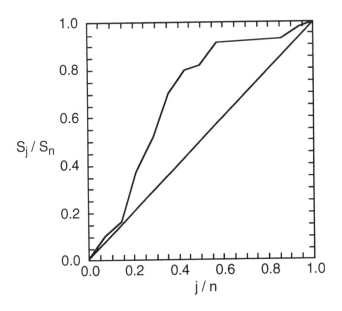

Figure 6.3   *TTT-plot showing the material in Example 6.2.*

When the number of failure times n increases, the TTT-plot approaches a curve which is characteristic of the underlying life distribution F(t). This curve is called the *scaled TTT-transform.* Accordingly, the TTT-plot can be interpreted as an estimator of the scaled TTT-transform of F(t).

Hence we may find a suitable life distribution model of our failure data by comparing the TTT-plot to scaled TTT-transforms of different life distributions and then choosing the life distribution whose TTT-transform best corresponds to the TTT-plot. This was the first application of the TTT-plotting technique that was introduced by Barlow & Campo (1975). How the TTT-plot approaches the TTT-transform is illustrated in Figure 6.4.

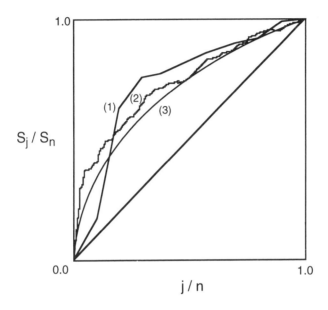

Figure 6.4   *TTT-plots based on simulated data from a Weibull distribution with $\beta = 2.0$, $n = 10$ i (1) and $\beta = 2.0$, $n = 100$ i (2) and the TTT-transform of a Weibull distribution with shape parameter $\beta = 2.0$ i (3). (From Bergman & Klefsjö, 1984.)*

The TTT-plot also gives information about the failure rate of the current kind of unit. It is possible to show that increasing failure rate of a life distribution corresponds to the fact that the TTT-transform is concave (i.e. the slope is declining). A TTT-plot that shows a concave pattern is therefore probably based on times to failure from a unit with increasing failure rate. Similarly, a convex

TTT-plot reveals that the current kind of unit probably has a decreasing failure rate. For example it seems reasonable that the distribution underlying the TTT-plot in Figure 6.3 has an increasing failure rate. The same conclusion can be drawn from the TTT-plot in Figure 6.5

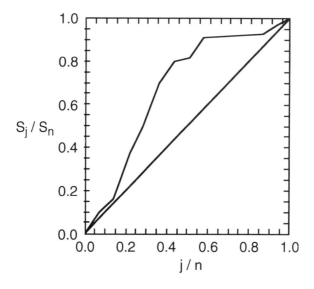

Figure 6.5   *TTT-plot showing times to failure from engines of dumpers that have been used in a Swedish mine. (From Kumar, et al., 1989.)*

The TTT-plotting technique is also useful in many other situations such as maintenance or burn-in optimization (see Bergman & Klefsjö, 1984, 1985). It is also possible to generalize the TTT-plot to the case where the data are not complete but contain different kinds of censored or truncated failure data; see e.g. Westberg & Klefsjö (1994).

6.1.3 Analysis on log-log-paper

When analysing data from a repairable system it is often assumed that the system has been restored to the "as-good-as-new" state, i.e. maximum repair has been done. This assumption means that all the failure times (time to the first failure, time between the first and second failure, etc) are observations from the same life distribution. It is then possible to analyse the failure data by using methods for non-repairable units, for instance those just studied.

However, generally an assumption of maximum repair is unrealistic and incorrect. Many times the truth is closer to a minimal repair than to a maximum one. Then the times between failures are neither independent nor do they originate from the same life distribution. It is then not possible to use the same methods as for non-repairable units. When analysing data from a repairable system it is therefore important to check whether a trend or any form of dependency can be found (techniques for that are described in e.g. Ascher & Feingold, 1984). Here we will very briefly discuss how it is possible to analyse failure data from a repairable system.

Under fairly general conditions, and above all in connection with minimal repair, the *failure intensity* $\lambda(t)$ at the time t can be approximated by a power of t, i.e.

$$\lambda(t) = \frac{\beta}{\alpha} \left(\frac{t}{\alpha} \right)^{\beta-1}$$

The expected number of failures before the time t, which we denote $E(N(t))$, can under the same conditions be written

$$E(N(t)) = \Lambda(t) = \int_0^t \lambda(s)ds = \left(\frac{t}{\alpha} \right)^{\beta}$$

It is said that the failures occur according to a *power law process*. For a power law process we therefore have

$$\ln E(N(t)) = \beta \ln t - \beta \ln \alpha \tag{6.1}$$

i.e. ln E(N(t)) is a linear function of ln t. A reasonable estimator of E(N(t)) is the number of failures that actually have occurred at t. If we accordingly estimate $E(N(t_j))$ by j we get the relation

$$\ln j = \beta \ln t_j - \beta \ln \alpha \tag{6.2}$$

In order to check whether the power law process is a suitable model we can plot ln j against ln t_j. If the power law process is suitable the plotted points are expected to coincide roughly with a straight line, the slope of which is then an estimate of β.

If failures occur according to a power law process with $\beta > 1$ the risk of a failure increases with the age of the system. The times between failures have in other words a tendency to decrease successively. If $\beta < 1$ the times between failures tend to become longer and if $\beta = 1$ the times between failures are independent and exponentially distributed.

Example 6.4

Assume that we have studied a system until seven failures have occurred and we have obtained the following times between the successive failures

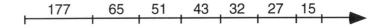

Figure 6.6   *Times between failures for a repairable system.*
(From Ascher, © 1981 IEEE).

In Figure 6.7 ln j is plotted against ln t_j. The figure does not indicate any objection against a power law process model since the points lie roughly on a line.

Furthermore, the slope of the adjusted line is k = 2.33, which will be our estimator of β. As $\beta > 1$ the intensity function increases with the age, i.e. the intervals between the failures tend to become shorter and shorter. This coincides well with Figure 6.6.

In order to estimate the parameter α in the power law process it is possible to use the linear relation (6.2) in different ways, depending on what the line looks like; see Figure 6.7.

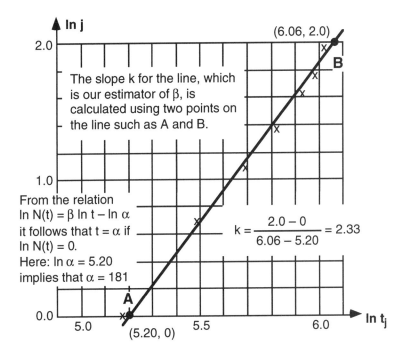

Figure 6.7   Illustration of ln j against ln t_j for the values in Figure 6.6.

6.2. System Reliability Analysis

When a system built of components or part systems is studied from a reliability point of view the structure is often illustrated with a *reliability block diagram* as illustrated in Figure 6.8.

117

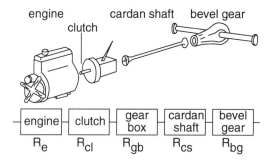

Figure 6.8   A simple system and its reliability block diagram.

6.2.1   Series Systems

Assume that we have n components with reliability functions $R_1(t)$, $R_2(t)$, ..., $R_n(t)$ and failure rates $z_1(t)$, $z_2(t)$, ..., $z_n(t)$, respectively. If a system works as long as all the components work we have, from a reliability point of view, a *series system*.

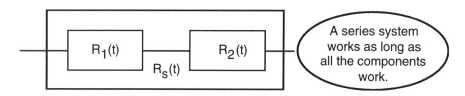

Figure 6.9   Reliability block diagram for a series system.

If a series system is to survive for the time t all the components have to survive for the time t. If the components fail independently of each other this means that the reliability function of the system is equal to the product of the reliability functions of the components, i.e.

$$R_s(t) = R_1(t)R_2(t) \ldots R_n(t)$$

The failure rate of the series system can then be shown to equal the sum of the failure rates of the components, i.e.

$$z_s(t) = z_1(t) + z_2(t) + \dots + z_n(t).$$

If especially the time to failure for every component is exponentially distributed with the same failure rate λ, i.e. $z_j(t) = \lambda$ for $j = 1$, $2, \dots, n$, the failure rate of the system is $z_s(t) = n\lambda$. This means that the system also has a constant failure rate, i.e. the time to failure of the system is also exponentially distributed. Its Mean Time to Failure, MTTF, becomes

$$\text{MTTF} = \int_0^\infty R_s(t)dt = \int_0^\infty e^{-n\lambda t}dt = \frac{1}{n\lambda}$$

where $1/\lambda$ is MTTF for an individual component. In other words, the MTTF of the system is in this case inversely proportional to the number of units connected in series.

6.2.2 Parallel Systems

If the system works as long as at least one component works we have a *parallel system*. Such a system is thus made up of a number of units in active redundancy; cf. 5.4.1. A parallel system has failed at the time t only if all the units have then failed. If failures of the different units occur independently of each other the life distribution $F_p(t)$ of the parallel system is equal to

$$F_p(t) = F_1(t)F_2(t) \dots F_n(t)$$

This means that the expression for the reliability function of the system $R_p(t)$ becomes

$$R_p(t) = 1 - (1-R_1(t))(1-R_2(t)) \dots (1-R_n(t))$$

When we are confronted with parallel structures, however, we cannot get a simple connection between the failure rate of the system and the failure rates of the components.

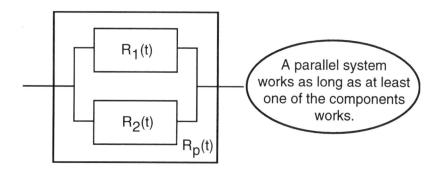

Figure 6.10   Reliability block diagram of a parallel structure.

Observe that a reliability block diagram can look different from "reality". If for instance two diodes are connected in series to rectify and the failure is a short circuit then, from a reliability point of view, the diodes are connected in parallel.

6.2.3   Other Systems

If the systems are simpler and built of series and parallel structures it is possible to derive the reliability function by using *successive reductions,* provided that the reliability functions of the components are known.

Example 6.3

Assume that the components in the reliability block diagram in Figure 6.11 are independent and that at a certain time t the reliability functions are

$$R_A(t) = R_B(t) = 0.90 \qquad R_C(t) = R_D(t) = 0.80 \qquad R_E(t) = 0.95$$

For the series system made up of the components A and B we get $R_{AB}(t) = R_A(t) R_B(t) = 0.81$. For the parallel system with C and D we get $R_{CD}(t) = R_C(t) + R_D(t) - R_{CD}(t) = 2 \cdot 0.80 - 0.64 = 0.96$. For the parallel block with AB and CD we get $R_{ABCD}(t) = 0.81 + 0.96 - 0.81 \cdot 0.96 = 0.9924$.

For the whole system we finally get $R_{syst}(t) = 0.9924 \cdot 0.95 = 0.94278 \approx 0.94$.

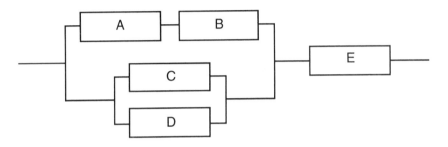

Figure 6.11 Reliability block diagram for Example 6.3.

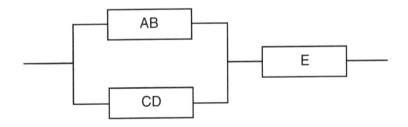

Figure 6.12 Reliability block diagram for Example 6.3.

6.2.4 Comments on the Independence Assumption

In Sections 6.2.1 - 6.2.3 we have assumed that failures of the different units occur independently of each other. However, this assumption is seldom true. For series systems an assumption of independence generally leads to the estimated value underestimating the true value of the reliability function. For a parallel system the corresponding assumption instead usually leads to a value which is too high.

It is very common when estimating reliability to assume that failures of the different units occur independently of each other. However, we would like to warn against uncritical assumptions of independence. Different kinds of dependency are discussed for instance in Barlow & Proschan (1981).

6.3 Reliability Prediction

To predict is to try to tell in advance what will happen. On the basis of available information the future reliability of a product or a system has to be predicted. The available information can be experience from usage or testing of the product, corresponding experience from similar products, experience from usage of the components included or basic data in general which in turn are based on material from which experience has been gained. A description of routines regarding reliability prediction is given in Figure 6.13.

6.3.1 Prediction by Using MIL-HDBK 217

For prediction, failure data can be found in many different data bases, whose contents vary in part. As far as electronics is concerned there are for instance prediction models based on large-scale data collected in the *Military Handbook 217, MIL-HDBK 217.*

The failure rate models in MIL-HDBK 217 are of the type

$$\lambda_p = \lambda_b \, \pi_Q \, \pi_E \, \pi_A \ldots$$

where λ_b is a base value of the failure rate and π_Q, π_E, π_A, ... are different correction factors. With the help of these correction factors it is possible to take into consideration factors such as quality level, environment and load.

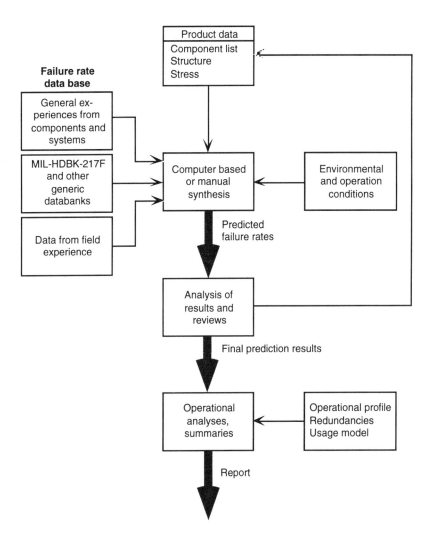

Figure 6.13   Routines regarding reliability prediction. (From Göran Holmberg, personal communication.)

The values of the failure rate and the correction factors in MIL-HDBK 217 are brought up to date regularly. The latest version is designated MIL-HDBK 217F and was published in 1991. The technique of using correction factors is still connected with great uncertainty and should be used with care.

The number of correction factors varies between different kinds of units. For the failure rates of resistors, for instance, this model applies

$$\lambda_p = \lambda_b \, \pi_E \, \pi_R \, \pi_Q.$$

Here π_E is an environmental factor, π_R is a factor dependent on the resistance and π_Q is a quality factor.

It should be mentioned that MIL-HDBK 217 always works with a constant failure rate, i.e. the time to failure is assumed to be exponentially distributed.

Likewise it should be mentioned that there are several other data bases regarding failure data. Examples of these data bases are OREDA (Offshore Reliability Data), meant for the off-shore industry, SYREL (System Reliability Service Data Bank) and NPRDS (Nuclear Plant Reliability Data System), both containing failure data from the nuclear power industry, and the T-book, which contains reliability data for components in Swedish boiling water reactors.

6.3.2 Use and Abuse of Predictions

The reliability data that are available in different data bases are of varying usefulness. The handbook MIL-HDBK 217 contains prediction models for electronic components. Such units are usually built of standard components with roughly the same level of stress and operating environment. This makes the prediction models based on failure data regarding electronic components fairly reliable. Still there is some criticism of prediction according to MIL-

HDBK 217. Reliability data for other units, for instance mechanical, should always be used with caution if they have not been produced under identical or very similar conditions. Furthermore, very few units have the same level of standardization. One exception is bearings.

If failure data have to be transferred from one kind of environment to another great caution must be taken. The definitions of failure used must be observed carefully. Furthermore, human management is of vital importance. If the conditions are different from those prevailing when collecting the data, reliability prediction is of little value. It is also important to remember that time to failure for many non-electronic units is heavily dependent on time, which makes prediction even harder.

Reliability predictions based on mathematical models and failure data from different sources such as MIL-HDBK 217 have to be used with caution and judgement. The predictions should not be used as absolute values of system reliability but rather as a source of information about where to allocate resources for different reliability improvement activities.

6.4 Failure Mode and Effects Analysis

Failure Mode and Effects Analysis, FMEA, is a very useful method for reliability analysis. It involves a systematic check-up of a product or a process, its function, failure modes, failure causes and failure consequences.

The idea is simple. For every failure mode at a low level, for instance the component level, the corresponding failure consequences are analysed at the local level and at the system level. This, however, demands a thorough knowledge of the functions of the components and their contributions to the function of the system. FMEA can be performed as a qualitative analysis of the connections between failure modes and the corresponding failure consequences at the system level and how it is possible to take measures to prevent failures or reduce the consequences of failures. But quantification of failures and the effects of failures can also take place.

FMEA can be used in many different ways. Qualitative and very rough analyses can suitably be initiated already during the stages of planning and definition of a project. The aim here can be to investigate whether it is possible to fullfil the reliability demands of the market. During the design and development stages a more detailed, quantitative FMEA may be used for various reliability activities. Such an FMEA can serve as a very good basis for a *design review,* which is a systematic analysis of the design by a group of persons with different knowledge and experience. These kinds of FMEA are called *design-FMEA.*

In connection with preproduction engineering, *process-FMEA* is a way of evaluating the manufacturing process. Generally, malfunctions of the product are studied and an analysis is made of how these malfunctions can be caused by disturbances in the manufacturing process. Process-FMEA can serve as a basis both for improving the process before and after the start of manufacturing and as a basis for the design of the process control.

The result of an FMEA is entered on an FMEA form. This form can be designed differently depending on the purpose of the failure effect analysis. Examples of forms are shown in Figures 6.14 and 6.15.

The planning of the work regarding design-FMEA may contain the following steps

- definition and limiting of the system
- choice of complexity level
- check-up of the functions of the system
- check-up of the functions of the components

- identification of possible failure modes
- identification of consequences of the possible failure modes
- possibilities of failure detection and localization of failures
- judgement of how serious the failure is
- identification of failure causes
- study dependence between failures
- documentation.

A similar list can be made for a process-FMEA.

FMEA is an efficient method when it is applied on systems where failures of components immediately lead to system failures. For complex systems where failures occur in connection with certain combinations of situations the analysis has to be supplemented, for instance by Fault Tree Analysis.

Sometimes a quantitative analysis also is done when using design-FMEA. In that case we often talk about *FMECA (Failure Mode, Effects and Criticality Analysis)*. The main idea is to consider each failure mode of every component of the system and quantify certain values in order to rank the different failure modes. There are several procedures for this numerical analysis. One is to quantify

- F: the probability of failure, i.e. quantify the risk for that failure mode to occur

- A: seriousness, i.e. are the consequences of that failure mode serious when it occurs

- U: probability of detection, i.e. how big the probability is that the failure mode will be detected when it occurs.

Often the assessments are based on subjective judgements on a scale of type 1-5 or 1-10. This three quantities are then summarized in a *Risk Priority Number RPN,* often defined as the product of F, A and U, but also other definitions and scales are common.

FAILURE MODE & EFFECT ANALYSIS - DESIGN / PROCESS

ITEM	PART No NAME ISSUE	FUNCTION OR PROCESS	FAILURE MODE	EFFECT OF FAILURE	CAUSE OF FAILURE	CURRENT CONTROLS	CURRENT STATUS				RECOMMENDED CORRECTIVE ACTION	ACTION BY	ACTION TAKEN	REVISED STATUS			
							OCC	SEV	DET	RPN				OCC	SEV	DET	RPN
1		Control of fuel flow	Crack	Reduced functionality	Material fault		2	6	...	12	No action	...	...	2	6	...	12
					High loading		6	6	...	36	Strengthen	Mary	Strengthened	1	6	...	6

Figure 6.14   A form intended for design-FMEA.

FAILURE MODE & EFFECT ANALYSIS - DESIGN / PROCESS

ITEM	PART No NAME ISSUE	FUNCTION OR PROCESS	FAILURE MODE	EFFECT OF FAILURE	CAUSE OF FAILURE	CURRENT CONTROLS	CURRENT STATUS				RECOMMENDED CORRECTIVE ACTION	ACTION BY	ACTION TAKEN	REVISED STATUS			
							OCC	SEV	DET	RPN				OCC	SEV	DET	RPN
3		Mounting of throttle valve on spindle	Throttle valve loose	Functional disturbance	Screws not tightened	…	6	6	2	72	Tighten with torque wrench	Neil	Tightened with torque wrench	2	6	2	24
					Wrong screw	…	1	6	2	.12	No action			1	6	2	12

Figure 6.15   A form intended for process-FMEA.

129

This RPN number indicates which failure mode is most critical and where improvement activities should be initiated. However, RPN numbers should be interpreted and used with great care. Only their relative size should be studied and not their numerical value. The difference between 100 and 110, say, is probably small,in particular when we consider the uncertainty included in the numbers which in general are based on subjective judgements.

6.5 Fault Tree Analysis

When performing a quantitative as well as a qualitative analysis of complex systems, *Fault Tree Analysis, FTA,* can be an excellent tool. The fault tree is a logical chart of occurrences which illustrates the connections between a non-desired occurrence on system level and the causes on lower system levels of this occurrence.

The very first application of Fault Tree Analysis was made in 1962 by Watson at Bell Telephone Laboratories to analyse the Minuteman Launch Control System. The technique was then further developed by the North American Space Industry and the method is now often used when analysing the reliability of a range of products. Names usually mentioned in connection with the development of FTA are D.F. Haasl, H.A. Watson, J.B. Fussell and W.E. Vesely.

The construction of fault trees often results in an increased understanding of how the system has been built and of its reliability. The fault tree also provides possibilities to detect critical failure modes even when component data are not at hand.

The design of a fault tree begins by specifying the non-desired top event. The immediate causes of this non-desired top event have to be considered and they are connected to the top event with a suitable logic gate, usually an "or-gate" or an "and-gate"; see Figure 6.16. This procedure is repeated until a basic fault occurrence level is reached.

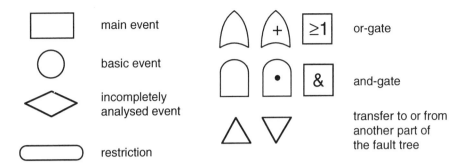

Figure 6.16   Some common symbols used in Fault Tree Analysis.

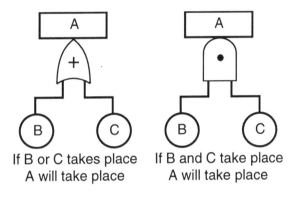

If B or C takes place
A will take place

If B and C take place
A will take place

Figure 6.17   Illustration of the usage of fault tree symbols.

A simple illustration of a comparison between a block diagram and a fault tree is shown in Figure 6.18.

It is important that the decomposition to the basic level takes place in as small steps as possible in order to make it possible to detect fault combinations that have not earlier been detected. If the system in question is made up of many components this might lead to trees that are big and hard to grasp. It is then possible to choose a lower level of decomposition provided that the basic occurrences are independent of each other.

131

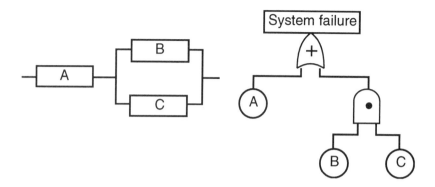

Figure 6.18   Illustration of a simple fault tree.

Let us study the simplified illustration of a hand-brake system in Figure 6.19.

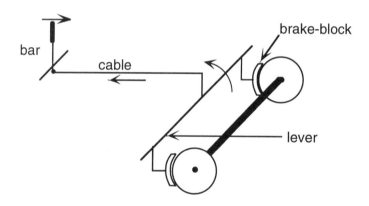

Figure 6.19 A simple hand brake system.

We only consider the failures "brake blocks worn" and "cable broken" and use the following notations

    A: no system brake action
    B: left wheel - no brake action
    C: right wheel - no brake action

X: left brake block worn

Y: right brake block worn

W: cable broken

The fault tree for the occurrence of A in this system can look like Figure 6.20.

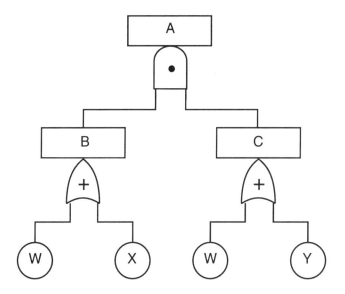

Figure 6.20 A fault tree for the system in Figure 6.19.

Today there are a number of computer programs for designing fault trees. Many of these also contain possibilities to make quantitative analyses based on the fault tree derived. One example of this can be found in Figure 6. 22.

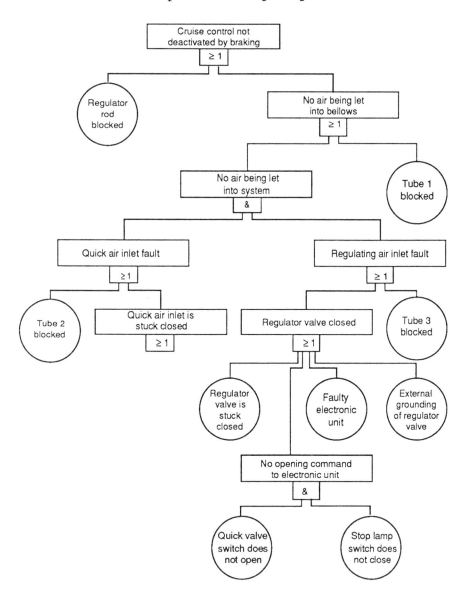

Figure 6.21   A fault tree describing the top event "cruise control not deactivated by braking". The fault tree was included in a safety analysis of a certain type of cruise control, which besides electronical components also has mechanical and pneumatic components. (From Gunnerhed, 1991.)

134

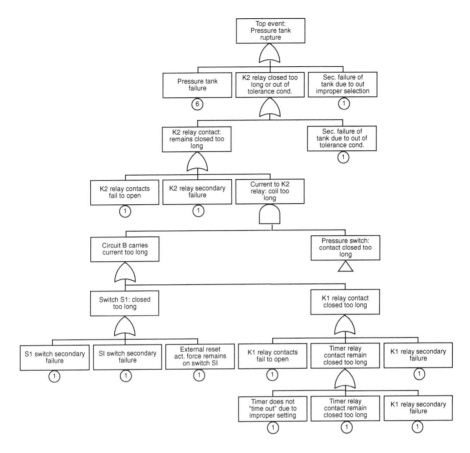

Figure 6.22   A fault tree drawn by RISK SPECTRUM, a software developed by RELCON Teknik AB, Stockholm. The top event is "a crack in the tank" of a nuclear power reactor.

6.6 Notes and References

Classic books on reliability are Mann, Schafer & Singpurwalla (1974), Kapur & Lamberson (1977), Henley & Kumamoto (1981), Cox (1984), Bain (1991) and O'Connor (1991). The books by Henley & Kumamoto and O'Conner are those that mostly have a practical approach. O'Connor's book is recommended in the first place.

135

A recent, rather practically oriented, book on reliability and risk assessment is Aven (1992). Also Kececioglu (1991) is practically oriented.

Ascher & Feingold (1984) provides an interesting discussion about analysis of data from repairable systems. Nelson (1982) deals with different kinds of statistical conclusions from complete as well as censored failure data from non-repairable systems. In Nelson (1990) statistical models regarding accelerated life tests are discussed. A more advanced book on the handling of reliability data when also explanatory variables are observed is Crowder et al. (1991). See also Lawless (1982) and Cox & Oakes (1984).

An easy-to-grasp article dealing with reliability has been written by Bergman (1985). The power law process and failure data analysis with the help of this model are described in a way that is fairly easy to grasp in Rigdon & Basu (1989, 1990). In all these articles there are also plenty of further references on this subject.

The two famous books by Barlow & Proschan (1965, 1981) deal with fairly advanced reliability theory. Bayesian methods in reliability analysis are discussed in Martz & Waller (1982).

FMEA can be read about in MIL-STD 1629 "Procedures for Performing a Failure Mode, Effects and Criticality Analysis" and in IEC Standard 812. FTA is described in Vesely et al. (1981), IEC Standard 1025 and Henley & Kumamoto (1981). A review paper of Fault Tree Analysis is Lee et al. (1985).

7   Design of Experiments

To be able to base decisions on facts and to perform quality improvements it is necessary to collect and treat data systematically. However, the facts naturally accumulated during product and process operation are not enough. Knowledge accumulation has to begin earlier and it has to be accelerated. For that purpose experiments also have to be planned and performed early in product and process development. Well planned experiments provide rapid knowledge of the values that have to be chosen for design and process parameters to achieve the best possible products or processes at the lowest cost level.

Design of experiments therefore is a very important stage in quality improvement. This is highlighted further in Chapter 8, where we also deal with a more advanced usage of design of experiments as a means of obtaining robust products and processes for design optimization. In this chapter we shall describe some basic principles in the design of experiments.

7.1   One-Factor-at-a-Time Experiments

The discussion in this section is based on an example from Box, Hunter & Hunter (1978). Suppose that a maximized yield from a chemical process is wanted. Influencing factors that have been identified are the time t in the reactor tank and the temperature T in the tank. Assume further that a *one-factor-at-a-time experiment* is used. At first the temperature is fixed at 225°C and then five tests are performed at different reaction times, see Figure 7.1.

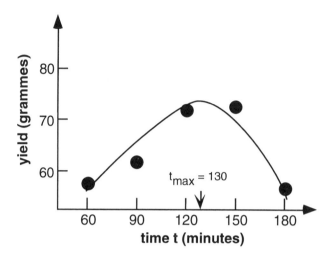

Figure 7.1   *The first test series, which for the set temperature 225°C gives the yield as a function of the reaction time. (From Box, Hunter & Hunter, 1978.)*

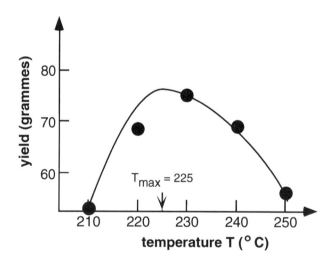

Figure 7.2   *The second test series, which for the set reaction time 130 minutes gives the yield as a function of the reaction temperature. (From Box, Hunter & Hunter, 1978.)*

From the test results in Figure 7.1 it is concluded that the reaction time that gives the best result is about 130 minutes. As it now "is known" that the reaction time 130 minutes gives the best result, another series of tests is performed. The time is set to 130 minutes but the temperature varies. In this series it is established that the "best" reaction temperature is T = 225°C; see Figure 7.2.

In both cases about the same maximum yield has been achieved, i.e. 75 grammes. This can easily be interpreted as if the best combination of time and temperature actually has been found. However, the situation might be far from optimal, which is illustrated in Figure 7.3.

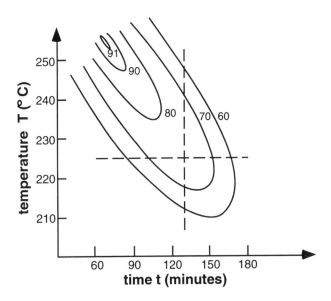

Figure 7.3   *The yield as a function of both time and temperature can look as above and still give the results shown in Figures 7.1 and 7.2 when tested according to a one-factor-at-a-time experiment. The figure shows response curves of the yield as a function of time and temperature. The figure indicates that t = 70 minutes and T = 255 °C is the best alternative. (From Box, Hunter & Hunter, 1978.)*

The moral of this example is that with a one-factor-at-a-time experiment it is not at all certain that the best yield is achieved. If two factors are interacting, i.e. the level of one factor influences the effect of changing the other, the "optimum" obtained may be far from optimal.

7.2 A Weighing Experiment

Assume that two objects A and B with the unknown weights w_A and w_B are to be weighed. At our disposal we have a balance scale giving a measurement error denoted e. Assume that this measurement error is completely random and has the known standard deviation $\sigma = 0.01$ in a suitable unit. Also assume that measurement errors that arise in different weighings are independent of each other. The task is to weigh the two objects with a measurement error whose standard deviation is at the most 0.0075. How many weighings have to be performed?

Assume that each of the objects is weighed twice and the values obtained are y_{A1} and y_{A2} for A and y_{B1} and y_{B2} for B. Each of these four values then has a measurement error with the standard deviation $\sigma = 0.01$. If then the mean values

$$\bar{y}_A = \frac{1}{2}(y_{A1} + y_{A2}) \quad \text{and} \quad \bar{y}_B = \frac{1}{2}(y_{B1} + y_{B2})$$

are formed, the standard deviation of these is equal to (see Appendix A)

$$\sqrt{\frac{0.01^2 + 0.01^2}{4}} = \frac{0.01}{\sqrt{2}} = 0.0071$$

Accordingly, these mean values do actually fulfil the set precision demands. With this technique every object is weighed twice, i.e. all in all four weighings are necessary.

In industry, experiments are often very expensive to perform. The number of experiments has therefore to be kept down. A natural question here is if it is possible to estimate the weights of the objects with the same precision using fewer than four weighings.

It is actually possible to solve the problem with two weighings. It is only necessary to determine the sum of the weights and the difference between them. Observe that the difference is easy to measure as there is a balance scale available.

Assume that the sum of the weights of the objects is $y_1 = w_A + w_B + e_1$, where e_1 is the measuring error from the first weighing and that the difference between the weights of the objects is $y_2 = w_A - w_B + e_2$, where e_2 is the measuring error from the second weighing. This gives

$$\frac{1}{2}(y_1 + y_2) = w_A + \frac{1}{2}(e_1 + e_2)$$

and

$$\frac{1}{2}(y_1 - y_2) = w_B + \frac{1}{2}(e_1 + e_2)$$

As $(e_1+e_2)/2$ and $(e_1-e_2)/2$ both have the standard deviation

$$\sqrt{\frac{0.01^2 + 0.01^2}{4}} = \frac{0.01}{\sqrt{2}} = 0.0071$$

$(y_1+y_2)/2$ and $(y_1-y_2)/2$ give the weights of the objects with sufficient accuracy.

By planning an experiment in a suitable way it is possible to reduce the costs of the experiment drastically. In order to achieve this effect a plan has to be drawn up before the experiment is started. Furthermore, we have to refrain from the fact that each of the experiments (in this case the weighing) gives immediate information about the things that attract our interest (in this case the individual weights). The interesting conclusion cannot be drawn until both the weighings have been performed. But this disadvantage is of limited importance in comparison with the fact that the experimental costs in this case have been halved.

7.3 A Factorial Design

The conclusion of the example in Section 7.1 is that wrong results might be achieved if a one-factor-at-a-time experiment is used. In the previous section it was illustrated that even if correct results are achieved, one-factor-at-a-time experiments might be very costly. This section shows what a simple alternative to one-factor-at-a-time experiments can look like. An example from Box & Bisgaard (1987) serves as a starting point.

It has been established from operating experience that the existence of cracks is a problem when using a certain kind of spring. Therefore there is a desire to examine what factors affect the crack initiation during usage. After a discussion it is decided that three factors are to be studied, namely

- the steel temperature before hardening (S)
- the oil temperature when hardening (O)
- the steel carbon content (C).

Level	Symbol	Steel temperature before hardening (°C)	Oil temperature (°C)	Carbon content (%)
Low	–	830	70	0.50
High	+	910	120	0.70

Table 7.1 The levels of the factors.

Two values, *levels,* are set for each factor. For each factor a low and a high value are chosen; see Table 7.1. For the low level we use the symbol "–" and for the high level "+".

If all possible combinations of the levels of the three factors are studied, eight different test situations result, see Table 7.2 and Figure 7.4. Such an experiment is called a *full factorial design.*

Run no.	Factor		
	S	O	C
1	–	–	–
2	+	–	–
3	–	+	–
4	+	+	–
5	–	–	+
6	+	–	+
7	–	+	+
8	+	+	+

Table 7.2   The eight test conditions

For each of these eight test conditions a batch of springs are manufactured. These springs are then exposed to a life test and the number of springs without cracks is observed. In order to avoid misleading influence from disturbing factors, like, say, parameter drifts in the manufacturing or measurement process, the tests are performed in a random order. The result can be illustrated using a cube, in which each corner represents a run, see Figure 7.5.

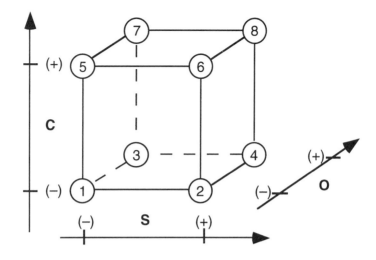

Figure 7.4   *The test conditions of the experiment illustrated as corners in a cube.*

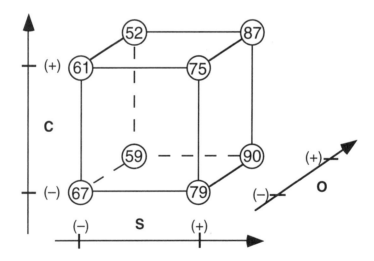

Figure 7.5   *Illustration of the test results obtained. For example "79" means that 79% of the springs that were produced at a high steel temperature, low carbon content and a low oil temperature did not have any cracks.*

It is now possible to estimate the effect of, say, raising the steel temperature S. For every combination of oil temperature (O) and carbon content (C) there are two observations, one for a low and one for a high steel temperature. Each of these differences gives an estimator of the effect of raising the steel temperature from 830°C to 910°C. The differences are $79 - 67 = 12$, $90 - 59 = 31$, $75 - 61 = 14$ and $87 - 52 = 35$, respectively. The arithmetic mean $(12+31+14+35)/4 = 23$ of these differences therefore results in an estimator of the average effect of raising the steel temperature from the low value to the high. Note that this value can also be obtained as the difference between the means $(79+90+75+87)/4$ and $(67+59+61+52)/4$ of the results achieved at low and high steel temperatures, respectively.

In the same way it is found that the average effect of raising the carbon content is $- 5$ and the average effect of raising the oil temperature is $+ 1.5$.

In order to get the same number of observations when estimating each of the three effects using a one-factor-at-a-time experiment, sixteen experiments would have been necessary. Such a plan of experiments still would not have given a fair result, because in this case the steel and oil temperatures seem to interact. When the oil temperature is low the effect of raising the steel temperature is not so high ($79 - 67 = 12$ and $75 - 61 = 14$, respectively) as when the oil temperature is high ($90 - 59 = 31$ and $87 - 52 = 35$, respectively). The interaction effect between the steel temperature and the oil temperature, which is designated SxO, can be estimated as half the difference between the average effects of a higher steel temperature when the oil temperature is high and low, respectively. Accordingly, the interaction effect can be estimated as

$$\left(\frac{31+35}{2} - \frac{12+14}{2} \right)\frac{1}{2} = 10$$

The halving of differencies can be considered as a pure convention. Note that it is not possible to estimate the effect of interaction with a simple one-factor-at-a-time experiment. In the same way as above it is possible to estimate the effects of interaction between steel temperature and carbon content (SxC gives 1.5) and between oil temperature and carbon content (OxC gives 0.0).

When estimating the various main effects S, C and O it is possible to use the signs in the table describing the experimental design, see Table 7.2. The different effects can be estimated as a quarter of the sum of the test results, where each test result has been taken with the sign that describes the level of the corresponding factor. If the test results are designated y_1, y_2, ..., y_8 the effect of an increased steel temperature can be estimated as

$$\frac{1}{4}(-y_1 + y_2 - y_3 + y_4 - y_5 + y_6 - y_7 + y_8)$$

It is also possible to estimate the other effects of interaction in a corresponding way using the so called *design matrix* illustrated in Table 7.3.

	Main factors and interactions							
Run no.	S	O	C	SxO	SxC	OxC	SxOxC	y
1	−	−	−	+	+	+	−	67
2	+	−	−	−	−	+	+	79
3	−	+	−	−	+	−	+	59
4	+	+	−	+	−	−	−	90
5	−	−	+	+	−	−	+	61
6	+	−	+	−	+	−	−	75
7	−	+	+	−	−	+	−	52
8	+	+	+	+	+	+	+	87
Estimated effects	23	1.5	−5.0	10	1.5	0.0	0.5	

Table 7.3   *The design matrix for the described experiment combined with the results from the runs and the estimated effects.*

The signs in the columns regarding interaction are obtained as products between the signs in the columns for the corresponding factors, where the product of two signs has to be interpreted as the sign of the product between two numbers with these signs. The first sign in the column regarding the interaction between S and O, SxO, is a plus since "minus multiplied by minus equals plus". In the same way the next sign is minus since "plus multiplied by minus equals minus". The interaction effect SxO can accordingly be estimated as

$$\frac{1}{4}(y_1 - y_2 - y_3 + y_4 + y_5 - y_6 - y_7 + y_8)$$

The bottom line in Table 7.3, which does not belong to the design matrix, gives the estimated effects.

Note that there might also be an interaction effect between all the three factors studied. In this case the interaction effect between steel temperature and oil temperature could be due to the carbon content. This interaction effect can be estimated with the help of the signs in the last column in Table 7.3, which gives 0.5.

The dominating factors seem to be the steel temperature and the interaction between the steel and oil temperatures. When interaction effects are at hand there is no point in describing the main effects of each effect separately. The result should instead be illustrated as in Figure 7.6.

When we are to decide if the estimated effect actually is the result of an actively influencing factor we have to consider the random variation in the experimental results. If every batch examined contains 200 springs we can estimate the standard deviation σ for the percentage of crackless springs p as $\sigma \leq 3.6$. This can be seen as follows. The number of springs without cracks is roughly binominally distributed with n = 200 and p unknown, i.e. Bin(200,p)-distributed. The standard deviation for the percentage of crackless springs is then $\sqrt{p(1-p)/200}$, which at most equals 3.6%. This occurs when p = 0.5. (See Appendix A.)

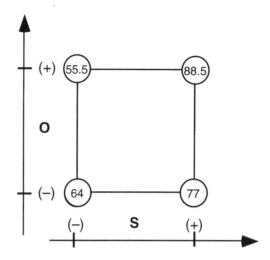

Figure 7.6   *The results of the experiment. Each result above is the arithmetic mean of the two test results with different carbon contents, but with the same steel and oil temperatures. Note that when the steel temperature is low, a negative effect is obtained when the oil temperature is raised, but the effect is positive when the steel temperature is high.*

Each effect is estimated as a sum of eight observations (with a plus or minus sign) divided by four. The random error of the estimator of an effect can thus be written as $(e_1+e_2+...+e_8)/4$, where all the e_j are independent and have a standard deviation which is less than 3.6. The standard deviation of the estimator then becomes

$$\frac{\sqrt{\sigma_1^2 + \sigma_2^2 + ... + \sigma_8^2}}{4} \leq \frac{\sqrt{8 \cdot 3.6^2}}{4} \leq 2.6$$

As each effect is estimated as the sum of a number of independent random variables, it follows, according to the Central Limit Theorem (see Appendix A), that the effect is roughly normally distributed.

Studying the estimates of the effects, we can establish that it is not probable that the estimated effect of steel temperature is a result of random variations. The same applies for the estimated interaction effect between steel and oil temperature. It is, as a matter of fact, not probable that an almost normally distributed random variable with expectation zero and standard deviation 2.6 is as large as 23, or even as 10, which corresponds to the estimated effects. The probability is roughly 0.1 % that a random variable which is normally distributed will attain a value that deviates by more than 3.3 times the standard deviation from the expectation; see also Figure 7.7.

On the other hand, the measured effect of the carbon content might possibly be due to random variation. It is not unrealistic that a normally distributed random variable with expectation 0 and a standard deviation of 2.6 may attain values around − 5. The chance of obtaining a value that deviates at least 1.9 times the standard deviation from the expectation is about 6%.

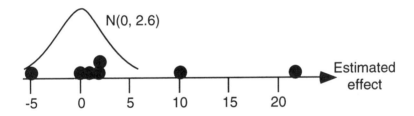

Figure 7.7   *Illustration of the estimated effects related to a normal distribution with expectation 0 and standard deviation 2.6, i.e. the distribution the estimated effects would have if no factor is active. This kind of distribution is called a reference distribution.*

Using a *factorial design*, it has proved possible to estimate the main effects of the factors with maximum precision. It was also possible to identify interaction effects. With a one-factor-at-a-time experiment this would not have been possible. More tests would have been necessary in order to reach the same accuracy when estimating the main effects and it would not have been possible to establish any interaction effects.

7.4 Fractional Factorial Designs

If it is considered that interaction effects can be disregarded it is possible to use fewer tests. In order to estimate the main effects of three factors, only four tests are necessary as is illustrated in Figure 7.8.

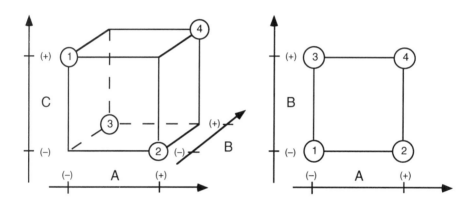

Figure 7.8   *Illustration of a fractional factorial design with three fac-*
tors. Using four runs, three main effects can be estimated.
Note that if one of the factors is disregarded the experiment
will in this case be complete in the other two. In figure to
the right factor C has been disregarded.

The design matrix for this *fractional factorial design* can be written as in Table 7.4.

Run no.	Main factors		
	A	B	C
1	−	−	+
2	+	−	−
3	−	+	−
4	+	+	+

Table 7.4   *The design matrix for a fractional factorial design with three factors.*

Note that if there is still an interaction between A and B it would according to the earlier discussion be estimated using the same sequence of "+" and "−" as the factor C. This means that it is not possible to distinguish between the effect of factor C and the interaction between A and B. In the same way the effect of A is mixed with the interaction effect between B and C. If, for instance, the estimator

$$\frac{1}{2}(y_1 - y_2 - y_3 + y_4)$$

is large it is not possible to know if it is the main effect C that is active or if it is the interaction between the two other factors A and B. In order to determine this the number of tests has to be extended, resulting in a full factorial design.

Often a large number of factors could affect the result. Then a fractional factorial design can be especially effective at the beginning of an investigation. Hence some of the factors have to be eliminated. Using the test results and estimates of the effects of the different factors, possibly mixed with interaction effects, it is possible to eliminate factors that are less "interesting". An example of an experimental design regarding seven factors in eight tests is illustrated in Table 7.5.

Run no.	Main factors						
	A	B	C	D	E	F	G
1	−	−	−	+	+	+	−
2	+	−	−	−	+	−	+
3	−	+	−	−	−	+	+
4	+	+	−	+	−	−	−
5	−	−	+	+	−	−	+
6	+	−	+	−	−	+	−
7	−	+	+	−	+	−	−
8	+	+	+	+	+	+	+

Table 7.5   A design matrix intended for seven factors in eight runs.

The reason why the fractional factorial design has proved to be so useful is that often only a few single factors and interactions turn out to be interesting. This is an example of the so called "80-20-rule", or as stated by Joseph Juran: "the vital few and trivial many". After the first fractional factorial design it is possible to design a more complete experiment with only the most important factors involved.

Observe that factors that do not give any visible effects are not necessarily of no interest. On the contrary, from an economic point of view they can be very interesting. By making a suitable choice it may be possible to choose the corresponding parameters in a way that is economically advantageous without affecting the function of the product or the process.

7.5 Studied Factors and Irrelevant Disturbing Factors

Before starting an experiment it is important to clarify what factors or parameters are interesting and what factors might disturb the outcome of the experiment. The factors that are to be studied depend on the situation. Often it might be advantageous to use guidance from previous experiments and other experience. In connection with quality improvement such experience might have been obtained with the help of "the seven QC-tools" mentioned in Figure 1.7 and further described in Chapter 11. For instance an Ishikawa diagram might be very useful.

Influence of irrelevant disturbing factors such as measurement errors has to be eliminated as far as possible. This can be done either by trying to keep them constant or by making blocks of experiments in which these disturbing factors are kept in fixed positions. The making of blocks is done in such a way that the effect of irrelevant disturbing factors is eliminated. Hereby the estimators of the effects of the studied factors are not affected. If for instance only four batches a day can be manufactured and it has been decided to study three factors in eight experiments, each in one batch, it might be possible to risk an irrelevant disturbing factor resulting in variations in the manufacturing process from one day to another. In this case blocks can be made with, say, four experiments per block, i.e. a day.

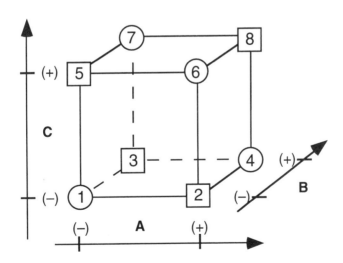

Figure 7.9   Illustration of the block design.

Then the tests are performed in such a way that the block effects are levelled out. It is for instance possible to distribute the blocks so that the block effect is mixed with the interaction effect among all the three factors since this interaction is the least probable one. The experiment can then be illustrated as in Figure 7.9, where round symbols describe the tests during the first day while the square ones symbolize the runs during the second day.

Observe that not all disturbing factors are irrelevant. If the disturbing factor affects the studied function of a product in use it has to be studied during product development, see also the next chapter.

7.6   Notes and References

The well-written book "Statistics for Experimenters" by Box, Hunter & Hunter (1978) tells more about design of experiments. This book is highly recommended. Montgomery (1991) is another book well worth reading. A classical book on design of experiments is Cochran & Cox (1957). Another book of interest is Daniels (1976). For more advanced material on the use of design of experiments for continuous improvements, see Box & Draper (1967) and Box & Draper (1987). Design of experiments, as presented in this book, is closely related to multiple regression analysis, see Draper & Smith (1981). The development in the field has also been dealt with briefly in Chapter 3 of this book.

Design of experiments is also used in connection with robust design described in the next chapter. In marketing research the same type of design can be used. It is then called Conjoint Analysis, see e.g. Green & Srinivasan (1978).

8 Robust Design

During the last few years Genichi Taguchi's view of quality and quality improvement has attracted great interest in Western industry. Sometimes , he has been mentioned as one of the men behind the Japanese success in the quality field. Bell Laboratories (nowadays American Telephone & Telegraph, AT & T) was one of the first companies outside Japan to take an interest in Taguchi's ideas. At about the same time, in 1979, Taguchi's book "Off-line Quality Control" was published in English. During 1984, thanks to the Ford car company, among others, a number of conferences and seminars were arranged where Taguchi's methods were discussed. Since then, discussion and interest have grown and the ideas have been presented in a number of articles in various journals. A large number of industrial applications have also been published.

8.1 Taguchi's Philosophy

The central idea in how Taguchi looks upon the quality concept is that he takes the use of the product as a base. According to Taguchi, product quality, or rather lack of quality, is the loss to society caused by the product after delivery. Taguchi restricts himself to the costs after delivery but he takes a practically global view. Only companies that take into consideration not only the consumer costs but also the costs to society will in the long run be competitive. The way Taguchi concentrates on the costs during product use brings *LCC (Life Cycle Cost)* to mind; see Section 5.6.

Taguchi makes a clear distinction between product characteristics and quality characteristics. Product characteristics have to be chosen in order to compete within a certain market segment. Quality characteristics, on the other hand, are set by the deviations of the product qualities from the ideal in the chosen market segment. Non-quality and variation of the product charcteristics are intimately connected. Every unit of a kind of product is exposed to disturbances of all kinds. This can affect product quality and thus contribute to its variation. If the product characteristics vary appreciably, poor quality is indicated. The disturbing factors can be of different kinds, from variations in the manufacturing process to environmental stress and wear. As it is impossible to eliminate the disturbances completely, Taguchi instead comes to the conclusion that the design has to be *robust,* that is insensitive to the disturbances to which the product might be exposed. How this aim is to be reached is a central element in Taguchi's quality philosophy.

Taguchi provides methods for quality engineering at early stages like product and process development. This is probably the reason why Taguchi's quality philosophy has received so much attention. Lots of people have been talking about the necessity of preventing quality problems right from the stage of product development. Not very many, however, have presented a well considered plan for how this should be done, reliability and design review activities excluded. Taguchi's quality philosophy, combined with the ideas regarding Quality Function Deployment, which were presented in Chapter 4, thus fullfills a need that has existed for a long time.

8.2 The Design Process

Taguchi identifies three phases during the design process. These are:

- system design
- parameter design
- tolerance design.

8.2.1 System Design

During system design the actual frame of the product is set. In this process the needs of the customers and the fact that it must be possible to manufacture the product have to be taken into consideration. Deep knowledge about the needs of the customers and the manufacturing possibilities is thus a basic requirement for system design. The final result of the system design is a prototype design which can satisfy the customer needs concerning the function, provided it is not exposed to disturbances. System design is a highly creative process.

8.2.2 Parameter Design

A design is said to be *robust* if it is insensitive to various disturbances both in the manufacturing process and during use. If, for instance, it is necessary to have a hole in a heavily loaded part of a structure, the aim is to keep as large a distance as possible between the edges. This should be done in order to reduce the sensitivity to inaccuracy in the manufacturing process and to load variations experienced in use. The aim is to make the design robust when deciding the parameter values.

A product's characteristic are often non-linearly dependent on the design parameters. The output voltage of a transistor depends for instance non-linearly on the transistor amplification, see Figure 8.1. By choosing the amplification x_1 with a nominal output voltage y_1 instead of x_0 and y_0, respectively, see Figure 8.1, the sensitivity to variations in the amplification has been reduced. By adding a resistor, the nominal output voltage y_0 can be achieved without affecting the sensitivity to variation in the amplification. In this way a robust design has been achieved.

Generally, the situation is not as simple as shown in the above example with the transistor. Usually, the relation between product characteristics and design parameters is not known. Instead, information about non-linearities and influencing disturbances has to be obtained by using design of experiments.

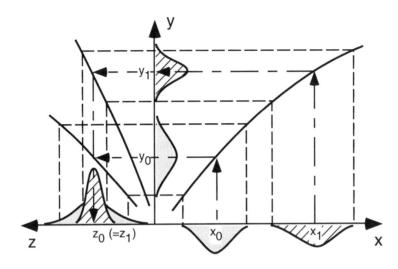

Figure 8.1   *It is often possible to choose parameter designs in order to make the design more or less sensitive to disturbances. In this figure x can illustrate the amplification of a transistor and y can illustrate its output voltage. By choosing a nominal amplification x_1 instead of x_0 the output voltage is much less affected by the spread of actual amplification. The level can then be controlled towards the target value z_0 with the help of a resistor.*

8.2.3   Tolerance Design

In parameter design the target values for the design parameters are set. During manufacturing the aim is to come as close as possible to these target values. As there is always a variation in the manufacturing process a tolerance interval has to be given.

As far as Taguchi's quality philosophy is concerned the tolerance interval must not, in connection with manufacturing, be interpreted as permission to be anywhere within the tolerance interval with the corresponding dimensions. Even if the variation of the

158

process is reduced, the target value has still to be aimed at. It is not permissible to get closer to one of the tolerance limits even if the manufacturer would profit from this through lower material costs. The total sum of the customer costs and the manufacturing costs should be considered when selecting the parameters. Tolerance should be selected by balancing the loss to society due to deviations from the target value and the cost to the producer of making an adjustment when an out-of-tolerance situation arises.

8.3   Robust Design

Every individual unit of a certain product is exposed to a number of disturbing factors during its entire life. These disturbances are deviations from what can be considered normal. They can be anything from the material of which the product is manufactured to a badly performed repair. Every factor that can make a product characteristic deviate from its target value should be considered a disturbing factor. Taguchi divides the disturbing factors into the following groups:

- *outer disturbances,* like variations of temperature, voltage fluctuation and other environmental factors during usage

- *inner disturbances,* like wear, tear, and deterioration within the individual unit, due to its operation

- *manufacturing variations,* i.e. deviations of the individual unit from the set target values due to manufacturing. This gives a variation between units manufactured under the same specification.

Typical of a robust design is that even if an individual unit is exposed to disturbances of the above mentioned kinds its important characteristics still do not vary. Design of experiments is, as mentioned earlier, an important means for finding necessary information to achieve this.

Not only the product design, but also the design of the manufacturing process is of major importance as far as the final product quality is concerned. The same methods as for the product design have to be applied when designing the manufacturing process. However, some new elements have to be added. An important one deals with the possibility of controlling the manufacturing process. Dealing further with these issues would, however, lead us too far away from the subject.

8.4 The Loss Function

The loss to society is important to Taguchi. He cannot accept the traditional view that as long as the parameter lies within the tolerance limits the loss to society is zero and as soon as the parameter value has exceeded one of the tolerance limits the financial loss is large. For Taguchi, every deviation from the target value means a loss which grows as the deviation increases, see Figure 8.2.

Instead of looking upon the deviations as losses, we can also say that as long as the quality measure coincides with the target value we will get a satisfied customer.

Taguchi also wants to quantify the financial loss when a parameter value deviates from its target value. He uses as an acceptable approximation a squared loss function. How this may be used is illustrated in Figure 8.3.

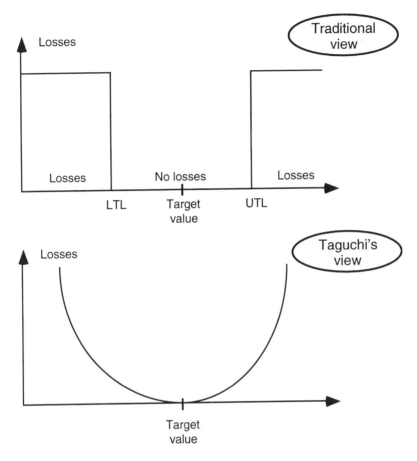

Figure 8.2   *(a) Traditionally a loss is considered to arise only when the parameter value is outside one of the tolerance limits. (b) Taguchi is of the opinion that every deviation from the target value causes a loss that grows with the deviation from the target value.*

In connection with tolerance design Taguchi wants to take into consideration the customer's costs as well as the manufacturer's costs. Every deviation from a parameter target value causes a customer loss whereas there may be costs for the manufacturer for reducing the variation of the manufacturing process.

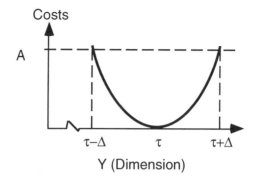

Figure 8.3   *Illustration of Taguchi's loss function. Taguchi uses a squared loss function $L(Y) = [A(Y-\tau)^2]/\Delta^2$, where A equals the expected costs if the deviation from the target value τ equals Δ. Every deviation from the target value means, according to Taguchi, that there is a cost. The larger this deviation is, the larger the average cost.*

For Taguchi it is obvious that it is the sum of the customer costs and the manufacturer costs that has to be minimized. An example in Figure 8.4 illustrates Taguchi's point of view.

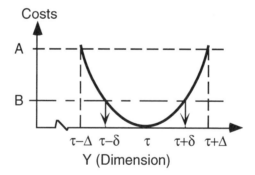

Figure 8.4   *This illustration shows how Taguchi suggests the tolerance limits should be chosen. First the loss function is chosen as in Figure 8.3. Then the tolerance limits are set in such a way that the scrap cost B is balanced against the customer loss. If scrap cost is less than the loss to the customer we should scrap the unit. We get the condition $B = A\delta^2/\Delta^2$, from which we obtain $\delta = \Delta\sqrt{B/A}$ and the tolerance limits $\tau \pm \delta$.*

8.5 Design of Experiments

Perhaps the most important message in Taguchi's quality philosophy is to be found in design of experiments. In Japan, millions of well planned experiments are performed each year to gain knowledge about the way the design parameters affect the product characteristics. In too many Western industries, however, only simple tests of a verifying kind are still used. When test series are actually performed, they are often only one-factor-at-a-time experiments. As shown in Chapter 7 this is a tremendous waste of money and information. The verifying tests do not generate new information and one-factor-at-a-time experiments are often not particularly efficient and they also constitute an inadequate way of collecting information. By using statistical design of experiments it is possible to obtain much more information at a lower cost.

Run no.	Parameter no.			
	1	2	3	4
1	−1	−1	−1	−1
2	−1	0	0	0
3	−1	1	1	1
4	0	−1	0	1
5	0	0	1	−1
6	0	1	−1	0
7	1	−1	1	0
8	1	0	−1	1
9	1	1	0	−1

Figure 8.5   *Example of an experimental design. The effects of four design parameters are examined. Every design parameter can be chosen at one of three levels (−1 = "low", 0 = "normal", 1 = "high"). In run number 1, for example, all the four design parameters are chosen at their low levels.*

In those experiments that have been carried out the interest has been concentrated on how the design parameters affect the level of the test results. Often, it is assumed that the variation of the experimental results is constant for different combinations of the design parameters. However, the interesting thing for Taguchi is variation. In order to create a robust design a combination of design parameter values has to be found. Otherwise, the desired product characteristics that show little variation, even when disturbing factors are allowed to affect the result, will not be achieved.

Taguchi is in favour of experiments where every factor studied, i.e. design parameters and disturbing factor, is allowed to have two or three values (levels). Combinations of design parameter values are chosen according to a fractional factorial design, see Figure 8.5. For each of these combinations the disturbing factors are chosen in the same way. The same combinations of the disturbing factor levels are represented in all the examined combinations of the design parameter levels; see Figure 8.6.

Run no.	Noise factor		
	1	2	3
1	−1	−1	−1
2	−1	1	1
3	1	−1	1
4	1	1	−1

Figure 8.6   *For every run according to Figure 8.5 the disturbing factors are varied according to this plan. The table illustrates how the effect of three disturbing factors can be studied using four tests in each series. Every disturbing factor is chosen at a low level (marked "−1") or at a high level (marked "1").*

Using the results from the experiment it is possible to estimate what average level different parameter combinations result in with regard taken to variations of the disturbing parameters. It is also possible to get information about how sensitive different choices of design parameter combinations are to variations of the disturbing factors. It is then possible to choose levels of the design parameters for which the sensitivity to disturbances is minimized and where on the average the target value has been reached. Design parameters that affect neither sensitivity nor level can be chosen at their most economical level; see Figure 8.7.

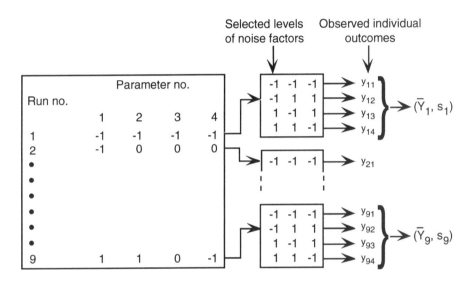

Figure 8.7   *From every test series an average level $\bar{Y}_i$ and a variation measure (or sensitivity measure) s_i, $i = 1, 2, ..., 9$, can be evaluated. These can then be used to choose the parameter combination which gives the most robust design.*

8.6 Taguchi's Quality Philosophy

In his quality philosophy and with his methods Taguchi has emphasized some very important points. Lack of quality is closely connected with the variation of the product characteristics. This variation is due to the effect of disturbing factors. The effect of the disturbing factors can however be reduced by choosing the best design parameters. The design can be made more robust. An important aid in this task is design of experiments, where the effects of the disturbing factors and different parameter combinations are studied.

Taguchi's Quality Philosophy in Seven Points

1. Lack of quality is the total cost society is caused by the product after delivery to the customer.

2. Continuous quality improvements and cost reductions are necessary for a company to stay in business.

3. A quality improvement program has to aim continuously at reducing the deviation of the product performance characteristics from their target values.

4. The customer loss due to the product performance variations can often be regarded as increasing as the square of the deviation from the target values.

5. The product quality is to a large extent determined by the design and manufacturing processes.

6. Often a non-linear relation exists between the design parameters and the product characteristics. This can be used to reduce the sensitivity to disturbances of the product characteristics. The same applies for production processes.

7. Design of experiments can be used to identify the parameter combinations that reduce the variation of the product characteristics.

Figure 8.8   Taguchi's quality philosophy summarized in seven points. (After Sullivan, 1984. © American Society for Quality Control. Reprinted with Permission.)

After having set the product design parameters, the tolerance limits have to be set as well. This should be done with the aim of minimizing the sum of the manufacturing costs and the customer costs due to deviations from the ideal parameter combination. According to Taguchi these costs can in many cases be described sufficiently well using a squared loss function.

8.7 Notes and References

There is no doubt that Taguchi's point of view regarding design of experiments and robust design methodology has succeeded in attracting industrial attention to very important areas. His way of looking at robust design has also created many new ideas. However, his methods are not always particularly well phrased. Sometimes they are even unsuitable.

Taguchi has written a number of books where he develops his ideas; see for instance Taguchi & Wu (1979), Taguchi (1986) and Taguchi, Elsayed & Hsiang (1989). A complete issue of the journal Quality and Reliability Engineering (1988:2) also deals with Taguchi's ideas and methods.

Some critical judgements of Taguchi's ideas are to be found in for instance Box, Bisgaard & Fung (1988). A review of Taguchi's books has been published by Bisgaard (1989) in Technometrics.

One of the persons who has best managed to explain Taguchi's ideas is R. N. Kackar from Bell Laboratories; see Kackar (1985) and Kackar & Shoemaker (1986).

Industrial design of experiments and robust design are also dealt with thoroughly in Ross (1988), Phadke (1989) and Lochner & Matar (1990). A number of industrial applications were presented in Bendell et al. (1989).

9 Software Quality

Computers are playing an increasingly important role in society. They are being used in many products and in the process of making new products the computer is becoming more and more important.

As a result of this, software quality has become more critical to the reliability of the product. Sadly, software quality is in many cases poor. There are many explanations for this. Software is often much more complex and, in addition, much harder to make tolerant to errors than hardware.

Another problem is that a lot of progress is still being made in this area and many new products are being developed without proper quality control. An additional problem is the immense variety of dimensions by which software must be evaluated.

In order to improve the situation we have to control the development of programs more effectively. Some measures could be:

- Produce a development model with regular check-ups to be carried out by independent examination teams.

- Make use of systematic test methods where tests will be developed along with the development of programs.

- Use a formal specification language.

- Use a thoroughly tested programming environment and a programming language that minimizes the danger of making errors.

- Follow up results from tests and error models for use in a continuous improvement program. Root causes of failures have to be found and eliminated. It is not enough to find errors in the software and correct them. Changes have to be made in the development process.

- Use a test environment that will prevent unreliable software from reaching the customers.

- Give attention to software maintainability. Even if a very reliable piece of software has been developed this could soon turn unreliable if it is difficult to make changes in the program. Often changes have to be carried out owing to new demands from the environment.

Here we will not try to give a comprehensive picture of the quality control and improvement activities in connection with software development. That would be almost impossible because of the width of the field. Furthermore, there is no homogenous picture of the field.

An interesting development is taking place in Japan, where among other things, attempts are being made to adapt Quality Function Deployment, QFD (see Chapter 4), to software quality. For instance in 1986, a project team from the Information-Processing Promotion Agency created a guideline for the application of QFD which after some company applications was published, see IPA (1989) and Yoshizawa et al. (1993). An example of a schematic concept of software development using QFD is shown in Figure 9.1

At IBM attempts are being made to develop a new way of looking at the whole development process, where statistical testing with customer-related problems plays a vital part. Based on Deming's philosophy of quality control and statistical process control, Chou (1987) has developed a method for *Quality Programming*. The *Cleanroom Methodology* is another attempt to find a development process supporting high software quality, see Section 9.3.

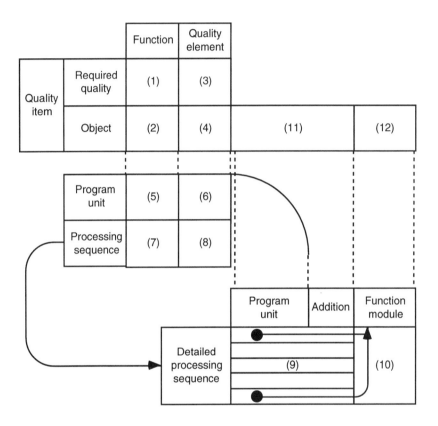

Figure 9.1   Schematic concept of software development employing *Quality Function Deployment. (From Yoshizawa et al., 1993.)*

Regarding the development of software as a process, it can continuously be improved by using statistical process control. Methods that can be used are very closely related to those we shall describe regarding manufacturing; see Part III. See also Chapter 18, where process thinking will be commented on further.

In this chapter we will only touch on some failure concepts and how they could be used for improving software quality. We will also briefly discuss some software reliability models.

9.1 Software Failures

Software failures differ in one vital aspect from hardware failures. All software failures are the result of design faults usually due to human errors. They originate in connection with specification, development or coding. The faults are not detected until the software is being tested or used in a specific way.

Even in hardware there can be a design fault from the very beginning. This applies particularly to advanced electronic circuits, whose design can to a great extent be compared to program development. Traditional analysis of hardware reliability shows that this type of fault has played only a minor part. The typical hardware fault appears as a rule at the same time as, or shortly after, it has arisen. There is a difference between software reliability and hardware reliability.

In this chapter we use the following terminology with respect to the concepts of error, fault, and failure. Somewhere in the program development process (specification, design, coding, or correction) an *error* is made. Then a *fault* is included in the software. For some input combination, this fault gives rise to a *failure* experienced during test or use. It should be mentioned here that in fault tolerant computing a somewhat different terminlogy is used.

9.2 Software Reliability

Software faults have to be discovered during testing. Otherwise the user will find them, with obvious consequences. Programs are tested quite intensively because of this. It is of vital importance to take care of the information from observed failures. The failures encountered are of great help when trying to predict software reliability. Such predictions can be made with the help of different kinds of models. With the assistance of a good model it is possible to avoid marketing unreliable software.

Existing models normally only use information on when failures have occurred and as a rule they are very simple models of reality. It is often assumed that new errors are never made when the faults discovered are corrected. Some models predict both the number of existing faults and software reliability, whereas other models only predict software reliability. In many of the earliest models, which were presented in the middle of the 1970s, efforts were made to predict the number of software faults. Usually, the time concept used is execution time.

Many of the models assume that the time T_i from the discovery of the i:th fault to the discovery of the (i+1):th fault is exponentially distributed with a parameter $\lambda(i)$ depending on the number of faults already discovered, i.e.

$$P(T_i > t) = \exp(-\lambda(i)t) \quad \text{for } t \geq 0$$

In such a model it is natural to assume that $\lambda(i)$ decreases with i. Thus the bigger i is, i.e. the more faults are discovered, the longer it takes to discover the next fault. Observe that a fault is usually discovered when a failure has occurred.

One of the very first and most frequently used models was presented by Jelinski & Moranda (1972). They assumed that $\lambda(i)$ = $\lambda_0(N-i)$, where λ_0 is a constant and N is the number of faults that existed in the original version.

Let us imagine that the time to discovery of each one of the faults is exponentially distributed with parameter λ_0. If the faults are discovered independently of each other the time T_i between the discovery of the i:th and (i+1):st faults is exponentially distributed with parameter $(N-i)\lambda_0$. This is because the time to the next failu-

re can be interpreted as the time to failure for a series system consisting of N–i units, whose times to failure all have the above mentioned exponential distribution (cf. Section 6.2.2).

Jelinski & Moranda's choice of $\lambda(i)$ means that all the remaining
faults in the program contribute with an equal probability of detection. This is hardly a realistic model. It should be easier to find the
errors in routines that are executed frequently than errors which
are to be found in less frequently used subroutines.

A natural generalization of the choice of $\lambda(i)$ from Jelinski &
Moranda (1972) is thus

$$\lambda(i) = \lambda_0(N{-}i)^\alpha, \text{ where } \alpha > 1.$$

This model has been introduced and studied by Xie & Åkerlund
(1989). Among other things they discuss the question of how the
original number of faults N should be estimated. Other questions
which are discussed there, are when to stop testing programs and
when they should be delivered to the user. One possible criterion is
to stop when n faults have been detected and where the estimated
value of $\lambda(n)$ is small enough, i.e. the probability that the next failure will be detected within a certain time is small enough.

The problem of estimating parameters which are part of the model,
like N and λ_0 in Jelinski & Moranda's model mentioned above, is
not an easy one. Normal statistical methods of estimation generally lead to fairly complicated equations, whose solutions often demand numerical methods and are fairly unstable. This means that
quite a long execution time and the occurrence of many faults are
necessary before the estimates are fairly correct.

The above description is, however, not the only way to use a software reliability model. With the help of such a model a measurement, of how reliable the software is, is achieved. Thus an evaluation can also be made of the quality control system that has been
used. System improvements can be evaluated. In the long run, this

field of use is perhaps the most important one. The aim is to avoid defects in software. Above all, improvements have to made in this respect. In order to make improvements, measurement and analysis of the errors that occur are necessary.

9.3   Cleanroom Methodology

A number of development models for software development have been suggested and practised. A recent one with some promising features from a TQM point of view is *Cleanroom Methodology,* which was originally suggested by Harlan Mills, see for example Mills et al. (1987). A number of successful examples from NASA and IBM, among others, have been reported.

Some features of Cleanroom Methodology challenge current tradition in software development. Firstly, a considerable amount of resources is expended on a functional specification and on a usage specification. Not only possible usage scenarios are described but also their relative frequence of occurrence. Secondly, the development is performed in incremental and verifiable stages from the outside and in. Thirdly, during development and coding only verification using more or less formal analytical methods is allowed, i.e. the programmers are not allowed to execute their own code. This means that testing is not looked upon as a method to debug the program, but rather as a means to verify reliability. Test cases are generated according to the probability distribution established during usage specification. Finally, the experience gained during software testing is fed back to the development process to improve this process in the future. The Cleanroom Methodology also challenges assumptions which traditionally hold true, e.g. that software faults are inevitable, that debugging works irrespective of program size, that it is uninteresting when faults are detected since the important thing is that they are removed, and that software is deterministic and statistical methods are of no use. A graphical illustration of the Cleanroom Methodology is given in Figure 9.2.

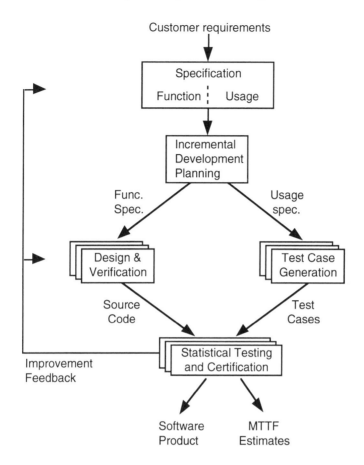

Figure 9.2   An illustration of the main features of the cleanroom development process. (From Mills et al., 1987)

9.4   Notes and References

We have chosen to relate only basic facts from this field. If a more complete presentation of this field is wanted, we refer to books by Myers (1976) and Kopetz (1979). Many different software reliability models are dealt with by Musa et al. (1987), Bendell et al. (1986), Littlewood (1987) and Xie (1991).

175

A large number of articles from technical journals deal with problems within the software quality field. These articles will for instance be found in recent issues of IEEE Software Engineering and IEEE Software. Many interesting views regarding software quality are to be found in the "Handbook of Software Quality Assurance" edited by Schulmeyer & McManus (1987).

Cleanroom Methodology is discussed by Selby et al. (1985), Mills et al. (1987) and Cobb & Mills (1990). A thorough description is given in Dyer (1992).

Standards regarding quality systems in connection with software development have been published by the IEEE (ANSI/IEEE Std730), NATO (AQAP-13) and the US Department of Defense. A British team has also developed TickIT, which defines a way to certify organizations working with software development according to the ISO 9000 system.

Part III

Production for Quality

Continuous improvement of the production process is of vital importance. In this part of the book, we will discuss tools for this task. We will present the seven QC-tools, which are very useful in Statistical Process Control (SPC) of manufacturing processes as well as other processes. We will also discuss the concept of capability, which deals with the ability of the process to meet set requirements on the results produced. Furthermore, we will discuss quality in the purchasing and supply processes.

10 Statistical Process Control

Every process, a manufacturing process as well as any other type of process, produces more or less varying results. Behind this variation there is an extensive system of causes. If enough information about the process is acquired, it is often possible to distinguish and identify some of the sources of variation. The next step is then to eliminate these causes, when this is suitable from a quality and cost point of view.

Examples of causes of variation in a manufacturing process can be play in bearings or spindles, vibrations, varying lighting conditions, inhomogeneous materials, and varying temperature or humidity. In a service process, information uncertainties and individual differences are important sources of variation. Since in each situation there are often many various causes of the variation, it can be hard to identify the contribution of the individual cause. If, on the other hand, we have a maladjusted machine, tool wear or defects in material lots, these causes may contribute so much to the variation that they become *assignable causes,* i.e. they can be identified and separated from the general noise. The other causes contributing to the noise are in general called *common causes.*

The purpose of *Statistical Process Control (SPC)* is to find as many sources of variation as possible and then eliminate them. When a stable process with small variation is achieved, the target is to maintain or, if possible, improve the process even further. In these cases it is often not possible to make improvements by eliminating sources of variation. Instead, a creative change in the process structure is needed.

10.1 Variation

The variation occurring from assignable causes is often called *systematic variation*, whereas the other part of the variation caused by common causes is called *random variation*. There is, however, no clear distinction between these two types of causes. What is an assignable cause and what is a common cause depends on the information acquired from the process.

When we have eliminated, or at least compensated for, the effect of the assignable causes, only the random variation remains in the process. As long as only this variation contributes to the dispersion, and no systematic variation occurs, we say that the process is *in statistical control* or that we have *a stable process,* see Figure 10.1.

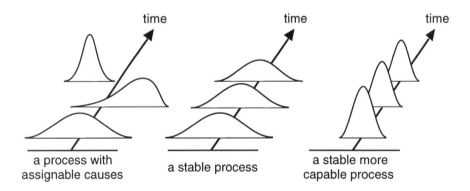

Figure 10.1 *By eliminating assignable causes we get a process in statistical control, a stable process. By gathering more information about the process we can eliminate more causes of variation and the process is further improved.*

When the process is stable we can predict its future results. Shewhart (1931, p.6) states this in the following way: "*A phenomenon will be said to be controlled when, through the use of past experience, we can predict, at least within limits, how the phenomenon may be expected to vary in the future*". The limits are set by the natural, random variation which the common causes bring about. These variations are often called *system dependent*.

The purpose of Statistical Process Control is, on the basis of data from the process, to

- identify assignable causes in order to eliminate them

- supervise the process when it is in statistical control so that no further assignable causes are introduced without the knowledge of the operator

- continuously give information from the process, so that new causes of variation can be identified as assignable and eliminated

Statistical Process Control is a vital part of the continuous improvement work. Using information from the process, new causes of variation can be identified as assignable and eliminated, or at least compensated for. Thus, the variation of the process will decrease, the costs of quality defects will decrease and quality will be improved.

Quite often people do not have a statistical approach to the process. This leads to their being misled by the random variation they are observing and believing that the observed variation is systematic. They then try to compensate for the variation in different ways. Instead, this results in increasing variation in the process. Decisions are not based on facts, but merely on misguided ambition. By using principles from statistical process control this kind of *overcontrol* can be avoided. Deming calls this problem *tempering*.

As emphasized earlier, variation is an important source of non-quality. The causes of variation often interact additively. The standard deviation of the different causes should therefore be added quadratically to get the variance of the total variation. Suppose, for example, that we have five independent sources of variation and that their contributions are added. If the various contributions have the standard deviations 4, 2, 1, 1, 1, respectively, the resulting standard deviation will be (see Appendix A)

$$\sqrt{4^2 + 2^2 + 1^2 + 1^2 + 1^2} = 4.8$$

Distribution of source no:

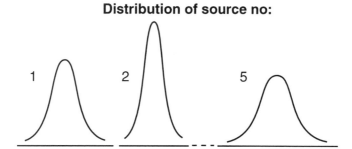

Distribution of the sum of sources:

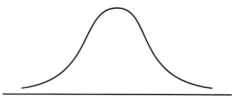

Figur 10.2   The total variation often depends on several more or less independent contributions. The variance of the total variation is then the sum of the variances of the different contributions.

Now, if we are successful in identifying the second largest source of variation and if we also manage to eliminate that completely, the resulting standard deviation will be

$$\sqrt{4^2 + 1^2 + 1^2 + 1^2} = 4.4$$

The standard deviation has then been reduced by about 10%. If, instead, we manage to identify and eliminate the largest source of variation this implies a much bigger reduction in the resulting standard deviation, which now equals

$$\sqrt{2^2 + 1^2 + 1^2 + 1^2} = 2.6$$

The variation measured as the standard deviation has now approximately been halved. Consequently, it is vital that we devote ourselves to the appropriate problem in our improvement work. Wasting a lot of energy on the second largest contributor to variation is not only less economical but may also be demoralizing. It will be difficult to see the result of all one's efforts, and the effect of seeing the results of one's improvement work is crucial for the motivation to move on.

10.2 Process Improvement

When we are looking for the causes of systematic variation, i.e. assignable causes, it is important to tackle the problems systematically and accurately. There are often several problems or causes present. It is a matter of first tackling the problem that is the most serious. When that problem is solved we move on to the next.

Figure 10.3 illustrates the improvement cycle: *Plan - Do - Study - Act.* The stages in that cycle are commented upon below. Another list with roughly the same contents can be found in Figure 10.4.

Plan. When problems are detected the first thing we have to do is to establish the principal causes of the problem. Large problems have to be broken down into small, manageable ones. The decision concerning changes must be based on facts. That means that we have to look systematically for different plausible causes of the problem using, say, the seven QC-tools (see Chapter 11). An Ishikawa diagram (see Section 11.4) can often give a hint as to the possible causes. Getting a group of people together, preferably with different backgrounds and skills, for a brain-storming session, where fantasy and ideas can flow freely without being criticized, is often productive. Other useful tools are FMEA (Failure Mode and Effects Analysis), see Chapter 6, and design of experiments, see Chapter 7.

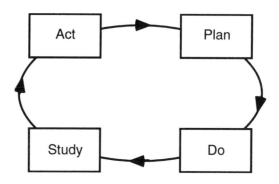

Figure 10.3   *A cycle for solving problems in the continuous improvement work presented by Deming (see Deming, 1986, 1993). Deming speaks of the PDSA-cycle, short for "Plan-Do-Study-Act", but he often refers to this cycle as the "Shewhart-cycle" after Walter A. Shewhart. In Deming (1986) he used the name PDCA-cycle since he used "Check" instead of "Study".*

After that we have to compile data in such a way that we can detect causes of error and variation. In such cases, a histogram and other simple ways of illustrating statistical data, Pareto diagrams, stratification, and scatter plots, will be of great help. It is vital not to "overreact" in such a way that the solution of a problem becomes a costly experience based on trial-and-error.

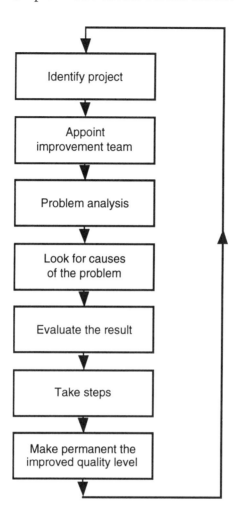

Figure 10.4   *An improvement cycle with contents similar to that in Figure 10.3.*

Do. When an important cause of a problem is found, an improvement team is given the task of carrying through the appropriate steps. It is of great importance to make everyone involved fully aware of the problem and of the improvement steps decided upon.

Study. When appropriate steps have been taken we shall investigate the result to see if the implementation of the improvement program was actually successful. Again, several of the seven QC-tools, such as histograms, Pareto diagrams and stratification, are important and useful tools. When we are convinced that the steps taken have had a positive effect and that the quality level has been raised, we have to make sure that the new improved level is retained. This can sometimes be made by utilizing a control chart; see Chapter 12.

Act. All the time it is a matter of learning and gaining experience from the improvement process in order to avoid the same type of problem the next time. If the steps taken were successful the new and better quality level should be made permanent. If we were not successful we have to go through the cycle once more. It is also very important to analyse the entire cycle of problem solving once again in order to learn and also improve the improvement process.

Then we go on with improvement by moving on to the next problem in the same process or proceed to the next process and repeat the improvement cycle once again.

10.3 Notes and References

As we have mentioned earlier Walter A. Shewhart was one of the first to realize the importance of a statistical approach to the manufacturing process. His books, Shewhart (1931, 1939), are still very well worth reading. He has also strongly influenced Juran and Deming, for example. Above all, his way of thinking about statistical process control has influenced Deming quite substantially; see Deming (1986). What we have called "assignable causes" of variation, with terminology from Shewhart, Deming calls "special causes". Shewhart uses the term "chance cause" for what Deming calls a "common cause".

One of those who most systematically and persistently has advocated the use of statistical techniques for problem solving is Ishikawa; see Ishikawa (1982). Also Juran, see for instance Juran (1986), has done a lot to spread the message of continuous quality improvement. "The Juran Trilogy": Planning – Control – Improvement, see Figure 10.5, plays a big part in his message.

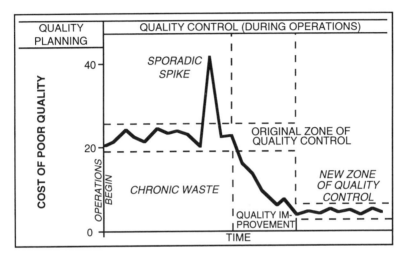

Figure 10.5   Illustration of "The Juran Trilogy". (From Juran, 1986. A similar figure is also given in Shewhart, 1939.)

11 The Seven QC-tools

As a basis for improvement work, data are required, together with an analysis of these data. In Japan it was quickly realized that everyone in a company had to participate in the improvement work. This meant that the statistical tools, which were to be used, had to be simple and yet efficient. Seven methods, or "tools", were put together by Dr Kaoru Ishikawa, among others. These methods have been given the name *the seven QC-tools*, where QC means Quality Control. Since the beginning of the 1960s these tools have been taught to workers and foremen in Japanese industry who have used them systematically for problem solving. An important educational vehicle has been QC circles, see Chapter 20.

In this chapter we will give a short description of these seven tools for quality improvement, namely

- data collection
- histograms
- Pareto charts
- Ishikawa diagrams
- stratification
- scatter plots
- control charts,

see also Figure 1.11. For a more complete presentation of the tools we refer to Ishikawa (1982).

11.1 Data Collection

The collection of data is one of the most important steps in a program for quality improvement. Having a substantial basis for decision-making is vital. It is, of course, also essential that the basis elucidates the topic in question. If incorrect or misleading data are collected, not even the most sophisticated methods will help in the analysis.

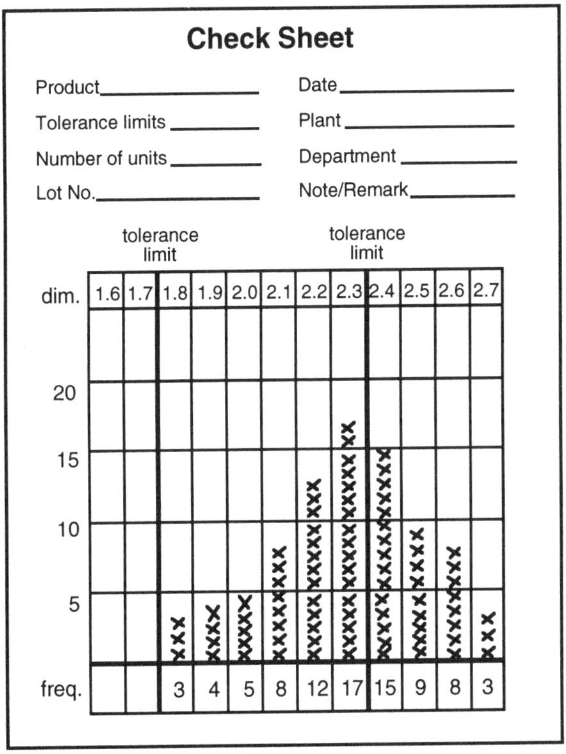

Figure 11.1   *A check sheet for continuous follow-up of a manufacturing process. This type of check sheet is also called a frequency table. In the case illustrated it is to be observed that the manufacturing process results in a large number of units with dimensions outside the tolerance limits.*

From the very start we have to be aware of the purpose of data collection.

- What is the quality problem?
- What facts are required to elucidate the problem?

Not until these questions have been answered is it possible to move on to collecting data. When we are collecting data, we can design a table in which each observation is represented, as it appears. Every new fact can be marked by a stroke or a cross. Sometimes it may be advisable to tick them off as in a check sheet. A few examples of check sheets are given in Figures 11.1 and 11.2.

Check Sheet

Product_____   Date_____
Manufacturing step_____   Plant_____
Number inspected _____   Inspector_____
Note/Remark _____   Lot No._____

Type		Number
scratches	ℋℋ ℋℋ ℋℋ ℋℋ ℋℋℋ //	32
cracks	ℋℋ ℋℋ ℋℋ ℋℋ ///	23
incomplete	ℋℋℋℋℋℋ ℋℋℋℋℋℋℋ ℋℋ ℋℋ ℋℋ	48
wrong shape	////	4
other	ℋℋ ///	8
	Total	115

Figure 11.2   An example of a check sheet intended for investigating what types of defects occur on a certain type of part.

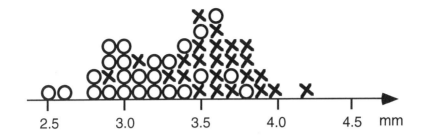

Figure 11.3   *Often the origin of the observations varies in some way.*
The measured units can, for example, be produced on dif-
ferent machines. It is then suitable to use different symbols
or colours for observations with different origins. See also
Section 11.5.

Different forms of simple check lists can also be assigned to the
group of check sheets.

11.2 Histograms

Often we have large amounts of data. Then we cannot represent
each observation in the figure. Instead we have to divide the measurement axis into different parts, *classes,* and let the number of
values in each class be represented by a rectangle. The area of this
rectangle is made proportional to the number of observations in
the class; see Figure 11.4. Also the sum of the areas of all these
rectangles is made equal to unity. This type of figure is called a
frequency histogram.

Using the histogram we can in an excellent way illustrate how a
product or process characteristic varies. Note that a histogram can
very easily be obtained using a frequency table as a basis. The big
difference is that the histogram generally describes relative frequencies and not numbers of observations.

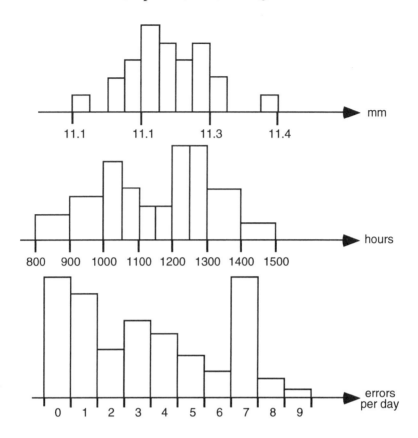

Figure 11.4   *An illustration of a frequency histogram.*
(a) The histogram illustrates the outcome from measure-
ments of the diameter of 30 shaft pivots. Each class has the
same class range, i.e. the same distance between upper and
lower limits in the class.
(b) The histogram illustrates times to failure for 50 electric
bulbs. Note that the classes do not have the same range.
(c) The histogram illustrates the number of errors per day
within a certain manufacturing section over a total of 132
days. In this case each integer corresponds to one class.

Tools similar in spirit to the histogram and very useful for illustra-
ting large amounts of data are referred to as *Exploratory Data*
Analysis, EDA. These tools were originally developed by John
Tukey; see Tukey (1977).

One example of tools from EDA is the *stem-and-leaf diagram,* which can be described as a histogram where the numerical values are still to be found, see Figure 11.5. Another EDA-tool for describing data and their dispersion is a *box-plot*; see Figure 11.6. In recent years the ideas from EDA have had a break-through in the work of process control. More about EDA can be found in Tukey (1977), for example .

7	10	32	17	21	29	13	3	18	28
18	6	12	14	25	27	33	29	17	12
8	35	16	31	11	15	22	7	20	9
19	19	5	21	8	13	17	30	14	15
33	18	7	11	13	25	15	16	23	28

Table 11.1   A data collection with 50 observations.

```
0 | 3                              (1)
0 | 5 6 7 7 7 8 8 9                (8)
1 | 0 1 1 2 2 3 3 3 4 4            (10)
1 | 5 5 5 6 6 7 7 7 8 8 8 9 9      (13)
2 | 0 1 1 2 3 3                    (6)
2 | 5 5 7 8 8 9 9                  (7)
3 | 0 1 2 3                        (4)
3 | 5                              (1)
                                  ‾‾‾‾
                                   (50)
```

Figure 11.5   Stem-and-leaf diagram of the material in Table 11.1. To the left of the stroke, i.e. the stem, in this case are the tens and to the right are the units. The top value is thus 3 and the bottom value 35. Last but one from the bottom are the values 30, 31, 32 and 33.

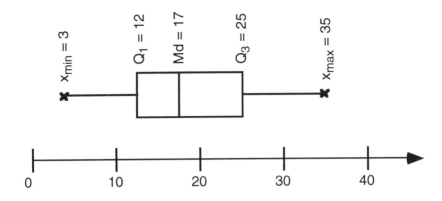

Figure 11.6   *A box-plot of the material in Table 11.1. Here Md stands for median, Q_1 has 25% of the observations to its left and Q_3 has 75% of the observations to its left. The notations x_{max} and x_{min} stand for the largest and smallest numerical value, respectively.*

11.3 Pareto Charts

There are several problems present in connection with a program for quality improvements. In general only one problem can be solved at a time. The *Pareto chart* (named by Juran after the Italian economist and statistician Vilfredo Pareto, 1848-1923) is then of great help when deciding in which order the problems should to be attacked.

The data, which were collected using for instance the check sheet in Figure 11.2, can be illustrated as in Table 11.2. In this table there is certainly all the information available to us at present, but it is not presented in a particularly lucid way. Therefore we will illustrate the data graphically. In the Pareto chart in Figure 11.7 we get a very clear picture of the frequency of the various error types.

Cause	Number of defectives	Number of total amount defectives
scratches	32	28
cracks	23	20
incomplete	48	42
wrong shape	4	3
other	8	7
sum	115	100

Table 11.2   Another way of presenting the data in Figure 11.2.

Note that in a Pareto chart:

• Each type of defect is illustrated by a rectangle whose height equals the number of defectives on the left-hand scale. Sometimes the accumulated number of defectives is also shown on the right-hand scale.

• The order between the different types of defects is such that the one with the largest frequency is placed furthest to the left. After that the number of defectives decreases to the right. The smallest columns furthest to the right can possibly be put together in one group "others", if each one of them contributes too little.

• A line illustrating the cumulative number of defectives or the fraction defectives is often drawn. (This line does not appear in all Pareto charts.)

• It is important always to state where and when data have been collected.

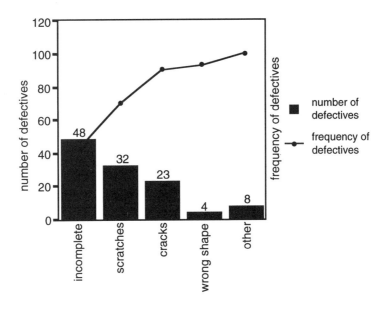

Figure 11.7   A Pareto chart based on the material in Figure 11.2.

On the bases of the Pareto chart the most serious problem is very clearly made visible. When that problem is solved we can move on to the next. In this way each problem is focused on, one at a time.

Often the Pareto chart shows that very few problems account for a large number of the errors or the non-quality costs. Juran, therefore, speaks of *"the vital few and the trivial many"*. The so-called *80- 20- rule*, which is often found in the field of business economics, states the same thing.

It is important to emphasize that it is not only the total number of errors or complaints that determines what step to take. It is also possible to draw a Pareto chart based on the experienced consequence costs of the different types of defects.

11.4 Ishikawa Diagrams

Once we have selected a quality problem its root causes have to be found. Here a systematic analysis can be made using an *Ishikawa diagram*, which is also called a *fishbone diagram* or a *cause-and-effect diagram*. This type of diagram was introduced for the first time by Dr Kaoru Ishikawa in 1943 in connection with a quality program at the Kawasaki Steel Works in Japan. Its construction resembles a simplified fault tree, see Chapter 6.

In the diagram we first roughly describe those types of causes that can possibly produce the observed quality problem. Then we concentrate on one of these roughly described causes and try to investigate it in more detail.

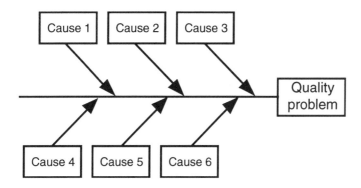

Figure 11.8   An Ishikawa diagram is designed by first sorting out the main causes of the problem. Then we refine the diagram as shown in Figure 11.10. An Ishikawa diagram may not, in its final version, look as in this figure. If it does, the causes of the main causes are not evident to us. A finished diagram should, as a rule, be very "bony"; see Figure 11.11.

When this is done we take one of these causes described in more detail and refine the classification further, see Figures 11.8 and 11.9. Only when we have investigated all the detailed cause descriptions for a main cause, do we move on to the next one. Note that even here it is important to concentrate our efforts and analyse one problem at a time.

It is, however, essential to point out that once it is finished an Ishikawa diagram must never look like the one in Figure 11.8. If it does, we have a poor grasp of causes and effects. An Ishikawa diagram must, in order to be useful, have a lot of "bones" on its skeleton; see Figure 11.11.

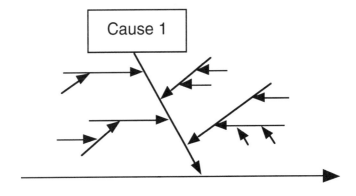

Figure 11.9   *For each main cause of a quality problem we must try to find the causes of the main cause. An Ishikawa diagram should thus be "bony" when it is finished.*

The causes of a quality problem can often be referred to any of the following seven M's:

- *Management.* Does the management provide sufficient information, support and means for the improvement activities?

- *Man.* Does the operator have adequate training, motivation and experience?

- *Method.* Are the proper tools available? Are the process parameters properly specified and are they possible to control?

- *Measurement.* Are the testing devices properly calibrated? Are there any disturbing environmental factors?

- *Machine.* Is preventive maintenance adequately executed? Has the machine the capability to produce units with a variation which is suffiently small?

- *Material.* What about the material used in the process? Are the supplier's quality activities enough?

- *Milieu.* Does the environment affect production outcome?

The beginning of an Ishikawa diagram can thus look as shown in Figure 11.10. We then sometimes speak of a *7M-diagram.* Figure 11.11 illustrates another Ishikawa diagram.

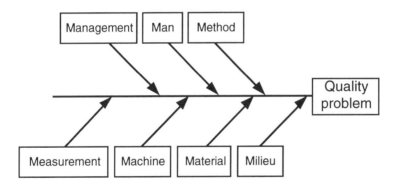

Figure 11.10 The principle of an Ishikawa diagram in the shape of a 7M-diagram.

Ishikawa diagrams provide an excellent basis for problem solving. An Ishikawa diagram and data collected earlier often point to a plausible cause of the observed problem. On other occasions the Ishikawa diagram can give clear indications as to whether a larger amount of data is required and how it is to be collected or how a well planned statistical experiment is to be conducted.

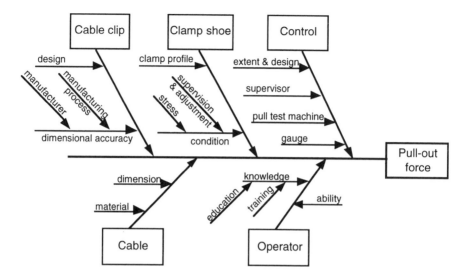

Figure 11.11 An Ishikawa diagram illustrating a problem with inadequate pull-out force after the clamping of a connector to a clamp-shoe.

11.5 Stratification

One way of deducing causes of variation is through *stratification.* If, as in the basis for Figure 11.3, we have data collected from different sources, then we should classify these data into subgroups and illustrate each group separately, for instance by using a histogram.

If these histograms differ substantially, as in Figure 11.12, we may have found a cause of the problem. Then it is a matter of going further to rectify the problem. Maybe an additional refinement of the Ishikawa diagram is required?

A basic rule closely related to the stratification principle is that we must avoid mixing data of different origins. Through stratification we can obtain important information for the improvement work.

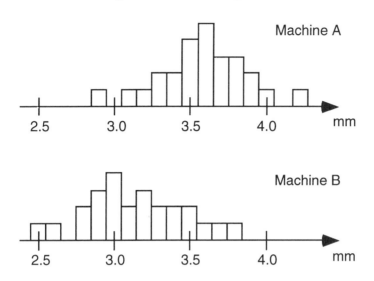

Figure 11.12   Stratification of data from Figure 11.3.

Stratification can be performed with respect to a number of classi-
fications. Some of these may be

- Material   – Supplier
              – Store
              – Time of purchase

- Machine   – Type
              – Age
              – Factory

- Operator   – Experience
              – Shift
              – Individual

- Time   – Time of day
              – Season

- Environment   – Temperature
              – Humidity

11.6 Scatter Plots

In cases where original conditions vary continuously it may be unsuitable, or in some cases impossible, to stratify. Instead a *scatter plot* can be used to illustrate how a process or product characteristic varies due to an explanatory variable, see Figure 11.13. Maybe the variation of the explanatory variables explains a great deal of the observed variation of the product characteristic. In that case, we have a good basis for quality improvement.

There are often many parameters influencing the product characteristic of interest. In such cases we should draw a series of scatter plots, one diagram for each combination of the parameters, and of the product characteristic in combination with the parameters.

The kind of covariation which can be interpreted from a scatter plot can also be used for controlling and supervising the process. Instead of measuring a product characteristic it is better to measure an explanatory parameter directly in the process. Figure 11.13 illustrates, for instance, that it may be more appropriate to supervise temperature during hardening than hardness itself in the finished product.

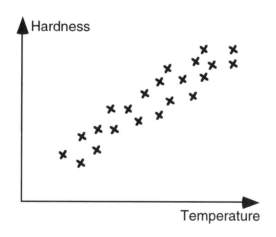

Figure 11.13 A scatter plot illustrating how a result, hardness, is due to a process parameter, temperature.

By studying a process parameter instead of measuring on a produced product, we can more rapidly prevent the problem of process variation.

Note, however, that we have to be on guard against nonsense correlations. Perhaps both the product characteristic and an "explanatory" parameter vary together with a third parameter, see Figure 11.14.

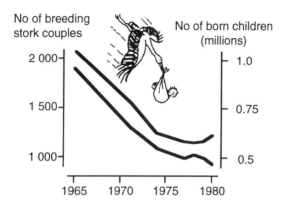

Figure 11.14 This diagram illustrates the number of children born and the number of breeding storks in former West Germany during 1965-1980. Although the curves are parallel we should not conclude that the nativity is due to the number of storks or vice versa. (The idea for the picture is from Nature, 1988, p. 495.)

11.7 Control Charts

As mentioned earlier it is always essential to try to illustrate data graphically. The interpretation of the result is then often more easily done. One of the most useful ways of presenting data from a process is the *control chart*. This is a type of chart in which the process result is illustrated in a time perspective.

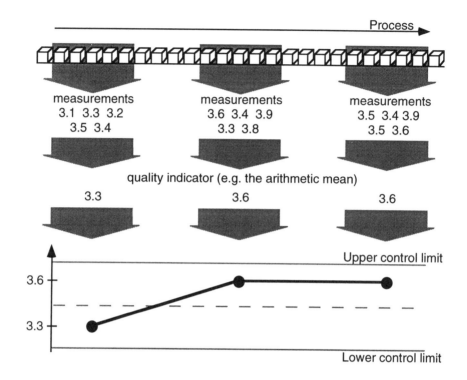

Figure 11.15   *The idea behind control charts. At regular time intervals a number of units are checked. The information is weighed together to a quality indiactor, which is plotted in the control chart.*

The idea of a control chart is to take a number of units produced by the process at regular intervals and check one or more characteristics of these. This information is then weighed together in a suitable manner, for instance to an aritmethic mean or to a standard deviation, and plotted in a diagram. Not only is the process variation illustrated as a function of time but also process changes are indicated.

The primary purpose of a control chart is thus to quickly detect whenever a change has occurred in a process resulting in an alteration in the mean value or in the dispersion. We will discuss control charts more thoroughly in Chapter 12.

204

11.8 Notes and References

More about "the seven QC-tools" can be found in the book "Guide to Quality Control" by Kaoru Ishikawa (1982). The book was written at the end of the 1960s to be used in a very ambitious training program for members of QC-circles in Japan. Nowadays these simple statistical means are standard procedures in QC-circles all over Japan as a step in quality improvement work. In fact one of the main purposes of QC-circles is to provide education in the use of these improvement tools. The idea of QC-circles also originates from Kaoru Ishikawa.

In a series of articles in Quality Progress 1990, starting in the June issue, "the seven QC-tools" are described and how they can be used for solving quality problems. In that series the tool "stratification" is exchanged to "flow chart", an important tool for process mapping, which will be discussed in Chapter 18.

For more about Exploratory Data Analysis we refer to Tukey (1977), Chambers et al. (1983) and Hoaglin et al. (1983).

12 Control Charts

An important tool in statistical process control for finding assignable causes and for supervising a process is the use of *control charts.* The idea is that we take a number of observations from the process at certain time intervals. Using these we calculate some form of *process quality indicator,* which is plotted in a diagram. A process quality indicator is an observable quantity based on the observations indicating the status of the process. It can, for example, be their arithmetic mean, the standard deviation of the sample or the total number of defective units in the sample. A manufacturing process is sometimes supervised by using several process quality indicators simultaneously.

As a process quality indicator we can use any quantity that in some way indicates the value of the process characteristic or how it can be changed. Consequently, it is not necessarily based on measurements on the results produced in the process. Instead it is an advantage if the indicator is based on measurements made directly in the process, since an indication of a change in the process will then be caught earlier.

As long as the plotted quality indicator remains within prescribed limits, we say that the process is *in statistical control* or that we have *a stable process.* These limits are called *control limits.* Very often a *central line* is indicated between the control limits, see Figure 12.1. A point outside any of the control limits is the most commonly used indication that an assignable cause has appeared.

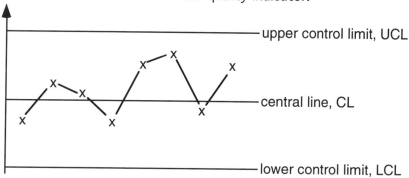

Figure 12.1   *The principles of a control chart.*

12.1 Requirements on Control Charts

A control chart should meet the following requirements:

- quickly indicate when a systematic change has occurred in the process and thereby contribute to the identification of assignable causes of variation

- "false alarms" should be rare, i.e. the risk must be small that a plotted point is outside the control limits when no systematic change has occurred

- it must be easy to handle

- in the control chart it should be possible to estimate the time of a change and the type of change in order to facilitate the identification of causes

- it has to function as a receipt proving that the process has been stable

- it should strengthen motivation and continuously bring attention back to variations in the process and to quality issues

- it has to serve as a basis for evaluation of process dispersion, i.e. its capability (see Chapter 13)

- is should provide information for improvements of its future operation.

The first two items above give rise to a conflict. If the sensitivity of the diagram is increased by narrowing the distance from the central line to the control limits the risk of false alarms tends to increase. As a rule this problem is solved in the following way. The random dispersion in the observed quality indicator is reduced by using several observations and not marking an isolated observation. Furthermore, the control limits are usually set so that the difference between the upper and lower control limit is six times the standard deviation for the plotted process quality indicator, when the process is in statistical control. As we will see later, this principle implies that in general the risk of false alarms becomes insignificant, even if it varies considerably between different types of control charts.

12.2 Principles for Control Charts

Henceforth we will exemplify ideas and concepts concerning control charts using a control chart for upervision of the average level of a certain characteristic. We can think of a diameter of a bolt, the time to delivery or the time to failure of a certain type of unit. In this case it is suitable to use an $\bar{x}$-*chart*, i.e. plot the mean $\bar{x}$ of the observations in the chart.

At certain regular time intervals we take a number of observations, a *sample*, from the process. Each observation is here presumed to be a numerical value. Then we calculate the arithmetic mean $\bar{x} = (x_1 + x_2 + ... + x_n)/n$ of the n observations and use this mean as a quality indicator of the process. Suppose that the quantity we want to control has the average level (expectation) μ and the standard deviation σ, both of which are assumed to be known when the process is in statistical control. Then the mean $\bar{x}$ is an observation from a distribution with the same average value (expectation) μ as the individual observations $x_1, x_2, ..., x_n$, but with the standard deviation $\sigma/\sqrt{n}$. In other words we have a larger chance of detecting a deviation from the average level μ by observing the arithmetic mean $\bar{x}$ instead of an isolated observation. How large then should n be?

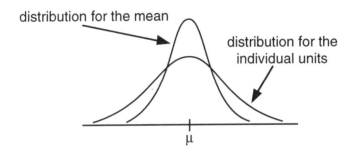

Figure 12.2 If the observations are from a distribution with mean μ and standard deviation σ the arithmetic mean has the same expectation μ as the individual observations, but a standard deviation that is σ/ √n.

Guidance as to the choice of n is given by Figure 12.3, where the standard deviation of the distribution for $\bar{x}$ is illustrated as a function of the number of observations n. We can clearly see that the reduction of the standard deviation of $\bar{x}$ due to adding another observation, is considerable for values of n up to about 4, but then gradually decreases. That is why it is common that 4, 5 or 6 is chosen. For historical reasons n = 5 is frequently chosen, since this facilitates the calculation of the mean $\bar{x}$. When n = 5 we just add the observations, multiply the sum by two and finally move the decimal point one step to the left.

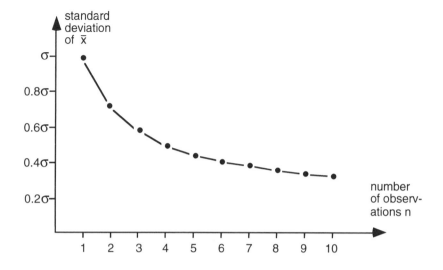

Figure 12.3   The standard deviation of the distribution for $\bar{x}$ as a function of n,   the number of observations in the sample.

12.3   Choice of Control Limits

The choice of control limits must be made in such a way that false alarms become rare. Let us assume for the moment that the distribution of $\bar{x}$ is approximately normally distributed. Then the probability of an $\bar{x}$-value deviating more than $3\sigma/\sqrt{n}$ from the process mean μ, when the process is in statistical control, is merely 0.0027 (see Appendix A). If we stop the process when an $\bar{x}$-value deviates more than $3\sigma/\sqrt{n}$ from μ, we therefore stop the process unnecessarily in about 0.3% of the cases. This means that, when the process is stable, on the average there are about 300 samples taken between false alarms. This is generally considered to be a reasonable risk. Often, in situations like this, we therefore use the control limits $\mu \pm 3\sigma/\sqrt{n}$ and the central line μ, in a control chart in which $\bar{x}$ is plotted. Since the distance between each control limit and the central line is three times the standard deviation of our quality indicator $\bar{x}$, the control chart is said to have *3-sigma limits.* Control charts designed according to this principle are sometimes called *Shewhart diagrams* or *Shewhart charts* after their originator Walter A. Shewhart.

The risk calculation above is based on the assumption that $\bar{x}$ can be regarded as an observation from a normal distribution, which often is a plausible assumption. This is due in part to the fact that many measurement quantities can be said to be approximately normally distributed. Another reason is that a mean, such as $\bar{x}$, is an observation from a distribution tending to resemble more closely the normal distribution than that of the individual observations, see the Central Limit Theorem in Appendix A.

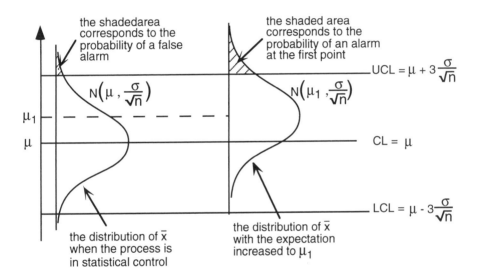

Figure 12.4   *The distribution of the quality indicator $\bar{x}$ in relation to the control limits, when the process is in statistical control and when the average value has increased from μ to μ_1.*

Control charts with 3-sigma limits provide different risks of false alarm depending on which quality indicator is used. This is due to the fact that different quality indicators are observations from different distributions. In some odd situations it is possible to get a risk of false alarm, when using 3-sigma limits, which is as large as 0.11. However, in most practical situations the 3-sigma limits give a rate of false alarms which is reasonably small.

The risk of a false alarm has to be put in relation to how difficult it is to decide that an alarm in the control chart really is false. If this is easy, perhaps we should take an even bigger risk of false alarms and thus obtain improved sensitivity in the diagram, i.e. getting an *alarm* more quickly when an assignable cause has occurred.

12.4 Control Charts for Mean

The control charts that are used can be classified according to the type of quantity that is supervised. If we are supervising an average value (expectation), we can talk of a *mean value chart* or an *average chart*. If, on the other hand, we are interested in the size of the temporary variations in the process, i.e. the dispersion between the measurements of various manufactured units, then we speak of a *dispersion chart*.

12.4.1 An x̄-chart when μ and σ are unknown

When we are going to start a process or restart it after a stop we do not, as a rule, know the expectation μ and/or the standard deviation σ. We then have to estimate these parameters in order to get the limits of the control chart. To get estimators we let the process run for a while and at regular intervals we take samples. Suppose that we take k samples of n units each. A common rule of thumb is that k should be at least 20-25, preferably up towards 40. This is partly because the risk of a false alarm is affected by the number of samples. Another reason is that we should not use control limits based on measurements from a process which is not in statistical control and we need at least 20 samples to decide if the process is in statistical control.

As an estimator of μ we take the mean value $\bar{\bar{x}}$ of the mean values of the samples $\bar{x}_1, \bar{x}_2, ..., \bar{x}_k$, i.e.

$$\bar{\bar{x}} = \frac{1}{k}(\bar{x}_1 + \bar{x}_2 + ... + \bar{x}_k)$$

Sample	Measurement			Sample mean	Range	Stand. dev.
1	x_{11} x_{12} ...		x_{1n}	$\bar{x}_1$	R_1	s_1
2	x_{21} x_{22} ...		x_{2n}	$\bar{x}_2$	R_2	s_2
3	x_{31} x_{32}		x_{3n}	$\bar{x}_3$	R_3	s_3
...						
k	x_{k1} x_{k2} ...		x_{kn}	$\bar{x}_k$	R_k	s_k
Mean				$\bar{\bar{x}}$	$\bar{R}$	$\bar{s}$

Table 12.1 A few notations for the calculation of control limits.

We will get the same numeric result if we calculate the arithmetic mean of all n times k measurement values.

If σ is known we can then use the control limits

$$UCL = \bar{\bar{x}} + \frac{3\sigma}{\sqrt{n}} \quad \text{and} \quad LCL = \bar{\bar{x}} - \frac{3\sigma}{\sqrt{n}}$$

If σ is also unknown we have to estimate σ by using our measurement values. The standard deviation σ can be estimated using two different methods, namely the *s-method* or the *R-method*.

The s-method. If we use the s-method, we first calculate the standard deviations $s_1, s_2, ..., s_k$ for the various samples and then take

$$\frac{s_1 + s_2 + ... + s_k}{k} \frac{1}{c_4} = \frac{\bar{s}}{c_4}$$

as an estimator of σ, where c_4 is a constant, depending only on the sample size n. The reason for this procedure is that the arithmetic mean of the unbiased estimators $s_1/c_4, s_2/c_4, ..., s_k/c_4$ of σ is an unbiased estimator of σ with less uncertainty. Values of the constant c_4 for different values of n can be found in Table B.4.

By introducing the notation $A_3 = 3/(c_4\sqrt{n})$, where A_3 is a constant which can be found in Table B.4, the control limits can be written as

$$\text{UCL} = \bar{\bar{x}} + A_3\bar{s} \quad \text{and} \quad \text{LCL} = \bar{\bar{x}} - A_3\bar{s}$$

The R-method. If, on the other hand, we use the R-method to estimate σ, we first calculate the range R in each sample, i.e. the difference between the largest and the smallest value within the sample. From these ranges $R_1, R_2, ..., R_k$, we estimate σ as

$$\frac{R_1/d_2 + R_2/d_2 + ... + R_k/d_2}{k} = \frac{\bar{R}}{d_2}$$

where d_2 is a constant that makes the estimator unbiased. The constant d_2, which in books dealing with statistics is often denoted α_n, is merely dependent on the number of observations in the samples and can be found in Table B.4 (see also Appendix A). The reason for this estimation procedure is, as with the s-method above, that the mean value of the unbiased estimators R_1/d_2, R_2/d_2, ..., R_k/d_2 is a new unbiased estimator of σ with less dispersion.

With this estimator of σ we get the control limits $\bar{\bar{x}} \pm 3\bar{R}/(d_2\sqrt{n})$. If we introduce the constant $A_2 = 3/(d_2\sqrt{n})$, which can be found in Table B.4, we get

$$\text{UCL} = \bar{\bar{x}} + A_2\bar{R} \quad \text{and} \quad \text{LCL} = \bar{\bar{x}} - A_2\bar{R}$$

This is the most common type of control limits for an $\bar{x}$ -chart.

Example 12.1

When a certain mechanical unit was produced, measurements were carried out every 45 minutes and the deviations from the average level $\mu = 3.2$ mm were noted in units of 0.1 mm. The values presented in the control chart in Figure 12.5 were obtained. In order to get control limits for the $\bar{x}$-chart, we first calculate $\bar{x}$ and R for the different samples (see the control chart) and then calculate

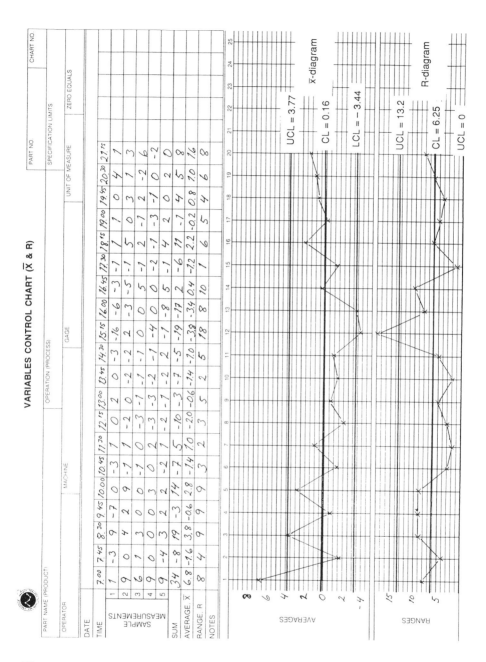

Figure 12.5 An x̄-diagram and an R-diagram illustrating Examples 12.1 and 12.2.

$$\bar{\bar{x}} = \frac{1}{20}(6.8 + 3.8 + \dots + 1.6) = 0.16$$

and

$$\bar{R} = \frac{1}{20}(8 + 9 + \dots + 8) = 6.25.$$

Since n = 5 we get $A_2 = 0.577$ from Table B.4. We then get

UCL = 0.16 + 0.577·6.25 = 3.77

LCL = 0.16 − 0.577·6.25 = − 3.44.

The control limits and the x̄-values are shown in the control chart in Figure 12.5. We observe that three of the x̄-values are outside the control limits. In other words the process is not in statistical control. Therefore it is not recommended to use the calculated control limits for further production without any further investigations as to why the points are outside the control limits. If we can find an assignable cause and eliminate that cause we delete the corresponding points and recalculate the control limits and then check again whether the process is in statistical control.

12.5 Control Charts for Dispersion

For supervision of the standard deviation σ we can use either of the process quality indicators s or R. The standard deviation s of the sample has the advantage of containing more information about σ, whereas the range R is easier to calculate and is therefore more common. In both the methods described below it is assumed that the characteristic being studied is normally distributed.

12.5.1 R-charts

The range R, i.e. the difference between the largest and the smallest observations, is a measure of the dispersion of the quality characteristic. Since the distribution from which R is an observation has the expectation $d_2\sigma$ and the standard deviation $d_3\sigma$, where d_2 and d_3 are constants depending on n (see Table B.4), we have to plot R/d_2 in the control chart if we want to keep σ as central line.

To avoid dividing by d_2 in every sample, we instead mark R in the chart and use the central line $CL = d_2\sigma$. An R-chart with 3-sigma limits has then the control limits

$$UCL = d_2\sigma + 3d_3\sigma = (d_2 + 3d_3)\sigma$$

$$CL = d_2\sigma$$

$$LCL = d_2\sigma - 3d_3\sigma = (d_2 - 3d_3)\sigma$$

For $n \le 5$ we have $d_2 - 3d_3 < 0$ (see Table B.4). In this case we set LCL = 0 since the standard deviation is never negative. If we introduce the constants

$$D_1 = \max(0, d_2 - 3d_3) \quad \text{and} \quad D_2 = d_2 + 3d_3$$

we get

$$UCL = D_2\sigma \quad \text{and} \quad LCL = D_1\sigma$$

The values of the constants D_1 and D_2 are to be found in Table B.4.

If σ is unknown we instead use the estimator $\overline{R}/d_2$, where $\overline{R}$ is the mean value of the ranges of k samples. This gives the control limits

$$UCL = D_4\overline{R} \quad \text{and} \quad LCL = D_3\overline{R}$$

where the constants

$$D_4 = \frac{d_2 + 3d_3}{d_2} \quad \text{and} \quad D_3 = \frac{\max(0, d_2 - 3d_3)}{d_2}$$

are to be found in Table B.4.

Example 12.2

To be able to calculate the control limits of an R-chart for the production described in Example 12.1, we use the fact that for the ranges in the samples we get $\overline{R} = 6.25$.

Since n = 5 we get $D_3 = 0$ and $D_4 = 2.115$ (see Table B.4). That gives the control limits

UCL = 2.115·6.25 = 13.2.

LCL = 0·6.25 = 0

The upper control limit is marked in the control chart in Figure 12.5, as are the R-values of the different samples. We note that the range of sample number 12 lies above UCL.

12.5.2 s-charts

The standard deviation s of the sample from a normal distribution is an observation from a distribution with the expectation $c_4\sigma$ and the variance $(1 - c_4^2)\sigma^2$, where the constant c_4 can be found in Table B.4. If we plot s in a control chart with 3-sigma limits we get

$$\text{UCL} = c_4\sigma + 3\sigma\sqrt{1 - c_4^2} = \left(c_4 + 3\sqrt{1 - c_4^2}\right)\sigma$$

$$\text{CL} = c_4\sigma$$

$$\text{LCL} = c_4\sigma - 3\sigma\sqrt{1 - c_4^2} = \left(c_4 - 3\sqrt{1 - c_4^2}\right)\sigma$$

If σ is unknown we replace σ by an estimator of σ. If we use the s-method and estimate σ by $\overline{s}/c_4$, then we get the control limits

$$UCL = B_4 \bar{s} \quad \text{and} \quad LCL = B_3 \bar{s}$$

where

$$B_4 = \frac{c_4 + 3\sqrt{1 - c_4^2}}{c_4} \quad \text{and} \quad B_3 = \frac{\max\left(0, c_4 - 3\sqrt{1 - c_4^2}\right)}{c_4}$$

12.6 Combining $\bar{x}$-charts and R-charts

In practice it is often advisable to combine control charts for the mean and for the dispersion. Most often, $\bar{x}$-charts are combined with R-charts. We then get an $\bar{x}$-*R-chart*. Such a chart is illustrated in Figure 12.5.

Note that the plotted points in the two control charts are not at all independent. For instance, a point outside the control limits in the $\bar{x}$-chart may be caused by a point outside the control limits in the R-chart, i.e. the standard deviation has increased.

12.7 Sensitivity

The sensitivity of a control chart is best described by the average time until alarm after a certain change has occurred in the process. When independent samples are taken from the process this average is determined by the probability of alarm based on a single sample. This is described by the *OC-curve*.

12.7.1 The OC-Curve

How sensitive a control chart is to systematic changes in the process can be described by its *OC-curve (OC* stands for *Operating Characteristic)*. The OC-curve illustrates the probability of a plotted point ending up between the control limits. This probability is a function of the size of the real change in the process.

Let us study the OC-curve of an x̄-chart. Suppose that the process average value has been changed from μ to $\mu+\theta$, where μ is the average level of the process in statistical control. We also assume that this change does not influence the dispersion of the outcome; see Figure 12.6.

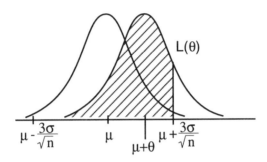

Figure 12.6   *The shaded area L(θ) corresponds to the probability that the quality indicator lies between the control limits when μ has changed to μ+θ, but the standard deviation is the same.*

In this case, the probability of not getting an alarm, i.e. the probability that the quality indicator x̄ lies between the control limits, is

$$L(\theta) = P(\mu - 3\sigma/\sqrt{n} < \bar{x} < \mu + 3\sigma/\sqrt{n} \text{ if the process average is } \mu+\theta)$$
$$= \Phi(3 - \theta\sqrt{n}/\sigma) - \Phi(-3 - \theta\sqrt{n}/\sigma)$$

where $\Phi(x)$ is the cumulative distribution function of $N(0,1)$. This function can be found in various tables (see Appendix B). For example, if we have $\theta = 2\sigma/\sqrt{n}$ we get

$$L(2\sigma/\sqrt{n}) = \Phi(1) - \Phi(-5) = 0.841.$$

This means that with the probability $1 - 0.841 = 0.159 \approx 16\%$ we will get an alarm in the x̄ -chart already with the first plotted point after the occurrence of a systematic deviation of $2\sigma/\sqrt{n}$. The function $L(\theta)$ is illustrated in Figure 12.7.

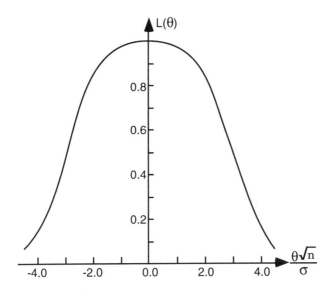

Figure 12.7 The OC-curve for an x̄-chart with 3-sigma-limits. If for example θ = 2σ/√n we get the value 0.84 in agreement with the calculations above. If instead θ = σ/√n we get the value 0.98.

12.7.2 The ARL-Curve

Another measure of the sensitivity of a control chart, in general more interesting than the OC-curve, is how long it will take until the control chart reacts after a systematic change in the process. The number of points plotted until the first one ends up outside one of the control limits is a random variable. Its average value (expectation) is usually called *ARL (Average Run Length)*. For a control chart with 3-sigma limits, this value can be calculated as $1/(1-L(\theta))$, where $L(\theta)$ is calculated in accordance with the last section, see e.g. Wadsworth et al. (1986). The ARL-value depends of course on the size of the systematic change. The ARL-curve for an x̄-chart with 3-sigma limits is illustrated in Figure 12.8.

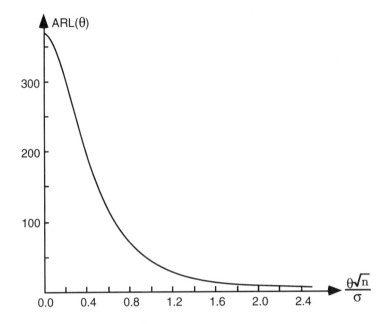

Figure 12.8 *Illustration of the ARL-curve of an* $\overline{x}$ *-chart with 3-sigma limits. If, for instance, θ is increased by* $\sigma/\sqrt{n}$, *i.e.* $\theta\sqrt{n}/\sigma =$ *1, the graph indicates an ARL-value around 40 (in fact, it is 44).*

The sampling frequency has also an important impact on the effectiveness of the control chart. The more often we take samples, the better supervision do we get against systematic changes. Only a small number of units are then produced before the control chart indicates the change. Sampling costs increase, however, and we will more often get false alarms when the process is in statistical control.

There is also another aspect of the time between samples. Sometimes production can be divided into different natural and homogeneous sections with respect to shifts, raw material deliveries or production equipment. Such natural sections of production are usually called *rational subgroups*. The idea is that within the different parts, subgroups, of production we should have as homogeneous a production as possible. If we succeed so well with the partition that a systematic change within a subgroup is hardly likely to occur, it is sufficient to take just one sample from each subgroup of the production. Using this sample we can then judge whether the part of the production examined has been subjected to any systematic changes.

12.8 Some Other Control Charts

As already mentioned, control charts need to have a small risk of false alarms but at the same time the chart should be sensitive, i.e. the chart should indicate a change in the process as soon as possible after its occurrence. In a Shewhart diagram one value for each sample is plotted and an alarm is received if that value lies outside any of the control limits. The only way to increase sensitivity in that type of diagram is to increase the sample size or the sample frequency.

Another way to increase sensitivity is to use more information from the collected data, for instance by also using results from earlier plotted points in the chart. We shall here just very briefly refer to some other types of control charts based on this principle.

One possibility is to use *modified Shewhart diagrams,* where some consideration also is taken of earlier plotted points and how these lie in relation to so-called *warning lines* within the control limits. These warning lines are often placed at 2-sigma limits. Here an alarm is defined as one point outside any of the control limits or two consecutive points outside the same warning line; see Figure 12.9.

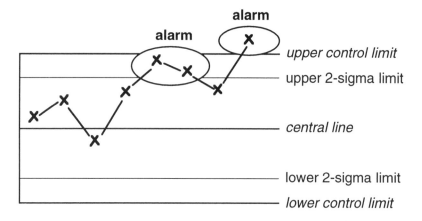

Figure 12.9   A control chart with warning lines at 2-sigma limits. The control limits are in general set at 3.1-sigma in order to get the same risk of false alarms in this chart as in the usual Shewhart diagram.

A generalization of this idea is to divide the area between the 3-sigma limits into several zones and use more rules for alarm. The most commonly used rules for alarm are (see Figure 12.10):

- Rule 1: One single point outside any of the 3-sigma limits, i.e. outside zone A.

- Rule 2: Two points out of three outside zone B on the same side of the central line but inside the corresponding control limit.

- Rule 3: Four out of five successive points fall on the same side of the central line outside zone C.

- Rule 4: Eight successive points fall on the same side of the central line.

These alarm rules, and some other, were developed by Western Electric (1956).

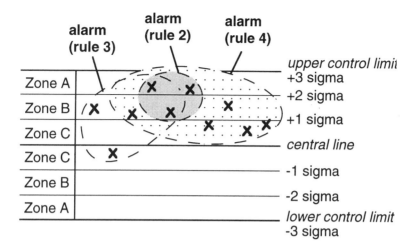

Figure 12.10 *Illustration of the Western Electric alarm rules indicating that assignable causes are disturbing the process.*

Note, however, that the use of several out-of-control rules increases not only the sensitivity of the chart but also the risk of false alarms. If, for instance, all the above mentioned four rules are used together, the ARL-length when the process is under control is about 90, instead of 370 when using only rule 1, i.e. one point outside any of the 3-sigma limits.

In a *cusum chart (cumulative sum chart)*, first proposed by Page (1954), the sum of the deviations from a target value is plotted. When we only have an upper tolerance limit the alarm signal often is based on plotting

$$u_n = \max(u_{n-1} + z_n - k, 0),$$

where u_{n-1} is the cusum value plotted at time n–1, z_n is the quality indicator at time n (which may be an average value), and k is the target value. An alarm is obtained when u_n is larger than a pre-determined limit; see Figure 12.11. If there is also a lower tolerance limit a corresponding chart can be used for that limit too.

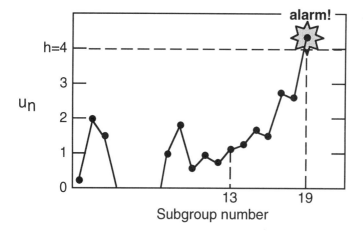

Figure 12.11   *Illustration of a cusum chart intended for use when we have an upper tolerance limit. The plotted points in the chart are based on simulated samples of size 4 from a normal distribution. The first 12 samples are from N(0,1), but after that the samples are from N(0.5,1). We get an alarm when u_n exceeds 4, which in the case illustrated happens after the 19th sample. However, we can see the tendency already after the 13th plotted point. (After Ryan, 1989.)*

Still another type is *EWMA (Exponentially Weighted Moving Average)*, first introduced by Roberts (1959), in which the plotted statistic is

$$v_n = (1-c)v_{n-1} + cx_n,$$

where v_n is the plotted quality indicator at time n, x_n is the observed value of the process characteristic at time n, and c, $0 < c < 1$, is a weighting factor. Often $c \approx 0.2$. This type of control chart is suitable in particular when only one observation per time may be available, for example in process and chemical industries. Here the control limits are often set at $\mu \pm 3\,\sigma\,\sqrt{c/(2-c)}$. For more about EWMA charts we refer for instance to Wadsworth et al. (1986) or Wetherill & Brown (1991).

An interesting and simple alternative to Shewhart charts is the *zone chart,* recently introduced by Jaehn (1987, 1989, 1991). The chart is divided into eight zones corresponding to 1-sigma intervals in the same manner as for the Western Electric alarm rules. Numerical scores are then assigned to the zones as follows:

Zone	Score
Between target and 1 sigma	0
Between 1 sigma and 2 sigma	2
Between 2 sigma and 3 sigma	4
Beyond 3 sigma	8

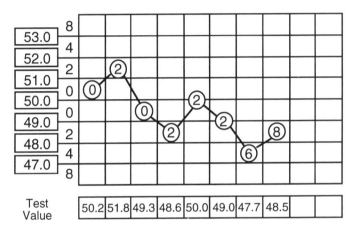

Figure 12.12   *The zone control chart procedure illustrated for a process quality indicator with target value 50.0 and a standard deviation of 1.0. The first test value 50.2 is marked in the region between the target value and the 1-sigma limit and gives, according to the rules above, a score of 0. The third test value crosses the central line and the scoring process restarts. At the eighth point the accumulated scores reach the alarm signal of 8 and we have a signal that the process is out of control. (From Jaehn, 1991. © American Society for Quality Control. Reprinted with Permission.)*

The scores are added unless the result falls on the other side of the central line. At that time, the score accumulation process restarts. A zone score of eight or more is a signal that the process is no

227

longer in statistical control. The score values and the value 8 as an alarm signal are chosen in order to get suitable ARL-values. The risk of false alarms is roughly the same as when we use a Shewhart chart with the Western Electric rules described above, i.e. about 90-95. The plotting procedure is illustrated in Figure 12.12.

All the types of diagram that we have discussed in this book are used when supervising some form of continuous measurement, i.e. we have *variable data*. It is also possible to design control charts for *attribute data,* such as the number of defective units produced per week or the number of signals before answering the telephone. We will, however, refrain from discussing such diagrams here. An example illustrating the ideas is however given in Section 18.3.

12.9 Notes and References

There are numerous books which in an elementary way give further details about statistical process control in general and control charts in particular. The very first, which is still very readable, is Shewhart's book from 1931. In the 1950s the first edition of Western Electric's (nowadays AT&T) "Statistical Quality Control Handbook" was published. Ishikawa's (1982) book "A Guide to Quality Control" is also pleasant to read.

Other recent good descriptions of different types of control charts are Wadsworth et al. (1986), Montgomery (1991), Wetherill & Brown (1991), Oakland & Followell (1990) , Wheeler & Chambers (1992) and Wheeler (1993). A book dealing with practical applications of some more special control charts is Pyzdek (1992).

13 Capability

The primary purpose of statistical process control is to reduce variation in the process and then supervise the process, so that new assignable causes do not appear.

In this chapter we will discuss ways of investigating and measuring the ability of a process to produce units within the set tolerance limits. To keep it simple we will only study one product characteristic and its variation.

The ability of a process to produce units with dimensions within the tolerance limits is called its *capability* (with respect to the characteristic in question). Utilizing the information obtained from statistical process control we can formulate various measures of this capability. Here we will formulate a few different capability measures and study the information they give about the process. We will also briefly discuss when and how studies of capability should be carried out. We also want to emphasize that although the capability concept today is used mostly for manufacturing processes it has the same relevance for other types of processes.

13.1 Capability Measures

The capability of the process is determined by the statistical distribution of the product characteristic being studied. When the process is in statistical control this distribution can often be described, at least approximately, by a normal distribution. The capability is then determined by the corresponding average value (expectation) μ and standard deviation σ together with the upper tolerance limit T_U and the lower tolerance limit T_L. This is illustrated in Figure 13.1. We would, however, like to point out that several situations may arise where the outcome hardly is normally distributed. The distribution can presumably be skewed when, for example, we are studying a resistance or surface smoothness.

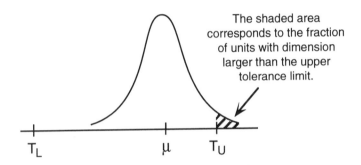

The shaded area corresponds to the fraction of units with dimension larger than the upper tolerance limit.

Figure 13.1   The capability to produce units within the tolerance limits T_U and T_L depends on the dispersion σ of the process and how the process is centered, i.e. where the average value μ is located

A simple and widely used measure of the ability of the process to produce units between the set tolerance limits is the *capability index*

$$C_p = \frac{T_U - T_L}{6\sigma}$$

This index states how large a part of *the natural variation* of the process, a common name for 6σ, is occupied by the tolerance interval (see Figure 13.2).

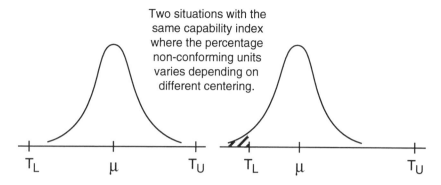

Two situations with the same capability index where the percentage non-conforming units varies depending on different centering.

T_L μ T_U T_L μ T_U

Figure 13.2 *Capability index is a measure of the dispersion of the process relative to the range of the tolerance interval. In order to avoid getting units with measurements outside the tolerance interval, a well-centered process is required in addition to a suitable value of capability index.*

$(T_U-T_L)/3\sigma$	Value of C_p	Defects per million units
4	0.67	46 000
5	0.83	12 500
6	1.00	2 700
7	1.17	500
8	1.33	60
9	1.50	7
10	1.67	0.6
11	1.83	0.04
12	2.00	0.002

Table 13.1 *The number of defective units for different values of the capability index C_p, assuming a stable and perfectly centered process. The fraction of units with a measurement outside one of the tolerance limits is under these circumstances equal to $2(1-\Phi(3C_p))$, where Φ is the cumulative distribution function of $N(0,1)$.*

A large value of this capability index C_p implies that the process, if well-centered, will produce units with measurements within the tolerance limits. But if C_p is too small, good centering is not enough. Far too large a part of the production will have measure-ments outside any of the tolerance limits, see Figure 13.3. Usually a value of C_p with $C_p \geq 4/3 = 1.33$ is recommended.

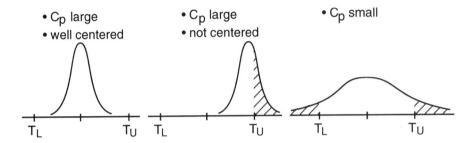

Figure 13.3 (a) A process with a large value of the capability index C_p will produce units within the tolerance limits if the process is well-centered.
(b) A process with a large value of the capability index C_p will produce a lot of units with measurement outside the tolerance limits if the process average is too far from the centre of the tolerance interval.
(c) A process with too small a value of the capability index C_p will produce units with measurement outside the tole-rance limits even if the process is perfectly centered.

Since capability is affected not only by dispersion but also by cen-tering, a measure is required that takes into account how well cen-tered the process is. One such measure is the *centering measure*

$$CM = \frac{|M - \mu|}{(T_U - T_L)/2}$$

where the target value $M = (T_U + T_L)/2$ is assumed to lie midway between T_U and T_L. This is a measure which is independent of scale and shows how well-centered the process is around M; see Figure 13.4.

When the target value does not lie in the middle of the tolerance interval, other measures have to be considered. We will not comment on this case any further here.

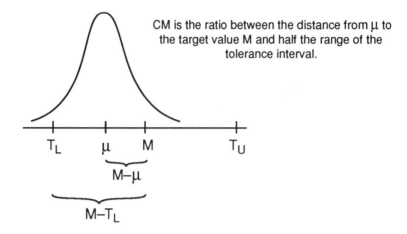

Figure 13.4 *The centering measure CM denotes how large a part of half the tolerance interval is absorbed by the distance between the target value M and the average value μ.*

A measure involving both the dispersion of the process and its centering is *the adjusted capability index*

$$C_{pk} = \min\left(\frac{T_U - \mu}{3\sigma}, \frac{\mu - T_L}{3\sigma}\right)$$

which measures the distance between the average value of the process and the nearest tolerance limit in relation to 3σ. The measure C_{pk} can also be expressed as a combination of the capability index C_p and the centering measure CM as

$$C_{pk} = C_p(1 - CM)$$

Note that here we assume that the target value is right in the middle of the tolerance interval.

If we only have one single tolerance limit, an upper tolerance limit T_U or a lower tolerance limit T_L, we can then use either of the following one-sided capability indices, the *upper adjusted capability index*

$$C_{pu} = \frac{T_U - \mu}{3\sigma}$$

or the *lower adjusted capability index*

$$C_{pl} = \frac{\mu - T_L}{3\sigma}$$

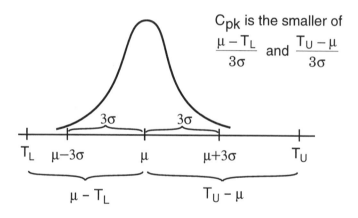

C_{pk} is the smaller of

$$\frac{\mu - T_L}{3\sigma} \quad \text{and} \quad \frac{T_U - \mu}{3\sigma}$$

Figure 13.5   *The adjusted capability index C_{pk} is equal to the smaller of the values C_{pu} and C_{pl}. Here C_{pl} is the distance between the average value μ and the lower tolerance limit T_L in relation to half the natural dispersion of the process, whereas C_{pu} is the corresponding relation between $T_U - \mu$ and 3σ.*

As a rule, the average value μ and the standard deviation σ are not known for the process. Thus, these measures have to be estimated using observations from the process. The common practice is to replace μ and σ by $\bar{x}$ and s. Such estimators of capability measures should be marked with a "*", for example C_{pk}* or CM* to distinuish them from the actual theoretical values. If these estimators are based on a small number of observations, the random uncertainty could be quite substantial. If for instance, $C_p = 1.0$ and $n = 30$ the probability is about 11% of getting $C_p^* \geq 1.20$ and about 3% of getting $C_p^* \geq 1.33$. If $C_p = 1.33$ and $n = 30$ the probability is about 18% of getting $C_p^* \leq 1.20$ and about 5% of getting $C_p^* \leq 1.10$, see Figure 13.6. A lucid discussion of uncertainties in estimators of different capability indices can be found in Pignatiello & Ramberg (1993).

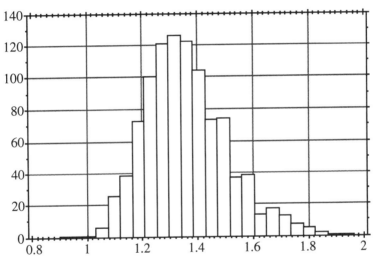

Figure 13.6   *The result of 1,000 simulated estimators of C_{pk} each one based on 50 observations from N(49.5, 1.0). The target value is assumed to be 50.0.*

13.2 Process and Machine Capability

Even if we have tried to eliminate all assignable causes of variation, the average value of the process may vary with time. This may, for instance, depend on variations between various shifts, different machines or varying material properties. We can then regard the variation in the average value of the process as a random variable, whose dispersion it is possible to estimate.

In this case there are two dispersion components: a variation from unit to unit and a variation that is due to the usually slower variation of the average level. If we only take the first mentioned variation into account, we would be dealing with *machine capability*, whereas *process capability* takes both dispersion components into account.

A capability index for a machine is usually indicated by "m", for example C_m and C_{mk}, in a similar way as C_p and C_{pk} refer to the capability index for the process.

To estimate machine capability we thus need homogeneous set of data, taken for instance from the same material, the same set-up, and the same shift.

To estimate process capability we need, on the other hand, to study the process during a longer period of time, and to pay attention to how we estimate the dispersion. An estimator of process capability cannot, for example, be based on R-values of a number of samples, taken during an extended period of time since we can have constant variation within the groups but a considerable variation of the average value over the same time period; see Figure 13.6.

Machine capability can be estimated by using $\bar{x}_j$ and s_j, $j = 1, 2,...,$ k, where k is the number of sample groups taken from the production. The quantities μ and σ can subsequently be estimated using

$$\bar{\bar{x}} = \frac{1}{k} \sum_{j=1}^{k} \bar{x}_j \quad \text{and} \quad s_I = \sqrt{\frac{1}{k} \sum_{j=1}^{k} s_j^2} \text{ , respectively}$$

Here s_I is an estimator of the dispersion within the same sample.

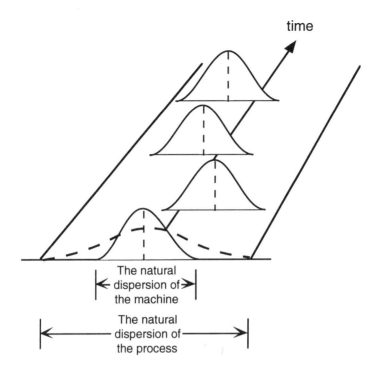

*Figure 13.6   Viewed over a longer period of time the average value va-
ries. Even if the dispersion of the machine is constant, the
dispersion of the process will then increase.*

Process variation can be described using two components. Both σ_I,
the dispersion within samples, and σ_M, the dispersion between
samples have to be considered. The total dispersion can then be described as

$$\sigma = \sqrt{\sigma_I^2 + \sigma_M^2}$$

By using $\bar{x}_j$ and s_j, $j = 1, 2, ..., k$, the total variation can be estimated as

$$\sigma^* = \sqrt{s_{\bar{x}}^2 + \frac{n-1}{n} s_I^2}$$

where

$$s_{\bar{x}}^2 = \frac{1}{k-1} \sum_{j=1}^{k} (\bar{x}_j - \bar{\bar{x}})^2$$

Sometimes more comprehensive statistical analyses have to be made in order to estimate the process capability in an accurate manner. Some of these methods are presented by Montgomery (1991) and Kotz & Johnson (1993).

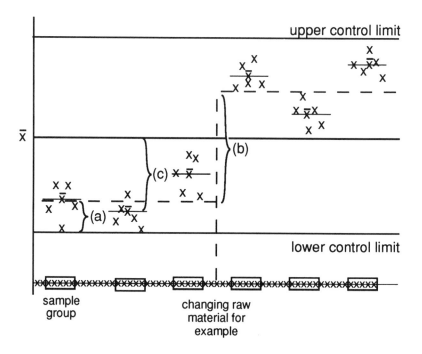

Figure 13.7   *An illustration of the dispersion components that are included in process capability.*
(a) Variation within the group causes the dispersion σ_I
(b) Variations in the process, which for example are due to change of shift or raw material, cause the dispersion σ_M
(c) Variation between sample means is described by $\sigma_{\bar{x}}$ where

$$\sigma_{\bar{x}}^2 = \frac{\sigma_I^2}{n} + \sigma_M^2$$

and n is the number of units in a sample.

13.3 Capability Studies

Capability studies should be carried out for each new process and, eventually, for all subprocesses that are regarded as important. The result of the studies can focus our attention on which processes ought first of all to be improved. Before making a capability study, it is important to assure that the machine or the process that is to be investigated is in statistical control. A description of the process outcome as a function of time is, therefore, an essential component of a capability study. A control chart should therefore be present as a basis for the final capability evaluation. It is equally important to try to split up the production into natural parts (e.g. each shift, each machine or each nozzle) and perform a capability study on each of these parts. This can be seen as a form of stratification.

Common requirements for the capability indices of a machine and a process are that they must be at least 1.5 and 1.33, respectively. These may perhaps seem to be very tough requirements. If the outcome is normally distributed, the capability index is 1.33 and the average value (which is assumed to coincide with the target value) lies midway between the tolerance limits, then only 0.007% of the units will have a measurement outside the tolerance limits, see Table 13.1. However, we should also take into consideration the possibility of large dispersion involved in the estimation of capability indices. Furthermore, we must remember then that it is not good enough to strive for zero defects only, i.e. no units with a measure outside the tolerance limits. We must also try to attain the target value with as little dispersion as possible.

In this context we could mention that Motorola, a large American electronics company which received the first Malcolm Baldrige National Quality Award in 1988, has a quality improvement program called "Six Sigma", see Figure 13.8. A program with the same name has also been accepted by IBM, the international computer company. One aim of the program is to keep the distance between the process average and the nearest tolerance limit to at least 6σ.

This means that the goal is that C_{pk} should be at least 2.0 for all the processes in the company, not only manufacturing processes.

Figure 13.8   *The Motorola quality improvement program is called "Six Sigma". The aim is that every process, manufacturing processes as well as administrative and economic processes, shall have a capability index C_p that is at least equal to 2.0. That means that although the process average deviates 1.5σ from M the fraction of defective units is as small as $\Phi(-7.5) + 1 - \Phi(4.5) \approx 3.4$ parts per million. Here Φ is the cumulative distribution function of $N(0,1)$.*

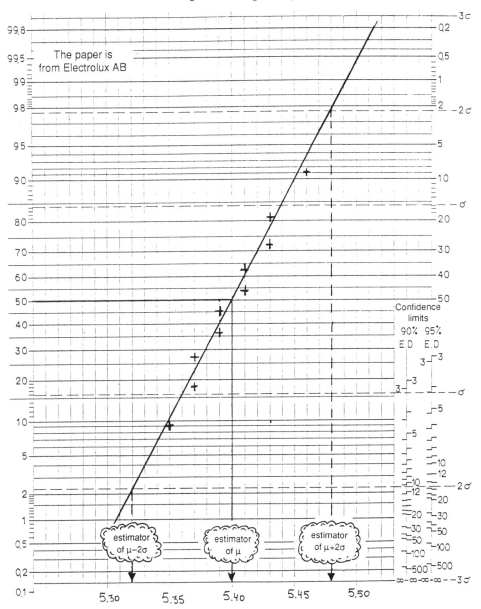

Figure 13.9   *By plotting the observations on probability paper for a normal distribution, we may conclude whether an assumption of normal distribution is realistic. At the same time we can also estimate the expectation μ and the standard deviation σ and thus also the capability index C_p.*

241

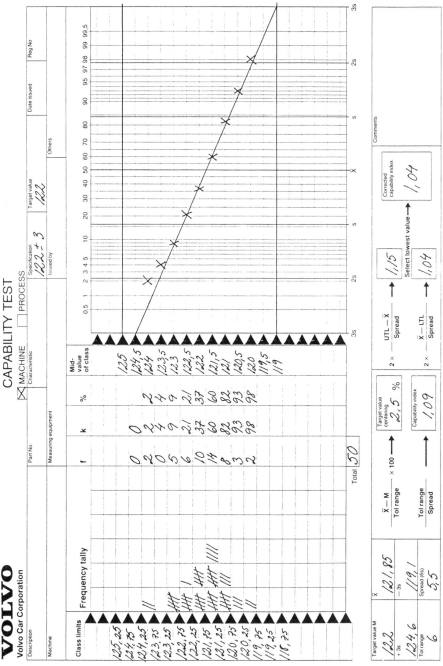

Figure 13.10 An example of a form intended for the capability study of a machine or a process.

A capability study can be carried out using the calculations presented in Section 13.2. However, it may then easily turn out to be a game with numbers. It is more appropriate to use probability plotting paper for the normal distribution to illustrate the data material. In that way we can at the same time check how plausible an assumption of normality is. If for example the plot gives a broken line this indicates a mixture of two normal distributions which in turn may indicate the existence of an assignable cause. The analysis also becomes much easier to interpret when done by graphical methods. See Figure 13.9 and Appendix A.

Some companies use special plotting papers for the investigation of capability. An example of this can be found in Figure 13.10.

13.4 Notes and References

More details about capability index and capability studies can be found for instance in Montgomery (1991). A unified approach to capability indices is presented in Vännman (1993). Furthermore, the book Kotz & Johnson (1993) is completely devoted to the capability concept.

The capability concept and its applications have also been discussed in numerous articles in recent years. The first comprehensive article was Kane (1986). Other interesting articles are for instance Chan et al. (1988) and Chou et al. (1990). Gunter (1989) has in a number of articles in Quality Progress discussed "use and abuse of capability indices". The whole October 1992 issue of the Journal of Quality Technology is also devoted to capability indices and their interpretations and properties. Several of the articles in that issue are well worth reading.

It should also be emphasized that the different capability indices, which in recent years has been rather popular, should be used with great care. The assumptions needed and the uncertainties involved makes this a complicated area. In his editorial note in the

October 1992 issue of the Journal of Quality Technology, Peter Nelson warns against uncritical use of capability indices and he states that devoting an issue to this topic "should not be construed as implying that JQT is promoting the use of capability indices. In fact, it is clear from a statistical perspective that the concept of attempting to characterize a process with a single number is fundamentally flawed". See also Pignatiello & Ramberg (1993).

14 Quality in the Supply Process

One of the fourteen points in Deming's quality philosophy (see Figure 3.5 and Chapter 21) is addressed to supplier relations:

End the practice of awarding business on the price tag alone

In the past, purchasing departments have frequently operated on orders to seek the lowest-priced vendor. This has often led to orders from suppliers with low product quality with consequential problems in the manufacturing process and sometimes also with consequences for the end user of the final product. In some companies as much as 70% of the total non-quality costs are related to poor quality of incoming goods.

In order to avoid severe problems extensive inspection has been made of received shipments. That is, however, an expensive and ineffective way of coping with the problem. It violates another of Deming's (1986) rules:

Cease dependence on inspection to achieve quality

Instead, buyers should strive to build a long-term relationship with one single supplier, or just a few, for each type of item in order to influence the quality improvement process of that supplier. For instance, Xerox, which produces and sells copiers, has reduced its number of suppliers from some 5,000 to about 400 in five years, and the multinational car manufacturer SEAT has reduced its number of suppliers from 1,500 to around 300 in less than two years.

In this chapter we shall in the following two sections, which mainly are inspired by Cali (1993), discuss the purchasing process and the important concept of *supplier partnership*. Then we shall discuss the practice of relying on acceptance sampling and mass inspection instead of supporting the suppliers in their improvement processes on their routes towards Total Quality Management.

14.1   The Purchasing Process

In a recent book Cali (1993) discusses the application of the TQM principles for purchasing management. He first notes that many leading companies today have changed their attitudes with respect to supplier relations. Some common themes that everybody seems to adhere to, and which are supported by purchasing practices from several American companies, are

- benchmarking provides the goal to strive for

- reducing the supplier base and heading towards single sources of supply provides a better vehicle for improved quality

- trust is the one element that will cement the relationships established.

- investment in the training and technical support of suppliers is a key to success

- focus on continuous improvement

- involving suppliers in the product design process yields the greatest benefits

- using metrics to measure performance is necessary in order to determine whether improvement is occurring

- the sharing of information, risks, and rewards with suppliers is the only way to establish long-term mutually beneficial partnerships

- multi-discipline involvement in supplier selection and relationships strengthens the relationship

The change currently going on is illustrated by an example from National Cash Register, NCR, see Figure 14.1.

NCR Purchasing Policies Then	NCR Purchasing Policies Now
Contracts renegotiated yearly	Evergreen contracts
Incoming inspection	Benchmarking
Purchasing components	Securing technology
Over 2000 suppliers	150 suppliers
Spotty parts quality	50 to 100 ppm rates on incoming parts

Figure 14.1   The current trend concerning purchasing policies in many companies illustrated by the change at NCR. (From Cali, 1993.)

In the "Total Quality Management Purchasing Model" in Figure 14.2 many of the ideas presented in Part I of this book are applied to the purchasing process. In the next section we shall focus on one part of Step 3, where supplier partnership is discussed. For the other steps we refer to Cali (1993).

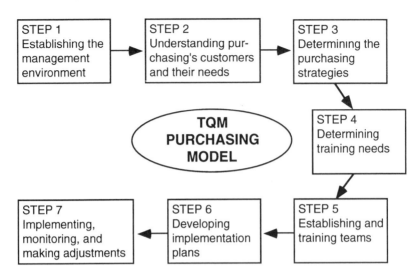

*Figure 14.2   A Total Quality Management Purchasing Model.
(After Cali, 1993.)*

14.2   Supplier Partnership

Some of the reasons for many companies to link the processes of their suppliers much closer to those of their own are:

- non-quality costs due to inferior quality of purchased goods
- the Just-In-Time philosophy
- necessity of having committed suppliers.

More generally, well developed process thinking makes this development inevitable.

In Cali (1993) supplier partnership is defined as

A mutual, ongoing relationship between a buying firm and a supplying firm involving a commitment over an extended time period, and entailing a sharing of information as well as a sharing of the risks and rewards of the relationship.

Some examples of partnership strategies are:

Intel, Inc. sets up "executive partners" at a high level. The executives from both parties act as the "godfathers" of the relationship and ensure that it is sound at all levels. A supplier's personnel is allowed to work at Intel for up to one year and then return to the supplier.

Federal Express recommends that partnerships should be developed with internal customers first, so that purchasing understands the requirements of a relationship before trying partnerships outside. They also have partnerships with several catalogue houses; customers calling the catalogue houses are actually talking to Federal Express employees who take and process orders.

The current strategy of many European firms today is to require their suppliers to be third party certified according to the ISO 9000 series. However, a quality system only fulfilling the requirements of ISO 9000 is not at all sufficient. A more progressive attitude has to be taken in order to be a trust-worthy supplier. It is also questionable whether such a claim is a major step towards a long lasting partnership. This is illustrated by the folllowing quotation from Henkoff (1993) in Fortune where Motorola's quality Manager Richard Buetow says: "If you're a Motorola supplier, an ISO 9000 certification won't even buy you a cup of coffee. We would never stop auditing a company with ISO 9000. It's just a fraction of what we're looking for."

In fact, the international series of quality systems, ISO 9000, is not mentioned at all by Cali (1993). It is also of interest to note that an increasing number of companies require their suppliers to apply for the Malcolm Baldrige National Quality Award. Comments on the criteria of the Malcolm Baldrige National Quality Award and the ISO 9000 series are to be found in Chapter 21.

In Japan, major suppliers join in already at the design stage. It is recognized that the supplier is the product specialist and has expertise to identify improvement opportunities. As well as the quality aspect, suppliers are expected to fully understand their processing capacity, cost assumption and delivery management in detail. It is understood that before any organisation can meet the requirements of its customers it must first fully understand in detail all aspects of its own business. To this end it is normal for the customer and supplier to conduct thorough discussions concerning operational details of the supplier's business. See also Dale & Allan (1993).

14.3 Acceptance Sampling

In modern quality philosophy, activities are guided towards process improvement so that defective units will not be produced. The practice of inspecting incoming goods is therefore no longer particularly interesting. Through active quality improvement together with the supplier, we can, in the long run abolish inspection. Faults are to be prevented or, at least, caught immediately at the source and not far downstream. However, since reality is not always so ideal, it might still sometimes be necessary to have a certain amount of inspection.

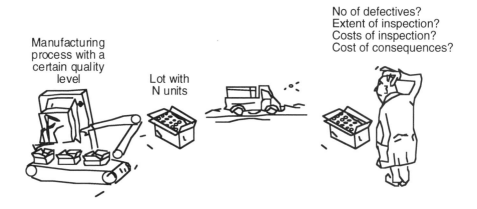

Figure 14.3   Illustration of the problem with acceptance sampling.

In the past, however, *acceptance sampling*, was considered very important within the quality field. We shall here, mainly for historical reasons, present some concepts in this area. In the following we thus study a situation where no partnership relation has been established and therefore some kind of inspection on incoming batches has been considered important. The aim is to decide whether the batch shall go straight into production or if the units of the batch must first be checked. What decision we make depends among other things on the consequences of letting a batch of inferior quality pass into production.

14.3.1 Deming's All-or-Nothing Rule

An important basis for a decision whether or not to inspect a lot is the available information on the lot. This can be based on

- experience of previous deliveries from the same supplier

- knowledge of the supplier's quality control system

- knowledge of the manufacturing process and the variation of characteristics among the units

- measurement results from the manufacturing process in which the units of the lot are produced.

All these sources of information are such that we, with some uncertainty, can estimate the probability that a manufactured unit in the supplier's manufacturing process is defective and that this is not detected before delivery. This probability is called the *process average* and is henceforth denoted by p. We are actually interested in the total number of defective units in the lot. This number, however, is unknown to us. We only know that they have been produced in a manufacturing process whose probability of producing a defective unit is p, a quantity we have some information about. The actual outcome of defective units in the process is then due to random variation in the manufacturing process. The number of defective units in the lot can thus be regarded as a random variable. (See Appendix A for a discussion on random variables and their distributions.)

Even if we cannot determine exactly the number of defective units in the lot, we can still say that the expected number of defective units in the lot is Np, where N is the size of the lot. This means that we will, on average, find Np defective units when we make a total inspection of a large number of lots coming from a process with the process average p. We then also assume that all units have been correctly classified as either "correct" or "defective", an assumption that is by no means always realistic.

Henceforth we will assume that the consequence of a defective unit getting into the manufacturing process is known, at least as an average value. We denote the *average consequence cost* by K. By using an appropriate follow-up on the costs of poor quality, it should, in many cases, be feasible to estimate K. Difficulties may arise if the probability of a defective unit not being detected is significant. In that case there is a risk that a defective unit coming out onto the market causes damage to customers and to company goodwill that is hard to measure. The estimation of these losses must be made in accordance with the company's quality policy.

The cost of inspecting a unit, the *inspection cost,* is very often easy to estimate. From now on we will denote this cost by C. There is often also a fixed cost that we will disregard in this fundamental discussion.

Suppose for a moment that we know the process average p. A randomly selected unit of the lot that passes on into manufacturing without inspection generates an average cost equal to pK. If, on the other hand, we check the unit we get an inspection cost C. The decision whether the unit is to be checked depends on whichever of these costs is larger. Since the reasoning concerned a randomly selected unit, it is also valid for the lot as a whole. Consequently, we get the decision rule

- a total inspection of the lot if p > C/K
- let the lot pass without any inspection if p < C/K.

This rule is sometimes called *Deming's All-or-Nothing Rule.* The only snag with this reasoning is that in practice we do not know p, at least not completely. Our uncertainty with respect to p can, under certain circumstances, make it financially worthwhile first of all to check a random sample in order to obtain further information about p. We can then make a decision whether the lot should be accepted as it is or if also the other units in the lot should be inspected; see Figure 14.4. This procedure can be called *statistical acceptance sampling.*

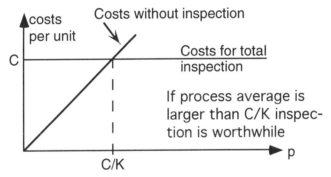

Figure 14.4   *The inspection cost per unit as a function of the process average p.*

14.3.2 Acceptance Sampling by Attributes

Suppose that we have a lot with N units and have to decide if it fulfills the requirements with respect to a certain characteristic such as colour, diameter or time to failure. From here on, in this chapter, we will measure the quality of a lot by *the lot fraction defective* p, i.e. the fraction of defective units in the batch. Please observe that when we say "a lot", it can refer to what has been produced during one shift or one day and not necessarily to the contents of "a box".

We evaluate the contents of the lot by randomly selecting units and then checking them with respect to the characteristic of interest. Each inspected unit is then classified as "correct" ("acceptable") or "defective". Depending on the number of defective units among those selected, we *accept* the lot (i.e. we consider the contents of the lot as acceptable) or we *reject* it.

This process of selecting and making decisions can be done in several different ways. We can for instance select a certain number of units out of the lot, which we denote n, and based on the number of defective units among these decide on either rejection (if $d > c$) or acceptance (if $d \leq c$); see Figure 14.5. This is called a *single sampling plan*.

Another way would be to first select a smaller sample of n_1 units. If the number of defective units d_1 in this sample is small, say $d_1 < c_1$, the lot is accepted and if it is large, say $d_1 > r_1$, the lot is rejected. If $c_1 < d_1 < r_1$ we take one more sample and base the decision of acceptance or rejection on the total number of defective units in the two samples. This is called a *double sampling plan*.

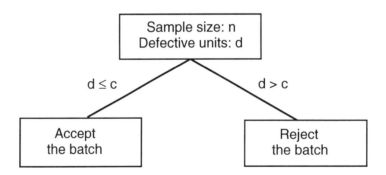

Figure 14.5   The principle of a single sampling plan.

One further alternative would be that after each inspected unit we make either of the three decisions "accept the lot", "reject the lot" or "checking yet another unit". This method is called *sequential sampling*.

Henceforth, we will only discuss simple sampling plans. A simple sampling plan is thus determined by *the size of the sample n* and *the acceptance number c*.

The OC-Curve

The ability of a sampling plan to separate out inferior lots and let good ones pass is dependent on which type of sampling plan we are using and on the choice of parameters in the sampling plan. The separating ability of a sampling plan is usually illustrated using the *OC-curve* (*OC* stands for *Operating Characteristic*). This curve illustrates the probability $L(p)$ that a lot with the lot fraction defectives equal to p is accepted as a function of p. Thus, with single sampling, $L(p)$ is the probability that when checking n units we will not find more than c defective ones when the lot fraction defective is p.

Figure 14.6 illustrates OC-curves of two simple sampling plans. We see that the sampling plan $n = 100$, $c = 2$ has a lower separating ability than $n = 500$, $c = 10$, since "good" lots (lots with a small fraction of defective units) have a high acceptance probability and "bad" lots (lots with a high lot fraction defective) have a larger acceptance probability. Please notice that in both sampling plans the same fraction of defective units is allowed for. In both cases $c/n = 2\%$. The steeper an OC-curve is, the better the separating ability of the corresponding sampling plan.

The ideal OC-curve, as in Figure 14.6, belongs to a sampling plan where each lot with a lot fraction defective lower than p is accepted whereas all lots with a lot fraction defective of at least p are rejected. This OC-curve cannot be obtained by using sampling theory. The monotony of the inspection work and other factors contribute to the fact that not even with a *total inspection* of the lot will we get this OC-curve. The ability to detect defective units is never perfect.

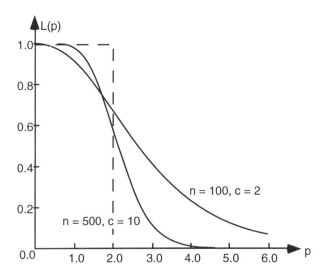

Figure 14.6   *OC-curves for the simple sampling plans n = 100, c = 2 and n = 500, c = 10. We observe that the steeper the OC-curve is, the better the corresponding sampling plan is for separating bad lots and accepting good ones. Compare with the dotted, "ideal", OC-curve.*

In order to determine a simple sampling plan we look for suitable values of the sample size n and the acceptance number c. This is preferably done in relation to the risks we are willing to take.

We want "good" lots to be accepted with high probability. In exceptional cases only lots with a lot fraction defective smaller than a certain value should be rejected. This limit of lot fraction defective is often denoted p_1 or *AQL (Acceptable Quality Level)*. The risk of rejecting a lot with the lot fraction defective equal to p_1 is usually denoted by α and is called the *producer's risk*. It is common for α to be set at 5%; see Figure 14.7.

Furthermore, we want "bad" lots, let us say with a lot fraction defective larger than p_2, to be rejected and only in exceptional cases accepted. This lot fraction defective limit is denoted *LTPD (Lot Tolerance Percent Defective)* or sometimes *LQ (Limit Quality)*. The corresponding probability of acceptance is denoted β and is called the *consumer's risk*. Often β is set at 10%.

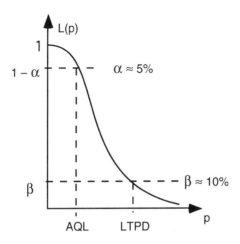

Figure 14.7 A few interesting points on the OC-curve.

According to ISO 2859, Standard Procedures and Tables for Inspection by Attributes, the concept of AQL is defined as the "maximum percent defective that, for pupoposes of sampling inspection, can be considered satisfactory as a process average". The concept of LTPD is defined as "a fraction of non-conforming units that should be accepted with a small given probability".

We would like to emphasize that it is not in compliance with the modern quality philosophy presented in the remaining parts of this book to say that a certain percentage of defective units could be acceptable.

How to Determine a Simple Sampling Plan

If we want to determine a simple sampling plan whose OC-curve passes through two given points, we can, as a rule, use a *binomial nomograph,* since the size of the lot N does not influence the OC-curve to any great extent if n/N < 10%. Figure 14.8 illustrates this when we are looking for a sampling plan whose OC-curve passes the points (0.018, 0.95) and (0.10, 0.40).

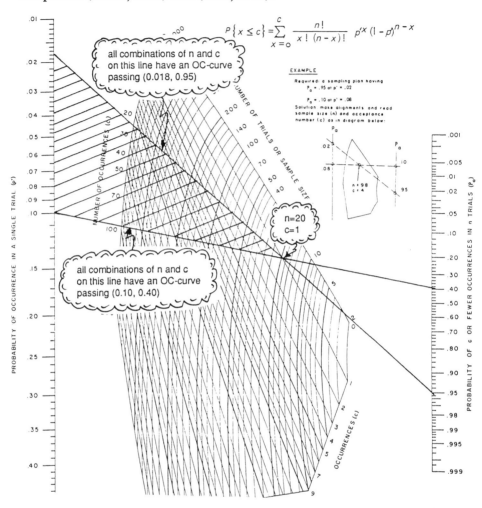

Figure 14.8   *The binomial nomograph illustrates how a single sampling plan with an OC-curve through (0.018, 0.95) and (0.10, 0.40) can be determined. When the lines of the binomial monograph do not intersect in a "cross", we should choose the combination of n and c that lies closest to the point of intersection, but still within the marked triangle. In this way we get a sampling plan with values of the risks α and β smaller than the specified ones.*

Sometimes sampling plans are determined by studying some measure of the necessary extent of inspection. Such measures are the concepts of ASN (Average Sample Number) and ATI (Average Total Inspection). The *Average Sample Number ASN(p)* is the average number of inspected units until a decision has been made whether to accept or reject the lot. However, this measure does not take into account what we do with the lot after the decision. In general, we submit the rejected lot to a total inspection. A better measure of the extent of inspection is hence often the *Average Total Inspection ATI(p)*, which is the average number of inspected units per lot, including the fact that a rejected lot is submitted to a total inspection.

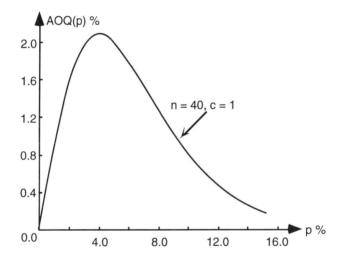

Figure 14.9   *The value of AOQ(p) as a function of p when n = 40 and c = 1. AOQ(p) is at most equal to 2.1%. This is the AOQL-value. The largest value AOQ(p) can achieve occurs when the lot fraction defectives of received lots is about 4%.*

Another measure of interest when determining sampling plans is the quality of the lot after inspection. A measure of interest here is *AOQ (Average Outgoing Quality)*, which is the average value of the lot fraction defectives after inspection. This quantity is a function of the lot fraction defectives p when studying a certain sampling plan. The maximum value of AOQ(p) as a function of p is usually denoted *AOQL (Average Outgoing Quality Limit);* see Figure 14.9.

14.3.3   Standard Systems for Acceptance Sampling

Over the years several different standard systems for acceptance sampling have been designed. Some are built up around the AQL concept, others around LTPD or AOQL. There are also systems designed on other principles.

The most frequently used system for acceptance sampling by attributes is the American system MIL-STD 105 from 1950 and its international equivalent ISO 2859 from 1974. The latest versions are MIL-STD 105E from 1989 and ISO 2859-1 from 1988. The title of the standard ISO 2859 is *Standard Procedures and Tables for Inspection by Attributes.*

The ISO 2859 system is an AQL system, which means that one of the entrance parameters is the AQL value. There are AQL values from 0.01% up to 1000%. Values up to 10% are intended for use when working with the fraction defective units of a lot. Values over 10% are used mainly when calculating the total number of defectives per 100 units. One unit can then have many defects.

The system includes sampling plans for single, double and multiple sampling (which is a generalization of double sampling using more than two samples).

One big advantage of this system is that it contains rules for transitions from normal to reduced and tightened inspection, respectively, depending on the inspection results of earlier lots from the same source, see Figure 14.10.

When using the transition rules in MIL-STD 105E or ISO 2859 between reduced, normal and tightened inspection, we get an OC-curve that is steeper than the one we would get working only with a normal inspection level. If most of the time we have lots with a low value of the lot fraction defectives, we often use reduced inspection, whereas we often have tightened inspection if that value is high. This is illustrated in Figure 14.10.

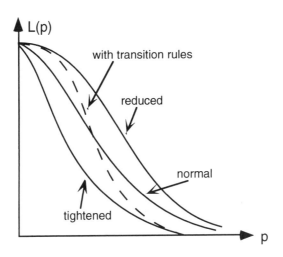

Figure 14.10 Sketch of OC-curves for normal, reduced and tightened inspection in ISO 2859 (MIL-STD 105) together with the OC-curve when the transition rules between the levels are used.

14.4   Notes and References

For a more thorough discussion about supplier quality we refer to Cali (1993) and Weber & Johnson (1993). The booklet "Elements of Successful Customer/Supplier Relationships" published by the British Deming Association also deals with supply quality. The October 1993 issue of The TQM Magazine is devoted to "building relationships with suppliers".

More about acceptance sampling by attributes can for instance be found in Shilling (1982), Montgomery (1991) and Wadsworth et al.

(1986). In these books acceptance control by the variable method is also discussed, which means that the decision concerning acceptance or rejection is based on measurement values of the quality variable. This can typically occur when studying quality characteristics which can attain several different values and which can be measured. Examples of such values are length, diameter or life time.

Part IV

Quality for Customer Satisfaction

Quality means customer satisfaction and delight. Here, service quality has become increasingly important. In this part we will briefly discuss some characteristics, models and techniques for achieving good service quality. More generally, we will discuss the formation of customer satisfaction and delight and how to measure and improve satisfaction of external as well as internal customers.

15 Service Quality

Awareness of the importance of service quality has increased rapidly. Since 1970, the number of employees in the service sector has increased by 60% in the USA and by 40% in Japan. Today about 70% of the GNP is coming from the service sector in the USA and several of the EC countries. Within the public sector we have, for example, schools, child care, health care, tax authorities and defence. Within the private sector we have banks, hotels, transportation, restaurants, hair-dressers, video agencies and so on. Besides the increase of the service sector, the amount of service and the importance of well delivered services in other parts of industry has also increased. It is difficult to mention any company for which service matters are not important. Often several services are associated with the goods a company is selling and these services are often as important as the product itself. When eating at a restaurant the service and the environment around the food are as important as the food itself and when hiring a car the reception and other services around the car are very important.

The costs for poor quality of services are even larger than those for goods. Crosby (1979) and others estimate the costs for poor quality to about 30-40% of the turnover. Just as an example, Arnerup & Edvardson (1992) state that the airline company SAS (Scandinavian Airlines Systems) had costs of SEK 100 million (about USD 12 million) during 1989 to look for or pay for luggage lost in transit.

This means that it has become increasingly important to focus on and improve service quality. In this chapter we will introduce some characteristics, models and techniques for improving service quality. In the next chapter we will discuss the relations to customer satisfaction.

15.1 Service Characteristics

As mentioned before in this book, many of the techniques and methods that we have discussed and that have earlier been used for quality improvements of goods are just as useful for services. However, there are some characteristics which differentiate services from goods. These are

- Services are intangible and may be difficult for a supplier to explain and specify and sometimes also difficult for the customer to assess.

- The customer often takes part directly in the production of a service.

- Services are consumed to a large extent at the same time as they are produced, i.e. services cannot be stored or transported.

- The customer has not become owner of something when buying a service.

- Services are activities or processes and cannot therefore be tested by the customer before they are bought.

- Services often consist of a system of subservices. The customer assesses the totality of these subservices. The quality and the attractiveness of the service depend on the customer's experience of the totality.

These characteristics must be taken care of when designing, marketing, producing and delivering services. In particular it is very important to realize that much of service quality is related to moments when the service supplier and the customer meet face to face. This moment is often named "the moment of truth", a concept introduced by Norman (1984) and relates to the moment in bull fighting when the matador meets the bull. The moment of truth is, however, also a "moment of possibilities" since the supplier can then really convince the customer of service excellence. On the other hand, if a problem has occurred it is in general too late to do anything about it when the customer has left. The most perfect system for delivering service is worthless if things do not work at the moments of truth.

Quality of a service has several dimensions. Some of these are (see Zeithaml et al., 1990):

- *tangibles,* which refers to the physical environment in which the service is presented, i.e. the organization, the equipment and the personal and their clothing

- *reliability,* which is the consistency of performance and dependability, e.g. punctuality and the correctness of service, information and invoice procedures

- *responsiveness,* which is the willingness to help the customer

- *competence,* which is the possessing of the required skills and knowledge to perform the service

- *courtesy,* which refers to the supplier's behaviour, e.g. politeness, consideration and kindness

- *credibility,* which means trustworthness, believability and honesty of the service provider

- *security,* which means freedom from danger, risk and doubt

- *access,* which is the ease of making contact with the supplier, e.g. the time the shop is open

- *communication,* which is the ability of talking in a way which is understandable to the customer

- *empathy,* which deals with the interest and possibility of becoming acqainted with the role of the customer.

In summary, many of these dimensions are related to the customers' confidence in those providing the service. A good discussion of dimensions of service quality is given in Zeithaml et al. (1990), which has to a great extent inspired this chapter.

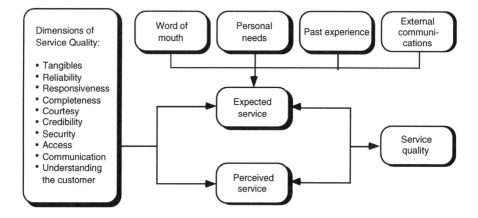

Figure 15.1 *Customer assessment of service quality. If the perceived service exceeds the expected service we get a satisfied customer. (From Zeithaml et al. 1990.)*

During the development of SERVQUAL, a methodology for measuring service quality, Zeithaml et al. (1990) found that some of the above mentioned ten dimensions are strongly correlated and as a result the number of dimensions was reduced in SERVQUAL to five, namely

- *tangibility*
- *reliability*
- *responsiveness*
- *assurance,*
- *empathy.*

Here *assurance* includes competence, courtesy, credibility and security and *empathy* includes access, communication and understanding the customer.

Investigations using SERVQUAL have proved that reliability is by far the most important of these dimensions and that tangibles is the least important. The other three dimensions are for many services of approximately the same importance. Similar results have also been obtained from other investigations.

In a specific case, however, the generic quality dimensions just mentioned have to be thought over again. In the end, service quality is most dependent on confidence in the service providers.

15.2 Models for Service Quality

15.2.1 Grönroos' Service Quality Model

One early model for service quality is the one described by Grönroos (1983). This model relates the service experienced by the customer to his expectations. The customer's experience of the service depends on the following two dimensions, see Figure 15.2:

- *technical quality,* which is related to the result of the service, e.g. the flight from New York to Amsterdam, the food in a restaurant or the result of preventive maintenance on the car. This dimension is related to the question: "what" has been provided.

- *functional quality,* which is related to the way the service has been delivered, e.g. the check-in at the airport, the environment in the restaurant or the help and the waiting time at the car service station. This dimension is related to the question: "how" has the service been provided.

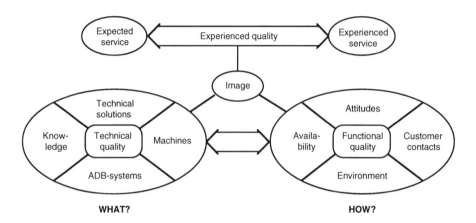

Figure 15.2 *Grönroos' Service Quality Model, separating the technical quality from the functional quality. (From Grönroos, 1987.)*

15.2.2 The Gap Model

Zeithaml et al. (1990) discuss a model explaining causes of customer dissatisfaction. The model is called *The Gap Model,* see Figure 15.3. This model illustrates the path from customer expectation to customer experience. Here, we will here just briefly discuss the different gaps in the model and refer to Zeithaml et al. (1990) for a more detailed discussion.

Gap 1: *Between customers' expectation and management's perceptions of those expectations.*

This gap consists of the discrepancies which arise because executives do not understand what customers consider to be high quality.

270

Knowing what the customers want and expect is the very first step in delivering service quality. It is also a critical step. To be able to provide services that customers perceive as excellent the firm has to know what the customers expect. Because services have few clearly defined and tangible quality dimensions, Gap 1 is in general considerably larger in service companies than it is in manufacturing firms. Some reasons for this gap are

- Lack of marketing research
- Inadequate upward communication
- Too many levels of management

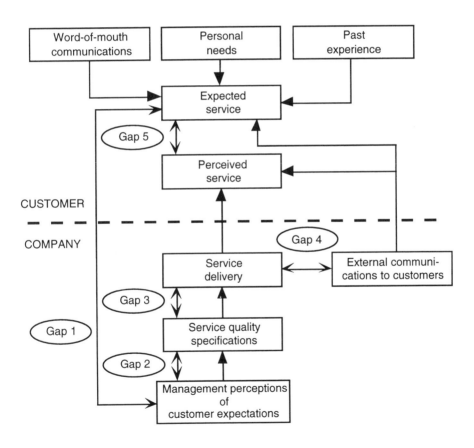

Figure 15.3   The Gap Model. (From Zeithaml et al.,1990.)

271

Gap 2:   *Between management's perceptions of customers' expectations and service quality specifications.*

This gap is a wide gap in many companies. Known customer expectations cannot be matched or exceeded because of difficulties in responding consistently to consumer demands and because of the absence of top management commitment to service quality. Some reasons for this gap are

- Inadequate management commitment to service quality
- Perception of infeasibility
- Inadequate task standardization
- Absence of goal setting

Top managers committed to quality must constantly and visibly express their commitment to the troops. Stew Leonard, in a highly respected dairy of the same name, demonstrates this, according to Zeithaml et al. (1990), in the two rules that can be read at the entrance to the store:

Rule 1:   The customer is always right

Rule 2:   If the customer is ever wrong, reread rule 1

These rules are worth thinking about. Although it can be discussed whether the customer is always right, as stated in the rules it is always the customer who judges the service.

Gap 3:   *Between service quality specifications and service delivery.*

Sometimes management really does understand customers' expectations and does set appropriate specifications and yet the service delivered by the organization does not reach the customers' expectations. The difference between service specifications and the actual service delivery is the service-performance gap caused by employees who are unable or unwilling to perform the service at the desired level. It is important to note that contact personnel delivering the service have a pivotal role. Even when service guidelines exist there may be a large variability in employee performance.

Some reasons for this gap may be

- Role ambiguity
- Role conflict
- Poor employee job fit
- Poor technology job fit
- Inappropriate supervisory control systems
- Lack of perceived control
- Lack of teamwork

Gap 4:   Between service delivery and external communications to customers about service delivery

This gap appears between what the firm promises about a service and what it actually delivers. Accurate and appropriate company communication, advertising and public relations that do not over-promise or misrepresent are essential to delivering services that customers perceive as high in quality. It is important to realize that customer expectations are affected by media advertising and other forms of communication. Because people cannot be controlled in the way machines that produce physical goods can be controlled, the potential for overpromising may be higher for services.

Some reasons for this gap are

- Inadequate horizontal communication among operations, marketing and human resources, i.e. between advertising, sales people and operations.

- Propensity for overpromising.

The result of these four gaps will be the fifth one:

Gap 5:   Between customers' expectation and perceived service.

A good service quality is one which matches or exceeds customer expectations. Judgements of high and low service quality depend on how consumers perceive the actual service performance in the context of what they expected.

15.2.3 Two Comments

Two aspects of importance not illustrated in the above mentioned models are

- the necessity to delight the customer (see also Section 16.1). The finding of exciting features of a service does not relate to any gap which can be removed by systematic methods. On the contrary, delight is formed by human interaction and by creative acts based on knowledge and understanding of the customer.

- services and hardware products are more and more often to be considered as elements in a value-creating network, i.e. there are a lot of interacting stake holders. A systems approach has to be taken in order to understand how customer delight and satisfaction are formed.

15.3   Design of Services

Interest for the process of designing services in order to meet customer requirements in an efficient and economic way has increased during the last few years. One reason for this may be the recent focus on quality activities during the design process for goods. As in many other situations, flowcharts are very helpful tools. Applied to design of services this tool is sometimes called *blueprinting*. Another useful tool for design of services is *QFD, Quality Function Deployment*, discussed already in Chapter 4.

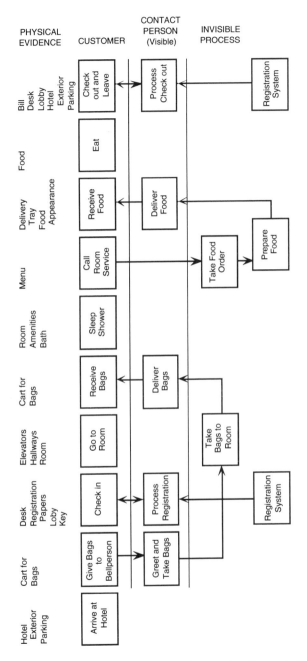

Figure 15.4   Example of blueprinting of the service "overnight hotel stay". (From Bitner, 1992.)

275

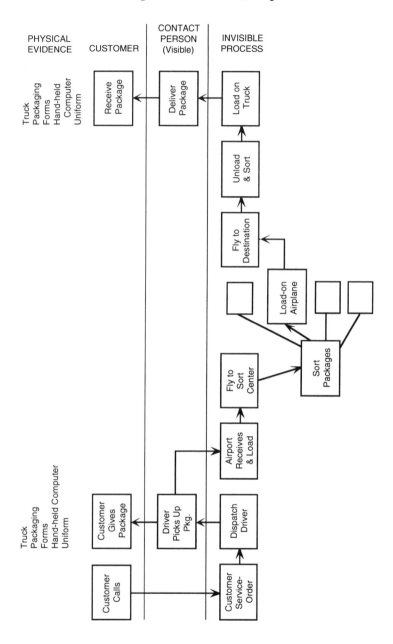

Figure 15.5   Example of blueprinting illustrating "express mail delivery service". (From Bitner, 1992.)

15.3.1 Blueprinting

Blueprinting is a systematic way of describing how a service is created by using a form of flow chart. It was first presented by Schostack (1984) but has still not been used to any great extent. It consists of a chart illustrating the service in detail. The design of the flow chart may sometimes be time consuming but at the same time it gives good opportunities for identifying and avoiding pitfalls regarding quality problems. By using a flow chart, the dependence between different departments, processes and people is clearly visualized. Often, a boundary is also marked between what the customer can see and what is made invisible, back-office, to the customer. Illustrations of blueprinting can be found in Figures 15.4 and 15.5.

15.3.2 Quality Function Deployment

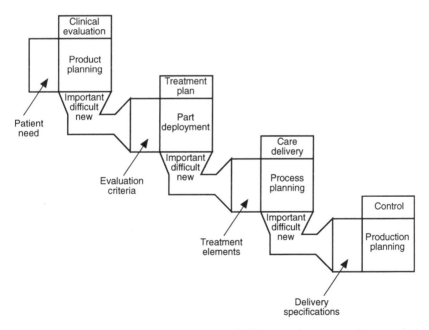

Figure 15.6   Illustration of how the QFD matrices can be used for deployment of patient needs throughout the hospital. (From Ferguson, 1991.)

Quality Function Deployment, QFD, as was discussed in Chapter 4, is as useful for design of services as for articles. The principles are roughly the same. Figure 15.6 is an overview of using QFD in health care and Figure 15.7 illustrates how the Quality House can be used when designing a course in Total Quality Management.

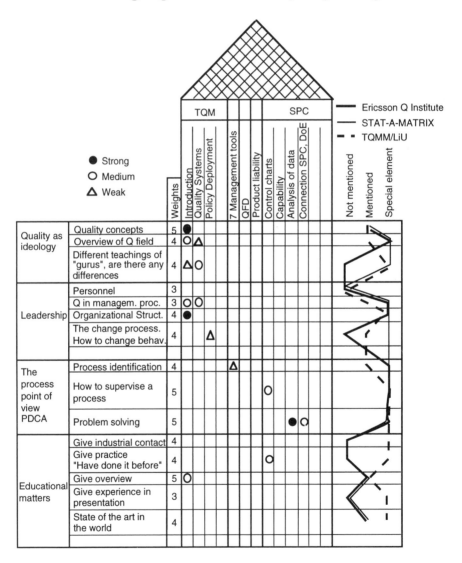

Figure 15.7   A QFD matrix illustrating the service "a course in TQM at university level". (After Bergman et al., 1991.)

15.4 Notes and References

Zeithaml et al. (1990) give a thorough discussion of quality dimensions. See also Parasuraman (1984, 1985). Zeithaml et al. (1990) also discuss in detail the Gap Model for understanding and achieving high service quality. Important contributions to service quality is also presented in Grönroos (1990) and Gummesson (1988).

Blueprinting was introduced by Shostack (1984). A generalization which attempts to achieve the aim of involving all employees in service quality diagnosis and improvement is the *perceptual blueprinting* technique introduced by Senior & Akehurst (1990). See also Randall (1993).

We also want to mention that there are also magazines devoted to service quality. One of these is Managing Service Quality.

16 Customer Satisfaction

Throughout this book we essentially identify quality as customer satisfaction and delight. It is always the customers who judge the quality of our products, whether these are goods or services, hardware or software. Those paying for, or using, the company's products are external customers. Among external customers we also have to remember all those who do not use the product but who will live in an environment possibly changed owing to pollution or other results of product manufacturing or use, including future generations. Among the external customers, or rather interested parties, are also the owners of the company and society in full. But there are also internal customers. Internal processes deliver products of different types, usually services, to other internal processes. Kaoru Ishikawa often said that "the next process is our customer". In addition, each individual employee is a customer of the leadership and management process and of other support processes of the company. In this chapter we shall discuss external as well as internal customer satisfaction, their formation and measurement.

16.1 External Customer Satisfaction

Traditionally, customer satisfaction has been studied within market research. However, in the past not much effort has been made to close the loops, i.e. to find out which specific factors are important to customer satisfaction and delight and then take action to make product improvements. One important reason for this is probably that it has been considered much more important to gain new customers than to retain old ones. It is, however, much more expensive to gain a new customer than to keep one who is satisfied or, even easier, who is delighted with our product. We have to reinforce positive cycles like the one depicted in Figure 16.1.

Figure 16.1   Reinforced sales process due to customer communication. (From Senge, 1990.)

Today, this has begun to be generally recognised. In fact, it has been argued that if we are striving today to reduce the number of suppliers, we will try tomorrow to limit the number of customers in order to tie them harder to us and to be better able to respond to their specific needs, see for example Bertsch & Williams (1993). Similar reports are coming from those actively working with Activity Based Costing.

In the future, customer loyalty will be of the utmost importance. We have to listen even more carefully to our customers to find out which factors lead to their satisfaction and delight and we have then to make serious efforts to deserve their loyalty.

16.1.1 Customer Satisfaction Formation

In Chapter 1 we defined quality of a product as its ability to satisfy the needs and expectations of the customers. However, that is not enough. We have to aim at exceeding these expectations, we have to delight our customers. Noriaki Kano has developed a model for customer satisfaction, where quality dimensions are separated into three goups: *basic needs, expected needs* and *exciting experiences.*

The *Kano model,* visualised in Figure 16.2, is discussed by King (1989), Slabey (1990), Gustafsson & Gustafsson (1993) and others. The model was introduced by Kano et al. (1984).

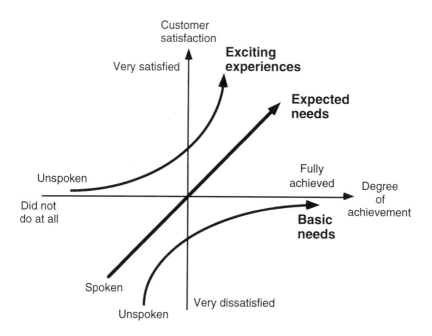

Figure 16.2   The Kano model of customer satisfaction. (From King, 1989.)

The basic needs are almost unconsciously expected to be there by the customer. They are so obvious to the customer that he usually would not describe these needs if asked. If dissatisfied with respect to these needs he will be most unhappy. We cannot, however, get a satisfied customer by fulfilling only the basic needs. Expected needs are such needs as the customer is aware of and wants to have satisfied but they are not always absolutely necessary. Some of these needs might be an extravagance. The exciting experiences, however, are items the producer has to find out by himself. They are surprises to the customer, who sometimes cannot imagine them. Technology development makes it possible to satisfy needs the customer is not even aware of. Here we may find opportunities to delight our customers. Of course, these surprises may also be services.

When we order a hotel room, for instance, a basic need is a bed which is carefully made up. Among expected needs are perhaps a TV set, a piece of soap and a tooth-brush and exciting experiences may include a dressing gown, a bowl of fruit or personal greetings from the manager.

The customer requirements also change with time. As an illustration of this we may think of the self-starter of a car. It was an exciting experience in the twenties, an expected need in the forties but is very basic today.

The degree of customer satisfaction depends on the correlation between the customer's expectations and his experience, but is also influenced by such things as the image of the company, as is illustrated in Figure 16.3. The Gap Model, discussed in Chapter 15, gives a deeper description of the relation between the expected and experienced service.

Sometimes it is possible to change dissatisfaction to excitement. By treating a disappointed customer very well you can win a loyal customer. Here it is important that people in the front line have sufficient knowledge and possibilities to act rapidly and take corrective action when faults occur. For instance, a car hiring company often gives you their very best car if some trouble occurs.

Figure 16.3   Illustration of the 4Q-model by Gummesson (1988).

An excellent way to find needs and wants of the customers is the use of *focus groups,* where potential customers discuss properties and use of products under consideration.

Today, many companies have taken customer satisfaction as their top priority with a carefully designed customer satisfaction framework. An illustration from Toyota is given in Figure 16.4. In the strategic plan for Toyota Motor Sales, USA, for the next five years the number one strategic objective is "to be number one in customer satisfaction". It is not to be profitable, to expand sales or to produce more units in the United States, see Powers (1993). Toyota has a large customer survey system that captures first-hand information about the customer's buying process, delivery experience, service experience and product quality. For instance, Toyota mails one survey monthly to all new customers who purchased a vehicle within the last month in order to collect information about their sales experience. Furthermore, the Toyota Service Survey is mailed every 10 days to those customers with a recent warranty repair. "These surveys are", according to Tom Gauer, the customer service manager at Toyota Motor Sales, "important because they put us in touch with what the customers' experience is. If you do not know what the customer expect, you have a very hard time trying to deliver that to him", see Powers (1993).

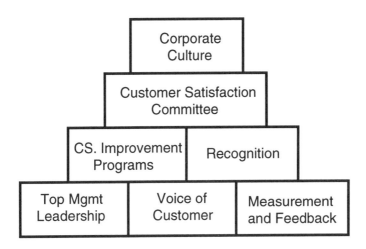

Figure 16.4   The Toyota Customer Satisfaction (CS) Framework. (From Powers, 1993.)

Another company well-known for its focus on customer satisfaction is the catalogue and retail giant L.L. Bean, which was founded in 1912 by Leon Leonwood Bean. The founder himself had a lot to say about customer relationships (Bowles & Hammond, 1991, p. 75): "A customer is the most important person ever in this company - in person or by mail. ... A customer is not dependent on us, we are dependent on him. ... A customer is not an interruption of work, he is the purpose of it. .... A customer is not someone to argue or match wits with. A customer is a person who brings us his wants. It is our job to handle them profitably to him and to ourselves." The Bean guarantee is also unequivocal: "All of our products are guaranteed to give 100 percent satisfaction in every way. Return anything purchased from us at any time that proves otherwise. We will replace it, refund your purchase price or credit your credit card, as you wish. We do not want you to have anything from L.L. Bean that is not completely satisfactory." According to Bowles & Hammond (1991), Bean's return rate is about 14 percent, which is well below the industry average.

16.1.2 Customer Satisfaction Measurement

For a long time many manufacturing companies have had a reasonable failure reporting system. Failures in operation have been reported and a reliability group has fed the information back to the design department. On the basis of this information, design changes have been initiated. Many companies have also had sensible treatment and feedback of warranty claims.

It was noted by Garvin (1988) in his study on air conditioning equipment that a major difference between successful and unsuccessful American companies with respect to customer satisfaction was the existence of a reliability department providing feedback to the organization. Good treatment of dissatisfaction reports is very important, see Figure 16.5.

Even if many companies still have deficiencies in their dissatisfaction measurements and feedback this is not the most important problem. Dissatisfaction measurements are not good indicators of customer satisfaction. It is important but not enough to know that customers are not dissatisfied. We need to know to what extent they are satisfied or, better, delighted. We also need to know what attribute to improve in order to make our customers even more delighted. That information can be obtained from systematic customer surveys, interviews and focus groups where representative groups from interesting market segments are asked to discuss the quality of products under study.

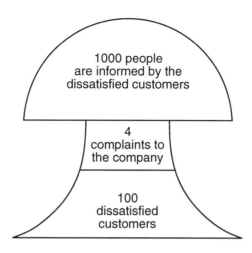

Figure 16.5   It is important to realize that the number of complaints is not a good measurement of customer dissatisfaction. Of 100 dissatisfied customers just a few, 4 say, complain, but they tell several of their friends and colleagues of their experiences from the company. Therefore, 100 dissatisfied customers can give 4 complaints but 1000 lost customers.

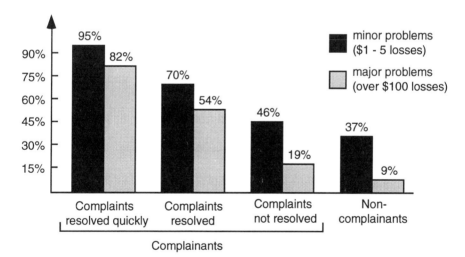

Figure 16.6   Most dissatisfied customers are lost to the company. This is illustrated here by the result from a national survey made by TARP, Technical Assistance Research Program, an American consulting firm. (From Bowles & Hammond, 1991.)

287

In recent years there has been an increasing interest in measuring customer satisfaction on a national scale in order to promote quality and make industry more competitive and market oriented. Since 1989 a Customer Satisfaction Barometer (CSB) has been in use in Sweden. This is an index based on annual survey data from customers of about 100 leading companies in some 30 industries, see Fornell (1992). Based on a set of questions used in telephone interviews, indices on product performance, customer satisfaction, voice and customer loyalty are estimated, see Figure 16.7. In total 100,000 possible customers are approached and 25,000 are telephone interviewed for about 8 minutes each. For each company the yearly sample size ranges from 250 to 400, making sampling errors reasonably small.

Empirical variables on a scale from 1 to 10	Unobservable endogenous variables
quality (given price) price (given quality)	performance
overall satisfaction conformation to expectation distance from ideal product	customer satisfaction (CSB)
complaints to personnel complaints to management	voice
price increase tolerance repurchase intention	loyalty

Figure 16.7 Variables in the Swedish Customer Satisfaction Barometer. (From Fornell, 1992.)

A general view of the results in the Swedish Customer Satisfaction Barometer is given in Figure 16.8

In Fornell (1992) it is also illustrated that customer loyalty is strongly correlated to customer satisfaction. A satisfied customer is very often a loyal one.

CSB Results 1989 to 1991

Industry	CSB			Leading Firms		
	1989	1990	1991	1989	1990	1991
Automobiles	77	76	78	Toyota (87)	Mazda (81)	Mazda (85)
Basic Foods	77	79	78	Jästbolaget (82)	Jästbolaget (83)	Jästbolaget (84)
Pharmacy	na	76	73	na		
Food processors	67	70	70	Marabou (78)	Marabou (79)	Marabou (80)
Oil (Gas stations)	67	68	70	Statoil (70)	Statoil (70)	BP (81)
Shipping	na	64	69	na	JetPak (70)	JetPak (73)
Airlines	67	67	68	SAS (67)	SAS (69)	SAS (69)
Charter travel	68	67	68	Spies (69)	Ving (70)	Atlas (69)
Banking, public	69	69	67	SHB (75)	SHB (73)	SHB (72)
Postal service, public	65	61	67	Letter (69)	Letter (62)	Letter (68)
Personal computers, business	70	66	67	Apple (76)	Apple (69)	Apple (73)
Insurance, property	65	63	66	Trygg-Hansa (66)	Trygg-Hansa (64)	Länsfskr. (69)
Postal service, business	59	62	65	Letter (62)	Letter (63)	Letter (67)
Supermarkets	66	68	65	ICA (70)	Vivo (70)	ICA (70)
Furniture, retail	64	63	65	MIO (68)	MIO (66)	MIO (71)
Vin & SpritCentralen	59	59	65			
Banking, business	70	66	64	SHB (75)	SHB (72)	SHB (68)
Newspapers	na	60	64	na	SvD (67)	SvD (72)
Insurance, business	64	62	64	Skandia (66)	Trygg-Hansa (63)	Trygg-Hansa (67)
Mainframe computers	68	64	64	IBM (70)	HP (70)	HP (70)
Mail order	na	64	63	na	Haléns (68)	HM&R (65)
Insurance, life	65	65	63	Trygg-Hansa (67)	Länsfskr. (69)	Länsfskr. (67)
Clothing, retail	63	62	62	Lindex (68)	Lindex (64)	Lindex (65)
Telecommunications, Public	55	59	61			
Department stores	62	63	61	NK (68)	NK (68)	NK (64)
Police	56	55	58			
Telecommunications, business	54	57	57			
Railroad	45	55	54			
TV broadcasting	44	43	47	TV3 (57)	TV3 (52)	TV3 (53)
Mean, all industries	64	64	65			

Figure 16.8   Some results from the Swedish Customer Satisfaction Barometer during 1989-1991. (From Fornell, 1992.)

According to Fornell (1992) efforts are made to measure customer satisfaction on a national basis also in the USA, Japan, Singapore, and in the EC countries. In the USA, for instance, such a barometer, inspired by the Swedish one, is planned to be in use from 1994.

In some branches, data bases on customer satisfaction have been compiled since long. In the car industry, for example, the JD Power Investigations are well-known.

16.1.3 Closing the Loop

One of the important improvement activities within the company is the process of providing the organization with information from customer satisfaction and dissatisfaction measurements in order to decrease customer dissatisfaction and increase customer satisfaction and delight. A well designed customer satisfaction model has to be developed. Two aspects are important here:

- the current product should be improved by eliminating common sources of customer dissatisfaction and, if possible, easily added sources of customer delight should be included

- the development and manufacturing processes should be revised on the basis of customer use information, so that the next product is better off right from market introduction.

A simple model for customer satisfaction growth is illustrated in Figure 16.9.

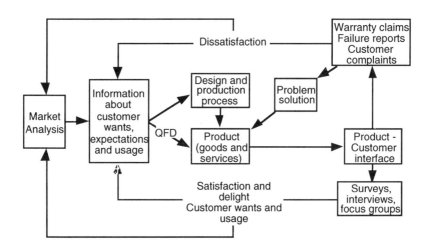

Figure 16.9   A simple model for customer satisfaction growth.

16.1.4 Loyalty Based Management

As noted above it is important to keep customers loyal to the company. The importance of this is stressed in what is called *Loyalty Based Management,* see for example Reichheld (1993), where it is noted that increase of customer retention is most profitable. Customer loyalty is becoming an important business strategy.

According to Reichheld (1993), Honda has emerged as the loyalty leader in the midpriced US auto market. Life-cycle marketing has helped propel Honda's owner repurchase rate to 65% versus an industri average rate of 40%. After the success of the subcompact Civic, Honda's next car, the Accord, was designed to meet the needs of Civic owners, who continued to care about reliability, conservative design, and value as they moved from their early twenties to marriage and family.

Another example is Banc One in the US, which according to Godfrey (1993) is the second most profitable bank in the world. Banc One has developed several statistical models to understand customer behaviour as a function of customer satisfaction. It has found that delighted customers, those who are much more than merely satisfied, are five times as likely to buy other financial products from the bank as customers who just are satisfied. Moreover, these delighted customers are also four times less likely to leave the bank than those who are just satisfied. See Godfrey (1993).

In the future we can foresee a far reaching integration with the customers. The traditional value-chain will in many situations be transformed into value-creating networks, where the strict borders between suppliers and customers will become unclear. Businesses will become knowledge intense. In this situation a great deal of trust between the interested parties is of utmost importance.

Loyalty will become crucial in the future. To obtain loyal customers we need loyal employees. That subject, with related issues, is discussed in the next section.

16.2 Internal Customer Satisfaction

There are two aspects of internal customer satisfaction. One is that "the next process is our customer" and one is the satisfaction of each individual employee. The first aspect can be handled by using Process Management in cross-functional teams. That aspect will be discussed in Chapter 18. We shall here focus on satisfaction of the individual employee as an important factor in human motivation.

16.2.1 Employee Satisfaction Formation

In the Tayloristic era, work planning and work execution were separated. Along with the elevation of income and educational level of employees, this has led to demotivation of employees, which in turn has led to a large number of other problems such as absenteeism and bad work performance. A new way of looking upon work has to be created, taking into account that we are are human beings with human wants and desires.

As discussed by Kondo (1991), two independent, but similar, definitions of work were developed in Japan and in the USA during the 1970s. O'Toole, heading a task force investigating the problems encountered in working life in America, defined work as "an activity that produces something of value for other people", see O'Toole (1974). Nishibori, leading a working group on human motivation in Japanese industry during the 1970s, stressed that work should always include the following three elements (see Kondo, 1991):

- creativity (joy of thinking)
- physical activity (joy of physical work)
- sociality (joy of sharing pleasure and pain with colleagues).

In his interesting book on human motivation, Kondo (1991) takes these aspects of work as a basis for a discussion of motivation in industry. As another basis he uses a combination of Maslow's hierarchy of human needs and Herzberg's theory of motivation.

Maslow's hierarchy of human needs is illustrated in Figure 16.10. When needs on lower levels are satisfied needs on higher levels become prominent. Kondo (1991) has added that for each single individual, needs on different levels may coexist but with different prominence. The human needs in Maslow's theory correspond to dissatisfiers and satisfiers in Herzberg's theory of motivation, where removal of dissatisfiers such as, say, hunger and fear has limited effect while adding satisfiers such as intellectual achievement is much more powerful.

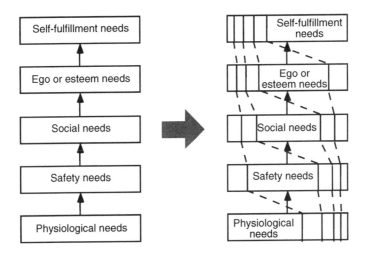

Figure 16.10 Maslow's hierarchy of human needs as described by Kondo (1991). All stages in the hierarchy of needs may be present but some stage is usually dominant. (From Kondo, 1991.)

A third basis is a comparison between sports and work. Why are people so motivated when participating in sporting activities but not when working? How can working life conditions be changed in such a way that the motivating aspects of sports are also manifested in working life?

From the three bases described above Kondo formulates a strategy for a change in working life, where human satisfiers such as a sense of free choice, creativity, responsibility, participation and teamwork are important elements. Monetary compensation, exemplifying elimination of a set of dissatisfiers – impossibilities to fulfill the basic needs on the lower levels of the hierarchy of Maslow – has come to play an insignificant role for the increase of motivation in modern society. Interestingly enough, this fact is supported by recent investigations of some successful companies studied by Kotter (1988). These companies had somewhat lower salaries than their competitors. On the other hand they provided better work environment in terms of honesty, integrity, fairness and justice, not only as honorary formulations but in real action. They also provided for challenging opportunities for development.

Modern theories within Total Quality Management with regard to employee participation, involvement and problem solving are exemplified in Kondo (1991). Another example is the contributions by Deming (1986, 1993), see also Chapter 22 in this book. These theories seem to have support also from recent developments in modern psychology.

Mihály Csíkszentmihályi, professor in psychology in Chicago, has developed a theory of "optimal experiences". He has tried to determine factors which are active when people feel a high degree of satisfaction. The state of optimal experience is called *flow* by Csíkszentmihályi and is explained as an ordered structure of the unconscious mind. The theory is based on a large number of interviews with people in ordinary activities. All types of people were interviewed, operators in mass production and professors, housewives and teenagers, Americans and Koreans and so on. Csíkszentmihályi found that at least one, and often all, of the following components were present in the interviewees' descriptions of highly satisfactory situations:

- a challenge which it is possible to tackle successfully
- concentration

- clear goals
- immediate feedback
- a deep and natural commitment, free of day-to-day concerns and frustrations
- disappearence of self-absorption
- loss of ordinary feeling for time; minutes can feel like hours and hours like minutes.

The first and very important component above is illustrated in Figure 16.11.

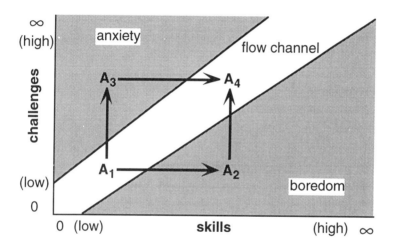

Figure 16.11 An illustration of the "flow channel" according to Csíkszentmihályi (1990). If flow is experienced at the point A_1 that would not last for ever since abilities are improved upon. The boring state A_2 will be reached. The only chance to reach flow is to increase the challenge. If challenge is increased earlier the abilities have to be increased before it is possible to feel high satisfaction.

16.2.2 Employee Commitment

Ideas on commitment formation are put forward by Kiesler (1971) Salancik (1977) and Oliver (1990). Salancik (1977) argues that it is coherence and environment that determine our behaviour and what responsibility we take on. In order for an action or an assignment to lead to participation and the assuming of responsibility it must, according to Salancik (1977), be

- clear
- final
- public
- self-chosen

Clear. If we are to assume responsibility for a task, we have first of all to understand what it really implies. If the definitions are vague and the contents poorly identified it is easy to regard vital parts as "someone else's" assignment. In other words it is a matter of making a clear delimitation of the field of responsibility and of specifying the contents.

Final. If the consequence cost due to mistakes increases, the importance of assuming responsibility also increases, according to Salancik. If we stop concentrating on inspection, the consequences of an error in a product can be disastrous. In a case like that we cannot think that it does not matter much what we do ourselves since there is no one present to remedy what has gone wrong. Today work is often organized in such a way that the consequences of errors, at least according to the organization plan, are dealt with by "someone else".

Public. We are all influenced by the way people around us look upon us. If the link between individuals and assignments is open and public, and if we are concerned that our environment regards us in a positive manner, our motivation will increase and we will do a good job. This element in Salancik's model for participation and taking responsibility emphasizes that responsibility and participation are not only an individual attitude but also a result of social pressure.

Self-chosen. If "clarity" sets limits to what we are responsible for, then the feeling of voluntariness matters a lot. We will appreciate to what extent we are responsible. It is important that we feel that we are the "owner" of our own actions. According to Salancik, it is of significance that

- we experience the possibility of choice
- we feel an external pressure to act
- we realize that result is important
- a lot of other people are involved.

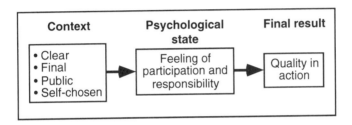

Figure 16.12   A model for how a situation affects the feeling of involvement and the assuming of responsibility. (After Oliver, 1990, but with a slightly different terminology)

From a model like the one in Figure 16.12 we can conclude that our activities should be organised so as to make it easy to identify the final result of the different assignments, the final goods or services. This can enhance both clarity and the feeling for the consequences of errors. In other words we should organize according to horizontal and not vertical, functional, processes. Self-governing groups working towards customer satisfaction may be an organization form where several of the above mentioned requirements are met. This is for instance how the T50-program of ABB, Sweden, is running, a program which is described in Section 20.6.1.

16.3 Conclusions

In conclusion, a new era of Total Quality Management is to begin. A better understanding of Quality of Life, whether associated with external customers or with employees, has far reaching implications for the continuing development of a theory for Total Quality Management and its application to the life of corporate and public organisations. We have passed from product quality and process quality to gain an understanding of the importance of Quality of Life. An integration of all these concepts requires a large portion of continuing creativity from all of us. The new era can perhaps be called the era of Total Quality Creativity.

16.4 Notes and References

In this chapter a lot of ideas have been briefly discussed and we have not given each of them a fair treatment. Therefore we urge the interested reader to go back to the basic sources. Especially, we want to refer the reader to Kondo (1991) and references cited there. See also Kondo (1993). Human motivation is also discussed in Maslow (1943) and Herzberg (1969). For a popular description of the theory of flow we recommend Csíkszentmihályi (1990). It is interesting to find that recent psychological research offers a lot of understanding for the TQM movement, which has been developed from quite different premises.

The premises for and consequences of the win-win strategy described by Deming are thoroughly discussed in a series of booklets from the British Deming Association.

A lot of research on customer satisfaction and dissatisfaction has been reported in market research. Models for customer satisfaction growth are discussed by Shores (1988), for example. It is also worth mentioning that Peters & Waterman (1982) is all about customer satisfaction. Furthermore, the November 1993 issue of Quality Progress is a special issue devoted to "customer service".

Part V

Leadership for Quality

The general principles of Total Quality Management have already been discussed in Chapter 1. In this part of the book the significance of top management commitment for successful work on continuous quality improvement is discussed. We also introduce a modern outlook on the continuous improvement work on all the company's processes and discuss "the seven management tools", which are designed to be of use in planning work. Also various company assessment criteria, for example quality awards and ISO 9000, are discussed from a TQM point of view.

17   Visions, Goals and Strategies

One of the most important tasks of top management is, with a vision of the company's future as a basis, to formulate long-term goals and state strategies for how to achieve these goals. In modern management, quality issues are of great significance in this process. To make this clear many companies have formulated a particular *quality policy*. In other companies the quality values are completely integrated into other strategic documents. Anyhow, it is important that the company's stated quality values are firmly established in the company's strategy process. It is also important to state improvement goals on the road towards the company vision and to deploy and to share these goals through all the company. This is what nowadays is called *Policy Deployment*.

17.1   Visions

In many of the companies that have been most successful in the quality field, top management have very distinctly expressed their vision of how the success of the company depends on quality. For instance, David Kearns, formerly chairman and Chief Executive Officer (CEO) of Xerox, played a very active part in the company's quality improvement process. He personally led the introduction of new methods and ideas for problem solving and improvements. Other examples of business leaders who quite clearly have shown their commitment to quality are John Young at Hewlett-Packard,

Robert Galvin at Motorola and Donald Peterson at Ford. Ford's vision and how they want to get there is illustrated in Figure 17.1.

Ford Vision

To be a low-cost producer of the highest quality products and services which provide the best customer value.

Mission

... to improve continually our products and services to meet our customers´ needs, allowing us to prosper as a business and to provide a reasonable return for our stock-holders, the owners of our business.

Values

• People ... people are the sources of our strength.
• Products ... products are the end result of our
                efforts... as our products are viewed,
                so are we viewed.
• Profits ... ultimate measure of our success.

Guiding principles

• Quality comes first.
• Customers are the focus of everything we do.
• Continuous improvement is essential to our success.
• Employee involvement is our way of life.
• Dealers and suppliers are our partners.
• Integrity is never compromised.

*Figure 17.1   The Ford vision and how they want to achieve it.
(From Smith, 1989.)*

17.2 Goals

Establishing the quality values of the company implies that we make it perfectly clear what role quality issues are to play in the future running of the company and in the corresponding long-term goals. The path by which these goals are to attained should also be stated.

A *quality policy* must be firmly established in the company's strategy process. It must be the guiding principle for all activities whenever quality is concerned, with respect to external as well as internal customers and also towards suppliers to the company. Not least does it imply an obligation on the management. Unless the management acts according to the quality policy, no other employee in the company will take it seriously. Consequently, the management must have pointed out extremely carefully what they want to achieve.

Here, we will not try to give a model for the design of a quality policy. Some of the elements that we consider important are however

- identification of the customers and their significance
- quality dimensions considered important by the company
- a process approach and continuous improvement work
- the company's attitude to their employees.

These elements were more or less fully discussed in the introductory chapters of this book. In particular we consider the attitude to continuous improvement as a question of vital importance.

Many successful companies have set high goals for quality improvements. John Young, CEO at Hewlett-Packard, set the goal already in 1979 that they should reduce product unreliability by a factor of ten. It took nine years until this goal was reached. Similar tenfold improvement goals were then set for other quality dimensions such as software errors and service. The reason for choosing a tenfold improvement as a goal, Young says was: "Because I wanted to force people to view their jobs in a different way. The magnitude of the challenge changed the way people in research and development and manufacturing viewed each other. It forced people to work across organizational boundaries. Research and development engineers could no longer simply design products and then ask manufacturing to build them. They had to involve manufacturing people in the design at the beginning of the project because if the design wasn't easy to build, product quality would suffer. Teamwork has always been a value at Hewlett-Packard. But Total Quality Control gave us a structured way to build on the tradition." (Bowles & Hammond, 1991, p. 49.)

In 1981 Anders Scharp, CEO at Electrolux, a Swedish white-goods company, formulated a quality improvement project called Q84, with the goal of halving the number of customer complaints by 1984 and at the same time focusing on quality in the Electrolux group. When they reached this goal in 1984, a new program was formulated (Q87) with the goal of halving the number of customer complaints once more by 1987. This project was equally successful. As a consequence of the necessarily improved internal quality, about USD 0.6 billion in locked-up capital could be set free. The improvement process at Electrolux has since continued.

17.3 Policy Deployment

Many leading Japanese companies have been very successful in deploying the company's goals and thus making them evident in all company processes, see for example Smith (1989) and Akao (1991). As we have seen earlier, Quality Function Deployment, QFD, elucidates the customer's needs and expectations in every step of the manufacturing process. In the same way we also have to understand in what direction these processes have to be developed in order to reach the company goals. This deployment of goals is called "hoshin kanri" in Japanese, where "hoshin" means "compass", i.e. pointing out the direction and "kanri" means "management" or "control". In English the process is called *Policy Deployment (PD)* or sometimes *Quality Policy Deployment (QPD)*.

Hewlett-Packard and Florida Power & Light (FPL) are two American companies which are successfully applying Policy

Deployment. Florida Power and Light, which in 1989 was the first Western enterprise to receive the Deming Application Prize, serves about 6 billion people in the USA with electricity. At FPL they consider Policy Deployment to be the most important reason for the phenomenal improvement process that has taken place within the company. According to Smith (1989), the saved about one million USD a week during the second half of the 1980s through quality improvement and substantially enhancing their service to customers. The company's comprehensive improvement goals, both on a medium long term (5-7 years) and in a short term (about 1 year), have systematically been deployed to measurable goals that can be understood by all employees. Lately, however, some questions concerning the amount of paper work have arisen.

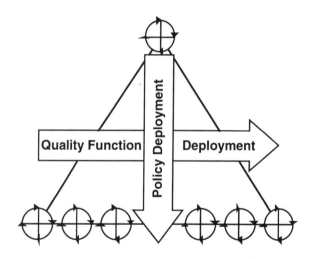

Figure 17.2   The customer oriented planning, Quality Function Deployment, cuts horizontally through the company, whereas Policy Deployment, deploys company goals vertically.

Policy Deployment is a top-down and bottom-up process aligning objectives through all levels. Objectives are identified at each level by top-down and bottom-up consultation and communication, thus translating overall goals of the company into specific targets for departments and groups. Once management prioritises areas for improvement and deploys time and resources accordingly, everybody is empowered to take initiatives in accordance with these priorities. The improvements towards the vision are taken in small steps utilizing the PDSA-cycle. In fact, it can be said to be the principle of the PDSA-cycle applied to the leadership process of the company.

Policy Deployment focuses on the question "what do we do first to be best?" In consultations between levels, priorities are set, the feasibility of plans are tested and the commitment of individuals and teams built. The aim is that everyone in the company pulls in the same direction towards clearly defined goals. Showing people what the overall goals are and where they fit in is the motor for mobilising efforts. People need to see that what they do is important for the company.

Once objectives are defined, critical processes can be identified. Teams agree on performance indicators for themselves. Setting challenging objectives at every level forces the organization to change the way it thinks and operates. Examples of goals set at different levels in the company are illustrated in Figure 17.3.

Level	Objective
Corporate	Improve customer satisfaction
Division	Reduce late shipment
Plant	Less than 10% late shipments this year
Manufacturing department	Less than 5% schedule misses this year
Maintenance group	Reduce machine downtime 25% this quarter

*Figure 17. 3   Examples of goals set at different levels of a company.
(From de Vries & Rodgers, 1991.)*

The consultative nature of Policy Deployment may make some managers wary. Sharing information means sharing power. However, in our view, sharing power strengthens the organization.

Policy Deployment should not be mixed up with *Management by Objectives (MBO)*, introduced by Drucker (1954). There are similarities between the two concepts but also essential differences. Some of these differences are presented in Figure 17.4

Management by Objectives	Policy Deployment
Focus on people	Focus on the process
Profit first	Quality first
Top-down	Top-down and bottom-up
Focus on "who?"	Focus on "how?"
Work harder	Work smarter
Look for whipping boys	Look for improvement possibilities

Figure 17.4   Some differences between the two concepts Policy Deployment and Management By Objectives.

17.4   TQM as Management Philosophy

The concept of *Total Quality Management (TQM)* was introduced in Chapter 1. The principles discussed there are the heart of Total Quality Management. Sometimes people also put into the TQM concept the methods that have to be used to deploy a quality strategy within the company. Here we choose to focus on management issues only.

At a meeting in 1987 between the EC president Jacques Delores and the executive board of the Philips group, the idea was born that a European platform for industrial managements should be created with focus on leadership and quality. In September 1988, fourteen European business leaders signed a "Letter of Intent" and the *European Foundation for Quality Management, EFQM,* was thus founded; see Figure 17.5. In December 1993 about 300 companies, organizations and administrations have various degrees of membership of the EFQM.

Robert Bosch GmbH
British Telecommunication plc
Bull SA
Ciba-Geigy AG
Avions Marcel Dassault-Breguet Aviation
AB Electrolux
Fiat Auto SpA
Koninklijke Luchtvaart Maatschappij N.V
Nestlé SA
Ing. C. Olivetti & C., SpA
N. V. Philips Gloeilampenfabrieken
Régie Nationale des Usines Renault
Gebr. Sulzer AG
Volkswagen AG

Figure 17.5   *The founders of EFQM, European Foundation for Quality Management.*

The fourteen business leaders stated that Europe is facing ever increasing competition with respect to both prices and quality. They claimed that this competition could be challenged if quality strategies are developed covering industry as well as the educational system, setting out from European culture and European values. Such a quality strategy is characterized by

- an ambition to be best in all management and business processes and in all administrative processes

- a culture of continuous improvement in all business processes as well as support processes of the company

- an understanding that quality improvements result in advantages of cost and improved prosperity

- profound relations between customers and suppliers

- commitment of all employees in improvement work

- an intention to find out what the market requires and have that influence the running of the company.

The development and realization of such a strategy implies in general a complete change in company culture and company organization. Therefore it can only be carried out through an active and visible leadership by the top management.

Within the framework of Total Quality Management we can attack many of the questions that are essential for companies today. The problem with inadequate productivity development in some countries, for example, could be a sign that continuous improvement of the company's processes is not working. This problem can hardly be solved by investments. Instead, we have to go to the root of the problems and create a culture for continuous improvement.

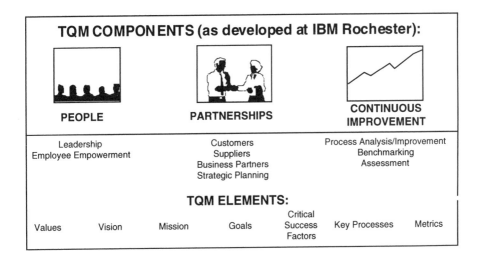

Figure 17. 6   The components of TQM, as seen by IBM Rochester, which recieved the Malcolm Baldrige National Quality Award in 1990 (see Section 21.2.)

Another problem, which partly links up with the productivity problem, is large absenteeism. This may to a large extent be due to people not finding inspiration and joy in their jobs. A bad psychological environment affects the physical power to resist illness. By using people's knowledge and desire for commitment, we can exert

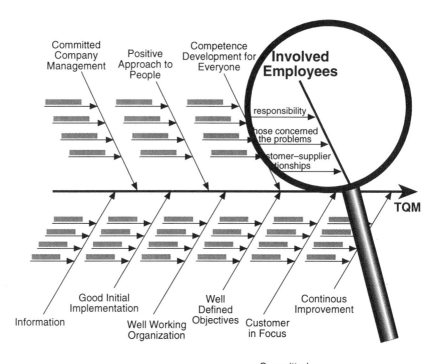

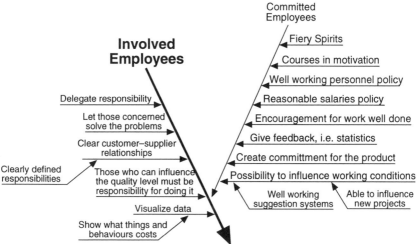

Figure 17.7   Elements of Total Quality Management illustrated using an Ishikawa diagram. (From Gunnarsson & Holmberg, 1993.)

a considerable influence on the psychological environment. Work must be joyful and stimulating. Using a company culture dominated by TQM, all employees become involved in the continuous improvement effort. Each individual is thus important and will have the possibility to influence his own situation and that of the company. The obstacles to taking pride in one's work, the fear of making a fool of oneself by suggesting changes and pointing out errors and deficiencies, barriers between different departments, all these have to be disposed of if we are to master the problems.

Many of the ideas making up the frame of TQM have their origin in Deming's management philosophy, which will be presented in Chapter 21 (see also Figure 3.5), and in the approach to quality work as advocated by Kaoru Ishikawa under the concept *Company Wide Quality Control (CWQC)*, which has been of great importance for the Japanese successes in the quality field.

17.5 Notes and References

Questions concerning TQM are often discussed in the magazines Quality Progress, Total Quality Management, The TQM Magazine and International Journal of Quality and Reliability Management. In the November 1988 issue of the TQM Magazine, for instance, the topic is "World-class manufacturers share their TQM secrets" and the May 1989 issue of the same magazine has the subheading "Implementing TQM". The introduction to this chapter goes back, to a large extent, to the article "Trends in TQM" by Smith (1989) in the TQM Magazine. A recent book describing TQM is Dahlgaard et al. (1993).

Ishikawa's concept Company Wide Quality Control (CWQC) is discussed by Sullivan (1986) and Mizuno (1988) among others.

In many successful companies quality improvement programs have a very central position. We have here mentioned the projects Q84 and Q87 at Electrolux. More about these projects can be found in Scharp (1988) and Stangenberg (1990). We will return to more improvement programs in Chapter 20.

Policy Deployment was developed in Japan in an effort to apply the quality methods to management. The Japanese concept "hoshin kanri", seems first to have been used by the Japanese company Bridgestone Tire in 1964. More about the history and the use of "hoshin kanri" in Japanese industry can be found in Akao (1991). Hudiberg (1991), the chairman of Florida Power & Light (FPL) during the 1980s, describes the FPL road towards TQM and their use of Policy Deployment as well as his personal experiences. Policy Deployment is also described in the book Sheridan (1993).

As long ago as about 500 BC, the Chinese philosopher Lao Tzu shows in his book "Tao Te Ching" a great awareness of problems lying close to the TQM concept.

18 The Process View

Every activity in a company or an organization has certain elements which are continuously repeated, whereas others are unique on each single occasion. In a research and development department unique items are designed. However, the same development facilities, the same kind of testing activity, the same type of design of experiments and the same inspection routines are used time and time again. Furthermore, it is the same people who are doing the job. When acquiring material, the same routines are used on the various occasions, even if each and every one of these acquisitions may be unique. In a project, unique decision matters are discussed, but with similar handling of the items and with the same kind of decision support.

In this chapter we will discuss the continuously utilized underlying structure of the activities, *the process*. By using the process as a basis we can implement improvements in the activities. Without a process it is difficult to talk about improvements. It is the process that ties history and future together, thus making future activities predictable.

Awareness of the significance of process thinking is essential in modern leadership for quality. In this chapter we discuss processes and process improvements, an area which sometimes is called *Process Management.* We will also study the concept of *benchmarking,* an important tool for process improvements based on the idea of thoroughly comparing your own process with another identical or similar process.

18.1 Processes

Processes in a company can be essentially of three different kinds:

- *individual processes,* carried out by separate individuals

- *functional processes* or *vertical processes,* belonging to activities associated with a certain department or unit

- *business processes* or *horizontal processes,* which cut through the company and whose final result provides the company with its profit.

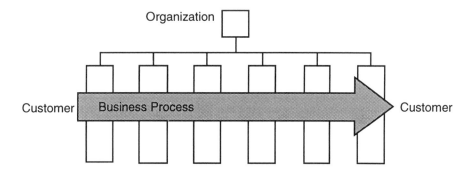

Figure 18.1   *A business process, e.g. an order process, cuts horizontally through the organization.*

It is characteristic of each process that it has one or more customers for the final results produced in the process. Running the process requires resources of various kinds, such as information, energy or working time. The goal of each process is to satisfy its customers using as small an amount of resources as possible. Careful planning is required as well as adequate resources needed to run the process. It is also required that the suppliers of the process are identified and that they receive the appropriate signals.

Each process should have a *process owner,* who is responsible for the improvement work of that process. A head of department is, for instance, responsible for a functional process and a lathe operator is the owner of the individual turning process. Horizontal processes, traditionally, do not have any owners. An owner should be appointed, however. The project leader, for instance, is not the owner of the project management process. His interest is the unique project, whereas the interest of the process owner is to improve the process. The project process, the process of projects run in the company, should be identified and a process owner appointed.

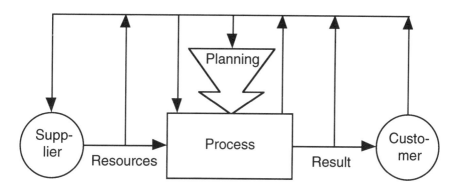

Figure 18.2   *The feedback of information as a basis for continuous improvement is vital. The process has to be planned as much as possible based on the customer's needs, available resources and process abilities. Once the process is under way we have to study the results of the process and learn from these so that in future the process will be better planned; Plan, Do, Study, Act, Plan, Do, Study, ...*

A company can be described as a network and hierarchical pattern of processes. The functional processes link up with the business processes and each process consists of other subprocesses down to individual processes. Strength analysis, for example, which in a certain company may be an individual process, is part of product design, which is a horizontal process, but it is also part of the functional process run by the stress and strength department. Company success depends on how well the customers of the different processes have been identified and how well and efficiently they have been satisfied.

Resources and energy should be devoted to continuous process improvement instead of using considerable resources for "fire-fighting", i.e. taking temporary steps in order to save critical situations. It is important not to react to "exceptionals". However, each separate error and each separate deviation from the expected result provides vital information about the process and must, therefore, be utilized and compiled. This information will help to improve our knowledge of the underlying causes of variations in the result of the process. We will be able to identify new sources of variations. These can then be eliminated, thus further reducing variation. In this way we can improve the process and achieve improved customer satisfaction.

18.2 Process Improvements

We are now studying more general processes than those discussed in Part III, which were mainly connected with manufacturing. However, the same facilities and ideas can still be used. "The seven QC-tools", introduced in Chapter 11 are not at all limited to treatment of variations and errors in a manufacturing process, but may just as well be used for all types of processes. Furthermore, the improvement cycle is equally applicable to general processes as it is to manufacturing processes, see Figure 18.3.

The importance of a process view and of continuously improving business processes has created the philosophy of *Process Management*. The idea was first developed at IBM, where examining business processes has become an important approach to quality improvement. The principles of Process Management have been applied to many key processes. Functions such as finance, purchasing, product release, marketing, and product development have applied this concept with excellent payback in terms of cost savings and operational effectiveness.

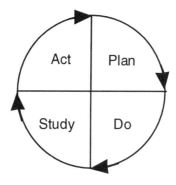

Figure 18.3   *The improvement cycle, which was discussed in Chapter 10, is equally applicable to general processes as it is to manufacturing processes. The cycle, which is inspired by Deming (see Deming, 1986, 1993), is sometimes referred to as the Deming cycle and occasionally the PDSA-cycle, where P = "Plan", D = "Do", S = "Study", A = "Act". Deming himself usually refers to this cycle as the "Shewhart cycle". In Deming (1986) "check" is used instead of "study". The cycle was then called the PDCA-cycle.*

The process management procedure consists of the following steps, see also Figure 18.4.

- Organize for improvement. Define ownership and a process improvement team.

- Understand the process. Define the boundaries, investigate who are the customers and suppliers. Document the flow of the work.

- Control the process. Establish control points and implement measurements.

- Improve the process continuously. Use the feedback from the measurement and control system to improve the process.

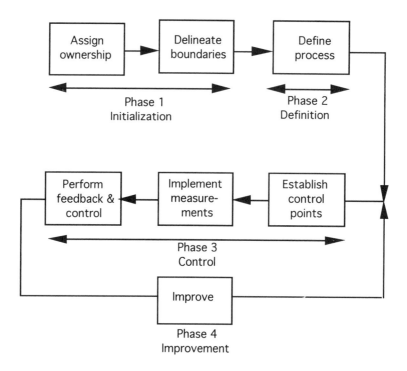

Figure 18.4   The steps in the process improvement process. (After a figure in Melan, 1993.)

Facts about the earlier behaviour of the process have to be used as a basis for improvement. Therefore, the results of the process have to be measured in different ways. Information concerning how well the final results of the process fit in with the customer's needs is vital, as is the amount of resources used. We also have to learn to what extent the internal process is successful, for example in the form of waste and resource utilization for changes and revisions.

An important step in productivity and quality improvement is simplification. Many of the processes in use today are unnecessarily complex. This is due to the many changes that with time have been made in conjunction with "fire-fighting". Quite often old routines live on, despite the fact that there are no longer any customers for them.

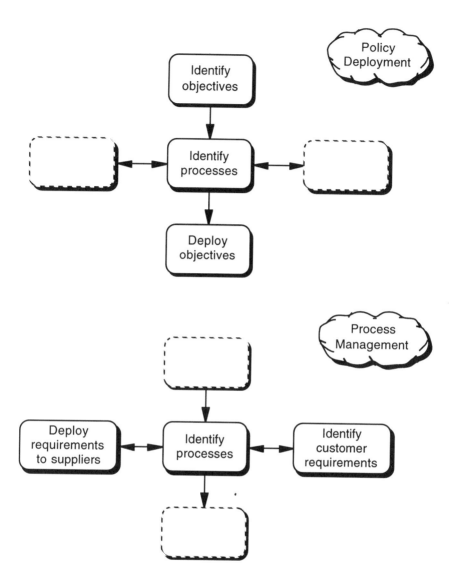

Figure 18.5 The idea of Policy Deployment (the figure at the top) together with that of Process Management (the figure at the bottom). Only the planning stages of the PDSA-cycles, so important for both Policy Deployment and Process Management, are displayed here. These two strategies together
give a good environment for quality improvements. (After
DeVries & Rodgers, 1991.)

319

For most processes there is a large potential for improvements in productivity and quality. Therefore, it can be worthwhile to be systematic when describing and understanding the present characteristics and behaviour of the process. A very important tool here is a *flow chart* of the process, see Figure 18.6.

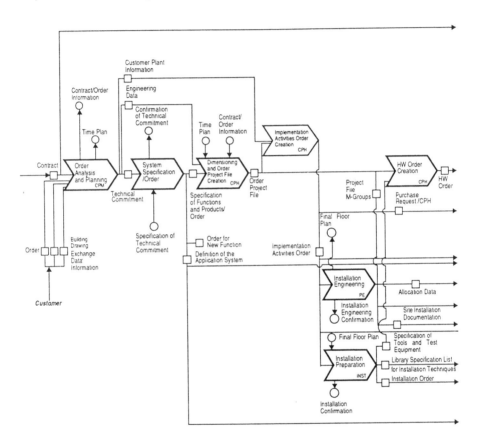

Figure 18.6   Example of a flow chart illustrating the "order process: prepare an order". (From Ericsson Telecom AB "Order Process Survey".)

18.3   An Illustration

In this section we will discuss an example taken from IBM, which is one of the companies that has put emphasis on process thinking. The discussion is based on an article by McCabe (1989).

In McCabe (1989) the purchasing process of a company is descri-bed. Evident measures of process efficiency are the time it takes to carry out a purchasing operation and the risk of anything going wrong. Variations in these measures can be due to the two diffe-rent kinds of causes: assignable causes of variation and common causes. Some sources of variation can be

- the people who do the job, i.e. the buyers and their educa-tion and training

- the reliability of the computer system and the equipment used

- the purchasing procedures that are followed and how well these are actually carried out

- work load.

Figure 18.7 illustrates how the percentage of errors over a certain amount of time varies among the 23 buyers at the department ob-served. It is apparent from the figure that there are two buyers whose patterns fall outside "normal" variation. It indicates that there may be assignable causes for the variation. A check showed that the buyer who had a small error percentage ordered on the basis of catalogue information and not like the others with engine-ering drawings as a basis. It also showed that the buyer with the high error percentage had not fully understood his assignment and needed further training and guidance in his work. The rest of the buyers had, as can be seen in the figure, roughly the same error percentage. The variation we can see probably reflects the natural variation of the process. The results from the remaining 21 buyers were now followed up in order to improve the process. The fraction faulty requisitions per week was analysed utilizing a control chart based on information from a period of 30 weeks; see Figure 18.8. On average the fraction faulty requisitions was 5.2%.

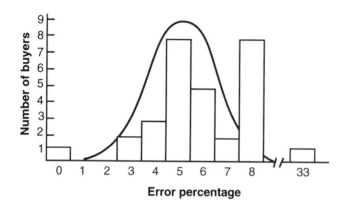

Figure 18.7   The fraction faulty requisitions per week for the 23 buyers at the department. (From McCabe, 1989.)

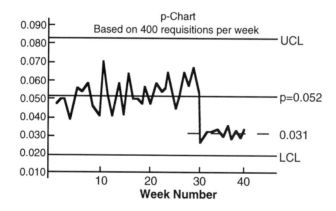

Figure 18.8   A control chart of the fraction faulty requisitions per week. The control limits are based on the result of 30 weeks' work. The limits of such a chart are in general set at $p \pm 3\sqrt{p(1-p)/n}$; see for instance Montgomery (1991). (From McCabe, 1989.)

The head of department then called the buyers together and described how important he considered it was to have a low error percentage. He also decided to start to register the number of errors per buyer and look into the error causes to be able to understand the sources of the variation. From Figure 18.8 it appears that the error percentage immediately dropped from 5.2% to 3.1%. The explanation lies in the process change that was the outcome of the buyers aquiring a new awareness of error significance. The control chart in Figure 18.8 also indicates that the fraction faulty requisitions had been stabilized at the level 3.1%.

Buyer	Wrong supplier	Exceeding commitment	Incomplete information	Other reasons
1	1	4	1	-
2	-	2	1	2
3	2	2	1	-
4	-	3	2	1
5	1	3	-	-
6	-	2	-	1
7	7	3	1	2
8	-	3	2	-
9	1	4	2	2
10	-	3	-	-
11	3	2	2	1
12	-	4	1	2
13	1	2	2	-
14	-	-	1	3
15	1	5	-	1
16	-	3	-	1
17	1	5	1	1
18	1	4	2	1
19	-	3	-	1
20	-	4	1	-
21	1	2	4	2
Total	15	63	24	21

Figure 18.9 An illustration of causes regarding faulty requisitions for the different buyers. (From McCabe, 1989. © American Society for Quality Control. Reprinted with Permission.)

In the new situation the cause of each occurring error was registered, see Figure 18.9. It turned out that all buyers had problems with exceeding commitments. As a consequence of this, procedures were changed and commitment reports were distributed to the buyers at shorter intervals. This improvement then reduced the error percentage to about 1.7%.

In McCabe (1989) some other examples of process improvements based on statistical process control are also described.

18.4 Benchmarking

Benchmarking is a way of finding opportunities for process improvements. It has become frequently used in recent years in many companies. The technique is now a systematic part of the quality improvement process at many successful companies such as AT&T, Digital (DEC), Ford Motor, DuPont, General Electric, IBM, ALCOA, Motorola, Milliken, NEC and Xerox. According to Camp (1989), benchmarking means "the search for best practices that will lead to superior performance". AT&T has described benchmarking as a "structured discipline for analysing a process to find improvement opportunities". In Japanese, the corresponding concept is called *dantotsu* which means roughly "striving to be the best of the best". The basic idea is to make a careful comparison of a process of the company with the same or a similar process at another company or another division of one's own company and benefit from the comparison.

As a consequence of the large interest in benchmarking, the American Productivity and Quality Center, APQC, started The International Benchmarking Clearinghouse (IBC) in Houston in 1991. It has already about 200 members. The organization helps its members in different ways with education and a network in promoting the benchmarking process and also by facilitating and improving the applications of benchmarking. Recently IBC has also created International Benchmarking Awards.

The first known formalized benchmarking process was carried out in 1976 by Xerox when they evaluated their warehouse operation by comparing with the legendary catalogue and retail giant L.L. Bean, with headquarters in Freeport, Maine (see Camp, 1989). In fact, much of the success at Xerox has been ascribed to their systematic work on improving their processes by using benchmarking.

When for instance they wanted to improve their invoicing process, they looked for a company that was good at that very process, not necessarily a company in the same business. Invoicing processes look almost the same irrespective of what product or service is to be invoiced. At Xerox they found a company, American Express, which was well-known for good invoicing service and precise invoicing. By comparing the invoicing processes of the two companies they could immediately find suggestions for improvements. Large parts of the improved process could then at once be used by Xerox. This and other examples are described in the article "Malcolm Baldrige Award Winners" in the TQM Magazine, April 1990.

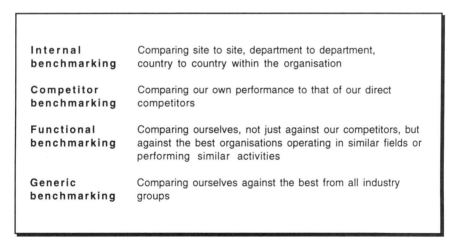

Internal benchmarking	Comparing site to site, department to department, country to country within the organisation
Competitor benchmarking	Comparing our own performance to that of our direct competitors
Functional benchmarking	Comparing ourselves, not just against our competitors, but against the best organisations operating in similar fields or performing similar activities
Generic benchmarking	Comparing ourselves against the best from all industry groups

Figure 18.10   Different types of benchmarking depending on where the comparison process is found. (From Hollings, 1992.)

The companies which have used benchmarking state that, in general, it is not too difficult to aquire sufficient insight. Generally, no company is interested in hiding anything from another company that is not competing with it. Furthermore, insight can be facilitated if we ourselves are experienced in these matters and are willing to share this with the other company.

It is important to emphasize that benchmarking is far more than copying. It requires deep self-assessment, and the ability to translate practices that work in another context into a process appropriate to our own organization. It is the essence of creativity. A basis for successful benchmarking is that our own company has adopted a process view. Benchmarking, in the sense that we use it here, means that we check, not our competitors products but their processes.

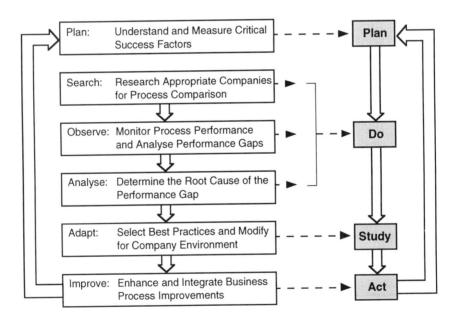

Figure 18.11 The benchmarking process according to Xerox. (From Watson, 1992.)

The benchmarking process can be described by the six steps: plan, search, observe, analyse, adapt, and improve (see Figure 18.11). Note the similarities between these steps and the Deming cycle: Plan-Do-Study-Act. The goal is to continuously improve a key business process with the objective of achieving customer satisfaction that exceeds the satisfaction delivered by our competitors.

Figure 18.12 contains a checklist that follows the six-step benchmarking process. It is further discussed in Watson (1992).

Plan	□ What is our process?
	□ How does our process work?
	□ How do we measure it?
	□ How well is our process performing today?
	□ Who are our customers?
	□ What products and services are we delivering to our customers?
	□ What do our customers expect or require of our products and services?
	□ What is our performance goal?
	□ How did we establish the goal?
	□ How does our products and service performance compare with our competitors?
Search	□ What companies perform this process better?
	□ Which company is the best at performing this process?
	□ What can we learn from that company?
	□ Whom should we contact to determine if they are willing to participate in our study?
Observe	□ What is their process?
	□ What is their performance goal?
	□ How well does their process perform over time and at multiple locations?
	□ How do they measure process performance?
	□ What enables the performance of their process?
	□ What factors could inhibit the adaptation of their process into our company?
Analyse	□ What is the nature of the performance gap?
	□ What is the magnitude of the performance gap?
	□ What characteristics distinguish their process as superior?
	□ What activities within our process are candidates for change?
Adapt	□ How does the knowledge of their process enable us to improve our process?
	□ Should we redefine our performance or reset our performance goal based upon this benchmark?
	□ What activities within their process would need to be modified to adapt it into our business environment?
Improve	□ What have we learned during this benchmarking study that will allow us to improve upon the "superior" process?
	□ How can we implement these changes into our process?

Figure 18.12   A checklist for benchmarking studies. (From Watson, 1992.)

18.5 Notes and References

The emphasis on processes and the continuous improvement work on them are discussed in Kane (1986), Melan (1986, 1993), Ackerman et al. (1988), McCabe (1989) and de Rosa et al. (1990).

The concept of Processs Management is discussed in the books Harrington (1991), Slater (1991) and Melan (1993).

We also want to mention the concept of *Business Reengineering* as described in Hammer & Champy (1993). The idea here is, according to Hammer & Champy (1993), to starting all over, starting from scratch putting aside much of the recieved wisdom of industrial management. At the heart of business reengineering lies in the notion of discontinuous thinking. See also Davenport (1992) and Johanson et al. (1993).

The concept of benchmarking is discussed in the book by Camp (1989) and in a series of articles in Quality Progress 1989 by the same author. Watson (1992) builds on the foundation laid in Camp's book, offering a practical guide that will be of good help when starting process benchmarking. Watson has also published two other books on benchmarking during 1993. Another recent book dealing with benchmarking is Spendolini (1992). The interest for benchmarking has also recently resulted in "International Benchmarking Awards" organised by the American Productivity & Quality Center through its International Benchmarking Clearinghouse. The assessment criteria are similar to those in the Malcolm Baldrige National Quality Award (see Chapter 21). The book "Benchmarking the Best. A Look at the Finalists' Applications for the 1992 International Awards" by APQC describes the applicatiosn from the seven finalists including Eastman Kodak, Digital Equipment and SunHealth Alliance.

The October/November 1992 issue of the journal Continuous Journey and the June 1992 issue of the TQM Magazine are also devoted to benchmarking.

19 The Seven Management Tools

In Chapter 11 we have discussed the seven QC-tools. We have also several times emphasized how useful these tools are in quality work. Most of them are aimed at analysing numerical data. However, facts are not always numerical in nature. In many cases opinions of customers, external as well as internal ones, are important facts to be considered for process planning and improvement. This, and a lot of other knowledge, cannot be displayed in numerical diagrams.

Therefore JUSE (Union of Japanese Scientists and Engineers) compiled, and to some extent simplified, some tools from various sciences such as behavioural science, operational analysis, optimization theory and statistics. This very powerful and useful tool-box is called *the seven management tools,* or sometimes *the seven new QC-tools*. The seven management tools are:

- affinity diagram
- relation diagram
- tree diagram
- matrix diagram
- matrix data analysis
- process decision program chart
- arrow diagram

Usually, data are gathered in brainstorming sessions. The brainstorming groups should contain all those who have important knowledge about the problem under study and they should be cross-functional. After the brainstorming session the data are compiled in different diagrams, such as the seven management tools. One important aspect of these tools is their support of teamwork and cross-functional co-operation.

In this chapter we will give a brief description of each of the seven management tools.

19.1 Affinity Diagram

The affinity diagram, sometimes also called the *KJ-method,* after its Japanese originator Jiro Kawakita, is a facility for organising large amounts of verbal data, such as ideas, customer desires or opinions in groups, according to some form of natural affinity. The affinity diagram illustrates associations rather than logical connections. The principle of an affinity diagram is shown in Figure 19.1.

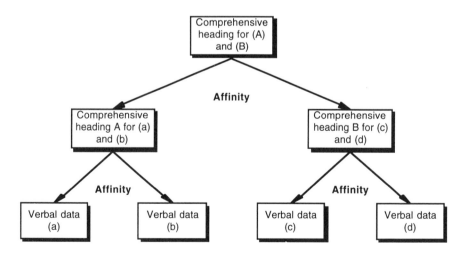

Figure 19.1   The principle of an affinity diagram.

The work of creating an affinity diagram is preferably done by a group. Experience shows that a suitable group size is 6-8 persons, who have worked together before.

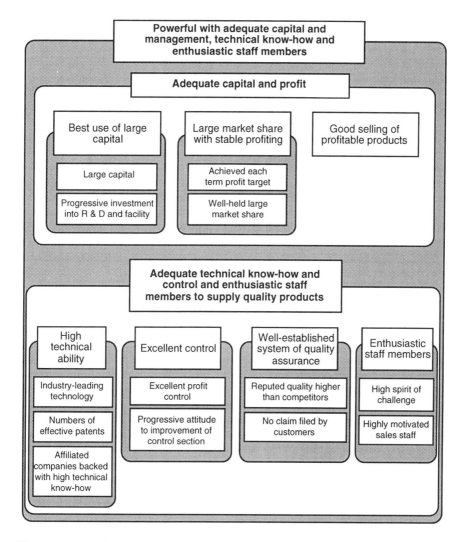

Figure 19.2   An affinity diagram concerning the question "what characterizes an attractive and reliable company". The example is from ReVelle (1989).

The procedure for designing the diagram can be as follows:

- Define the subject or matter that is to be the basis for the collection of verbal data. A vague definition like "what are the customers' requirements concerning the product?" is no disadvantage, because it can inspire new angles of approach.

- Take down the data that the group then generates in a "brainstorming" around the topical subject. It is important that data should be taken down without first having been arranged. Each statement can, for example, be registered on a small card by each participant.

- The task then is to group the related data together under subordinate headings at different levels according to the principles in Figure 19.1. This compilation can be done as follows:

  - Look for two cards that seem to be related in some way. Put these cards aside. Repeat this step.

  - This work should be done in silence to avoid discussions about, say, the semantic meaning of the words.

  - During this process divergent opinions concerning the relationship between different data will be discovered. Experience shows, however, that most of these conflicts will disappear during the continuing work.

  - Stop work when all data have been arranged into a limited number of groups and when the above-mentioned conflicts have been resolved. The remaining conflicts will be resolved by discussion.

  - Try to find a heading for each data group. This heading should in some sense sum up the group. This can

332

be done either by choosing one of the cards that is in the group and putting it at the top or by formulating a new heading.

This procedure can be repeated with the summarizing headlines regarded as data, thus creating a hierarchy. The analysis is finished when the data are grouped under a suitable number of headlines. Figure 19.2 illustrates part of an affinity diagram based on the question: "what characterizes an attractive and reliable company?".

19.2 Relation Diagram

A *relation diagram* illustrates the logical connections between an essential idea, a problem or a question at issue and various data. That is why there are certain similarities between relation diagrams and Ishikawa diagrams.

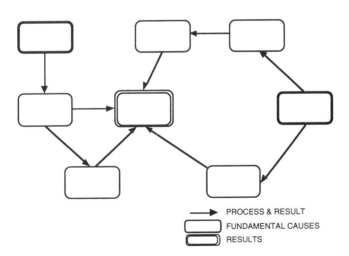

Figure 19.3   The principles of a relation diagram.

The data that are used can for example be generated using an affinity diagram. The relation diagram is mainly a logical tool as op-

333

posed to the affinity diagram, which is more creative. Examples of situations when the diagram may be useful are:

- When a topic is so complicated that relations between different ideas cannot be established through conventional reasoning.

- When the time sequence, according to which a number of steps are taken, is decisive.

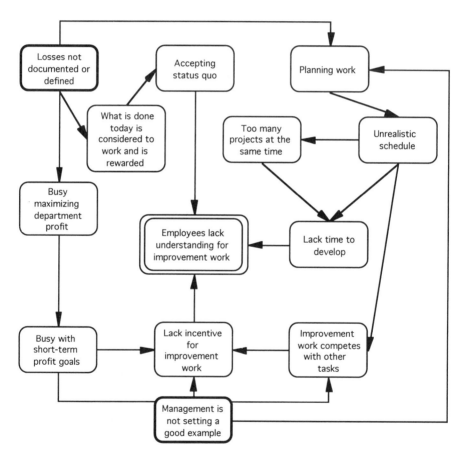

Figure 19.4   Relation diagram of the problem "employees lack understanding for the need for continuous quality improvement".

334

- When suspicions are raised that the problem in question is exclusively a symptom of a more fundamental underlying problem.

The principles of the relation diagram are shown in Figure 19.3.

As for affinity diagrams the work on the relation diagram should be conducted in groups. It is important that the topic (result) to be investigated has been carefully defined. The causes and the fundamental causes required for the work may have been generated, for example, from an affinity diagram or an Ishikawa diagram.

Figure 19.4 shows parts of a relation diagram designed to sort out the problem "employees lack understanding for the need for continuous quality improvement".

19.3 Tree Diagram

The *tree diagram,* or *systematic diagram,* provides a systematic way of breaking down an essential problem, a central idea or a need from the customers into its constituents at different levels. Unlike the affinity diagram and the relation diagram, this tool is more "goal-oriented". Fault Tree Analysis, which was discussed in Chapter 6, can be regarded as a development from this tool.
The principle of a tree diagram is illustrated in Figure 19.5.

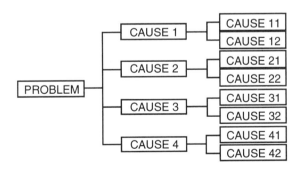

Figure 19.5   *The principle of a tree diagram.*

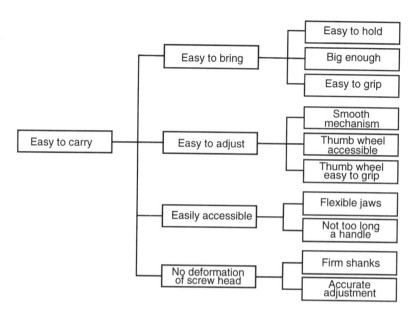

Figure 19.6 A tree diagram concerning the customer wish "easy to handle", which refers to an adjustable wrench.

The tree diagram is most efficient as a facility when designed by a group. The way of working resembles that described for the affinity diagram. However, it is important here that the topic (problem or similar), which is to be investigated is clearly identified. In Figure 19.6 a tree diagram is shown designed for the customer wish "easy to handle", which refers to an adjustable wrench.

The tree diagram is for instance appropriate to use in any of the following cases:

- To break down vaguely formulated customer wishes of a product into customer wishes on a managable level.

- When we need to investigate all possible parts that cause a problem.

- To investigate what short term goals have to be attained before a comprehensive goal can be reached.

19.4 Matrix Diagram

This tool organizes largest amounts of data so that the logical connections between various elements can be illustrated graphically. It also shows, using graphical symbols, the importance of the different relations.

The most common example of a matrix diagram are the matrices used in Quality Function Deployment, QFD (see Chapter 4). Figure 19.7 illustrates a few examples of how to design a matrix diagram.

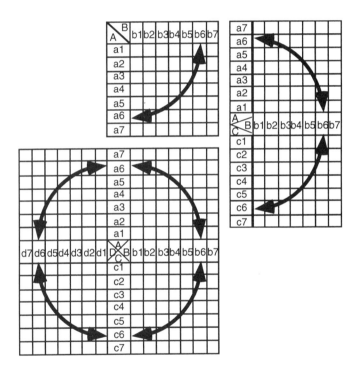

Figure 19.7   Examples of a number of different kinds of matrix diagrams. The diagrams in the figure, arranged according to size, are an L-diagram, a T-diagram and an X-chart. (From Mizuno, 1988.)

337

19.5 Matrix Data Analysis

Matrix Data Analysis is the only one of the seven management tools which is intended for analysing numerical data. It is equivalent to the statistical technique called *principal component analysis,* an important means of analysing multivariate data. Since its use requires statistical knowledge it is the least used of the seven management tools. The purpose of the method is to give a picture of numerical data from a matrix diagram in an efficient way. The matrix in Table 19.1 provides the result from an investigation of how a number of various foods attract different male and female age groups.

	Age group	Food 1	Food 2	......	Food 100
Men	≤ 15 years old	7.8	4.6		3.1
	16 to 29	5.4	3.8	·	2.8
	21 to 30	3.9	4.4		3.3
	31 to 40	3.5	4.0		3.0
	≥ 41	3.0	3.5		2.5
Women	≤ 15 years old	8.1	6.2		3.9
	16 to 29	6.0	7.2		3.5
	21 to 30	5.4	7.5		3.0
	31 to 40	3.8	7.0		2.8
	≥ 41	2.5	9.0		3.0

Table 19.1   The means of "taste points" for different foods distributed according to various age groups. (From Futami, 1986.)

In Table 19.2 we can see the correlation matrix for the data. Eigenvalues and eigenvectors for the first three principal components of the data are shown in Table 19.3.

From Table 19.3 we get the following:

(1) The cumulative share is 0.934, which implies that the 1st to the 3rd principal components account for 93.4% of the dispersion in the data.

	Male					Female				
	0-15	16-20	21-30	31-40	41-	0-15	16-20	21-30	31-40	41-
	1	2	3	4	5	6	7	8	9	10
2	0.871									
3	0.516	0.759								
4	0.370	0.604	0.852							
5	0.182	0.402	0.726	0.874						
6	0.938	0.821	0.517	0.358	0.208					
7	0.811	0.838	0.658	0.488	0.354	0.889				
8	0.615	0.709	0.698	0.620	0.523	0.746	0.894			
9	0.500	0.647	0.701	0.721	0.710	0.621	0.768	0.852		
10	0.330	0.457	0.558	0.632	0.748	0.493	0.642	0.773	0.911	

Table 19.2   *The correlation matrix for the data in Table 19.1. The matrix is symmetrical.*

Group	1st principal component	2nd principal component	3rd principal component
1	0.286	0.446	0.194
2	0.331	0.240	0.336
3	0.323	-0.166	0.442
4	0.266	-0.359	0.375
5	0.261	-0.507	0.128
6	0.306	0.408	-0.084
7	0.344	0.253	-0.171
8	0.348	0.032	-0.290
9	0.346	-0.164	-0.322
10	0.303	-0.267	-0.522
Eigenvalue	6.830	1.760	0.750
Frequency	0.683	0.176	0.075
Cumulative freq.	0.683	0.859	0.934

Table 19.3   *The 1st, 2nd and 3rd principal components of the data.*

(2) Groups 1 to 10 have about the same value of the eigen-vectors for the 1st principal component. This may indicate that it measures some sort of "general delight in food".

(3) Values of the eigenvalues for the 2nd principal component increase with rising age irrespective of sex. This probably shows that "food preferences vary with varying age".

(4) The 3rd principal component indicates that food preferences vary with sex, since the eigenvectors differ in size.

In Figure 19.8, preferences for different foods are plotted in the plane consisting of the 1st and 2nd principal components.

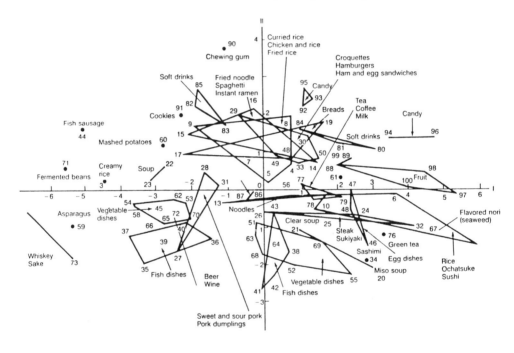

Figure 19.8   Preferences for different foods plotted in the plane determined by the 1st and 2nd principal component. (From Mizuno, 1988)

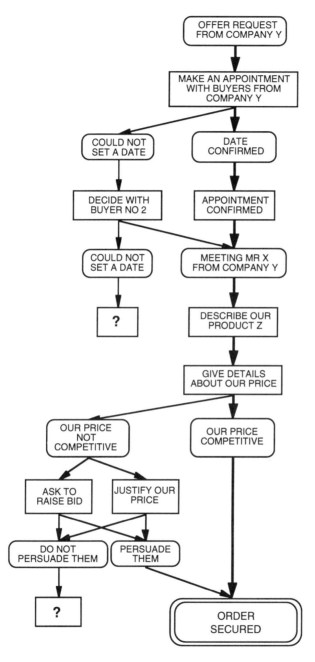

Figure 19.9   A process decision program chart describing how to assure the winning of an order.

341

19.6 Process Decision Program Chart

PDPC (Process Decision Program Chart) is a planning tool earlier used in operational analysis. It is used for displaying the sequence of actions and decisions needed to reach a desired result. The PDPC-tool has for example the following two applications:

- When designing a new plan to achieve a desired result. The tool provides the possibility of planning for, and subsequently taking care of, the problems that may arise in the line of work.

- For "catastrophe planning" to avoid a certain undesired event. The undesired event is typed out and the process steps that lead up to it are systematically listed.

Figure 19.9 shows a part of a process decision program chart, established to assure the winning of an order for a company.

19.7 Arrow Diagram

The arrow diagram is a diagram for day-to-day planning, very similar to the *PERT-method* (Program Evaluation and Review Technique), which is used in project and production planning. The tool is used to ensure the most suitable time planning for a certain task.

The arrow diagram also facilitates control in the course of work. The traditional way of executing such planning is to use a so-called *Gantt-chart*. Figures 19.10 and 19.11 illustrate the planning of a house construction, using a traditional Gantt-chart, and an arrow diagram.

Quite often the PERT-technique is combined with optimization of the sequence of activities to be planned. This optimization is not at all regarded as essential by the Japanese practitioners.

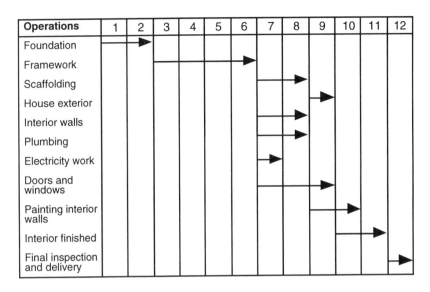

Figure 19.10 A Gantt-chart executed to plan the design of a house.

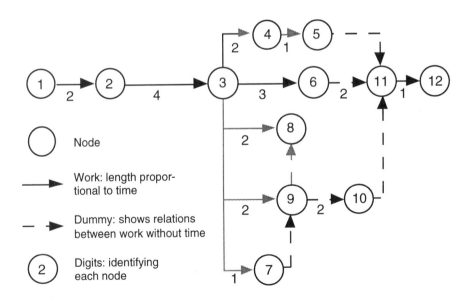

Figure 19.11 An arrow diagram executed to plan the same house construction as in Figure 19.10. Note that clarity increases dramatically compared to the Gantt-chart.

343

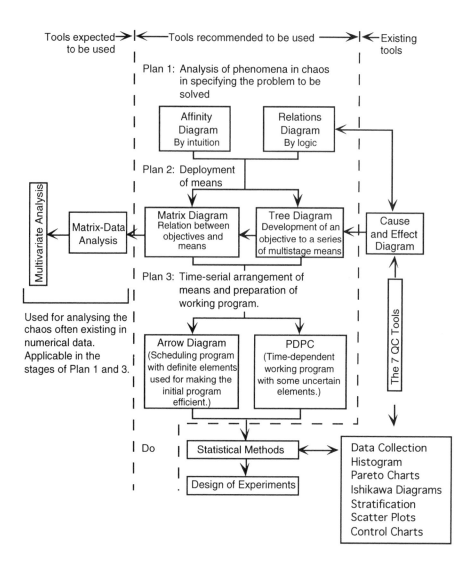

Figure 19.12 Relation between "the seven QC-tools" and "the seven management tools". (From Nayatani, 1986.)

344

19.8 Relations Between the Different Tools

It seems natural to wonder if there are any relations between the seven different management tools. When are the various tools to be used and what is the relation between the seven QC-tools and the seven management tools? In Figure 19.12 an attempt is made to illustrate the relation between the two tool groups. The idea for the figure comes from Nayatani (1986).

19.9 Notes and References

The seven management tools were compiled by JUSE (Union of Japanese Scientists and Engineers) in 1979. The book by Mizuno (1986) is an English translation of the Japanese compilation. Other references on this subject are Futami (1986), King (1987) and Asaka & Ozeki (1990).

For a description of the theory behind principal component analysis, one of the tools in multivariate analysis, we refer to Joliffe (1986).

20 Improvement Programs

Continuous improvement is in a way contradictory to the belief in optimization that was very strong in the 1960s and the 1970s. Optimization must be done within a fixed framework. Continuous improvement, however, is partly a matter of ridding ourselves of this framework and starting to think on entirely new lines.

To a great extent, successful companies are using special programs for quality improvement. In this chapter we will discuss some important elements of such a program. We will also briefly describe improvement programs at some companies.

20.1 Program Elements

We have earlier touched on several essential elements in an improvement program. One is management commitment and knowledge, with respect both to the significance of quality issues and to techniques for problem solving. Policy Deployment, which we mentioned in Chapter 17, is also an important ingredient. In this chapter we will discuss some other elements, namely *QC-circles* and *Suggestion Systems*. We will also discuss the Japanese *Kaizen philosophy* and describe a survey on quality activities performed at companies in Japan, Korea and Denmark.

20.2 QC-circles

One way to get all employees actively involved in improvement work is to form small groups who discuss different problems and come up with suggestions for improvement. This activity is usually referred to as *QC-circles (Quality Control Circles)*. However, this concept has for various reasons a slightly negative ring in Western industry, and today this activity is often referred to by other names. One of them is *improvement teams*.

The idea of QC-circles was developed in Japan back in the 1960s The first QC-circle was registered at the Japanese Telephone & Telegraph Corporation in May 1962 and the first nation-wide conference on this subject was held in November 1963.

From the very start QC-circles were meant to be study groups to encourage studies of some magazine or book on quality control. Thus self-development of the employees was at that time the primary goal. The educational element in QC-circles is still the most important one in many Japanese companies. The development of QC-circles has been rapid. According to Kondo (1993) there were more than 300,000 registered QC-circles in October 1991. Since a typical QC-circle in Japan consists of 6-10 members, more than 2 million employees are involved in these QC-circles. Furthermore, maybe twice as many circles are working without being registered. Several of the major and more successful companies have a large number of QC-circles. Toyota, for instance, had already in 1984 more than 5,800 QC-circles.

QC-circle activity is not only confined to manufacturing industry. There are, for example, QC-circles in sales organisations, department stores, hotels, banks and the restaurant business.

Sanwa Bank, one of Japan's biggest banks, had already in the middle of the 1980s about 2,400 QC-circles with nearly 13,000 employees involved. These offered an opportunity to discuss problems concerning miscoding, more efficient post handling, how to remember customers' names, how to save energy, how to reduce overtime work and how to get customers to open new accounts in the bank.

Using simple statistical tools, such as the seven QC-tools, people work in groups discussing, analysing and solving different problems, often aimed at costs, safety or productivity. The circle members in Japan are well-trained in data collecting and making statistical analyses based on these data thanks to the great efforts devoted to training. There are also different ways of encouraging circle members, for example, by rewards or by publishing their results on notice boards. An important reason for the success of QC-circles in Japan is presumably the fact that employees are well-trained and extremely problem oriented.

Taking part in the circles is voluntary and the circles themselves are free to choose their topic. Even if certain meetings take place during working hours, many are still held outside the working-day, for instance, during lunch breaks or when work is finished for the day.

QC-circles can be a useful method of teaching and encouraging the staff and arousing their interest in matters concerning quality improvements. This is an essential reason why so many companies start to concentrate on quality with the help of activities that resemble QC-circles. For QC-circles to be successful it is essential, however, as indeed for all other quality activities, that they have the management's support, and that management take an interest in the activity and in the results that are achieved. It is also their job to implement the suggested improvements. Contact and cooperation between the management and employees can also be improved in the course of this process. Today even employees from supplier's companies are involved in QC-circles in the customer's company, trying to arrive at joint solutions.

One of the traditional Western approaches to QC-circles was to have a team make recommendations. These suggestions more often than not fell into a "black hole" never to be heard of again. Improvement teams, however, are different from QC-circles in the sense that often they are empowered to implement what they recommend. They are given the resources (people, machines, and money) to ensure that their ideas are successfully used.

20.3 Suggestion Systems

An important way of making use of experience and knowledge from all employees is by stimulating them to contribute with improvement suggestions. In successful Japanese companies far more than half of all employees are active in quality improvement work, for instance through suggestion systems.

An example, maybe the most successful one, is provided by Toyota, who already at the beginning of the 1950s introduced a suggestion system among their employees. For the first few years the system did not work properly (see Table 20.1) but in the 1970s and above all in the 1980s the system has become very efficient. During 1986 about 95% of all employees contributed with improvement suggestions and there were on the average almost 50 suggestions per employee each year. There are many reasons why the system works so well at Toyota. One is that all suggestions are rapidly met with some kind of response, as a rule within twenty-four hours. The proposer does not have to wait and wonder whether anyone cares about the suggestion. Another reason is that they have a rewarding system for good suggestions. Good suggestions are rewarded with a medal, a sum of money or a membership of the "Good Idea Club". However, the most important reason as regards the efficiency of the system is probably that management look seriously at the submitted suggestions and actually make use of the improvement ideas. As can be seen in Table 20.1, 96% of the about 2.65 million suggestions submitted to Toyota during 1986 have resulted in some kind of change. This reflects not only the fact that the ideas are very well-founded, but also that management seriously consider the suggestions and try to implement them. It has been estimated that in 1986 Japanese companies received about 48 million suggestions from their employees while US employees only submitted about 1 million ideas for improvements.

Year	Total number of suggestions	Number per employee	Percentage of the employees involved	Percentage suggestions used
1951	789	0.1	8	23
1955	1087	0.2	10	43
1960	5001	0.6	20	36
1965	15968	0.7	30	39
1970	49414	1.3	54	72
1975	381438	8.7	81	83
1980	859039	19.2	92	93
1985	2453105	45.6	95	96
1986	2648710	47.7	95	96

Table 20.1   Development at Toyota as regards the number of submitted suggestions for quality improvements. (After Labovitz & Chang, 1990. © American Society for Quality Control. Reprinted with Permission.)

In certain companies illustrations of the number of submitted suggestions from different departments are put up on notice boards. This leads to competition between the different departments as regards the number of suggestions submitted and accepted.

20.4   Kaizen

"Kaizen" is Japanese and means roughly "change to the better"; see Figure 20.1. It is one of the most frequently used words in Japan. It is used in many different contexts. Politicians, for example, speak of "kaizen" for trade balance, "kaizen" for diplomatic relations and "kaizen" for social welfare. In the business world the "kaizen" concept is deeply rooted and has been so for a long time. The meaning is that all people involved contribute to the improvement of the different processes in the company or organization by continuous improvement work.

Figure 20.1 *The Japanese word "kaizen" consists of the symbols "kai", meaning "to change" and "zen", meaning "good". Together the meaning of the two words might be "change for the better".*

Behind the "kaizen" philosophy there lies an awareness of the necessity of satisfying the customers in order to keep the business alive and to be profitable. The "kaizen" philosophy is thus customer and process oriented, all in line with the views we have presented elsewhere in this book. The "kaizen" philosophy is based on people's commitment and participation by using the knowledge and experience of employees in continuous improvement work. This can be done, for example, via QC-circles (see Section 20.2) and suggestion systems (see Section 20.3). Important facilities are also "the seven QC-tools", which were discussed in Chapter 11. "Kaizen" can be regarded as a continuous journey in the PDSA-cycle: Plan - Do - Study - Act.

For a description of the "kaizen" philosophy and its significance we refer to Imai (1986).

20.5 A Comparison between East and West

Dahlgaard et al. (1990) describe a survey performed at companies in Japan, Korea, and Denmark. In Japan 300 companies were asked and the response frequency was 23%, in Korea 800 with a response frequency of 3% and in Denmark 118 companies with a response frequency of 35%. Even if the response frequency is unsatisfactory, the survey indicates, among other things, the following:

- Employees in Japan and Korea devote about three times as much time to training and education in quality issues as their Danish colleagues. The difference is even bigger for the newly employed.

- Management devote up to five times as much time to education in quality issues in Japan and Korea compared to Denmark.

- The number of companies with QC-circles is nearly 97% in Japan and Korea, to be compared with 12% in Denmark. About 70-80% of the employees in Japan and Korea take part in these QC-circles, but only 1% in Denmark. The survey also indicates that participation is fairly equally distributed among different departments, including administrative departments, in Japan and Korea. In Denmark, however, only staff from manufacturing, quality, and research and development participate.

- Suggestion systems, with or without a rewarding system, can be found at more than 95% of the companies in Japan and Korea. The corresponding figure in Denmark is 40-50%.

- Danish companies are bad at stimulating their employees into actively taking part in company quality improvement work. A Danish employee devotes about 5 minutes a week to quality meetings during and outside working hours compared with 75 minutes in Japan and Korea.

- In Japan "the seven QC-tools", in particular Pareto charts and Ishikawa diagrams, are the most important tools in quality work. In Korea check sheets and control charts are ranked highest. In Denmark, however, sampling plans head the list over the most frequently used tools in quality work. Thus the emphasis is still on inspection.

- Japan is much more active in looking for information regarding customer requirements and expectations through market surveys and analyses.

The survey thus indicates that management and employee commitment are much more substantial in Japanese and Korean companies than in Danish ones. It also shows that people in Denmark devote too much time to inspection and too little energy to actively obtaining information as to the needs of the customers. By spending more efforts on customer needs and wants they could more easily design and manufacture products fulfilling these needs and wants at lowest possible cost.

Even if Denmark was the only European country that participated in the survey, it is realistic to believe that the situation is roughly the same in several other European countries.

20.6 Some Applications

20.6.1 T50 - ABB Sweden's Customer Focus Program

According to the CEO Percy Barnevik, ABB Asea Brown Boveri, is a "multidomestic" company active in eight major business segments within electrical engineering located in 140 countries. ABB has 1,300 independent incorporated companies and about 5,000 autonomous profit centres with some 213,000 employees and revenues of USD 30 billion (1992). ABB Sweden has about 46,000 employees in 150 independent companies at 200 locations. In 1990 it booked about USD 8 billion in revenues. The average ABB company in Sweden has 200 to 400 employees.

In June 1990 ABB Sweden arranged two awareness meetings led by the President of ABB Sweden, Bert-Olof Svanholm, attended by four hundred company executives and union representatives. The purpose was to initiate a transformation process called "the most important task of this decade". This was the start of the *T50-program,* the customer and employee focused Time Based Management (TBM) program of ABB in Sweden. The urgency of the program was enhanced by focusing on threats such as the increase of cost without corresponding increase of productivity, the high turnover of personnel and absenteeism and the difficulties experienced in recruiting young people to industrial work.

Simplify job execution

Before

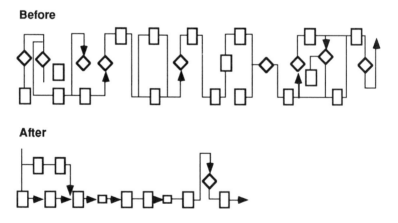

After

Figure 20.2 *By simplifying the processes the time in the different steps can be reduced considerably. The goal of ABB Sweden's improvement program is to reduce all lead times by 50%.*

The aim of the T50-program is to get satisfied customers and motivated employees and the means to reach this goal is primarily to focus on time objectives, i.e. all lead times (order, design, engineering, manufacturing, shipping) shall be halved by the end of 1993. Extracting time-oriented objectives was the method to meet the threats and thus force the organization to focus on the whole process from customer demand to customer satisfaction instead of on specialised functional parts of it. Time-reduction forces simplification of routines, increased parallel activities and improved quality. It is important to note that the time reduction was not aimed to be obtained through harder work but from smarter work, see Figure 20.2.

When the Customer Focus Program was launched in Spring 1990 an early conviction was that time-oriented objectives are concrete, visible and easy to communicate, but also that in the long run it is not sufficient to focus on time only. This led to the four components of the T50-symbol; see Figure 20.3. The name "T50" was chosen to give a strong encouragement to set challenging time goals; T for "time" and "50" for an average percentage reduction of times.

Figure 20.3   The logotype of the T50-program at ABB Sweden.

The leading internal example was provided by an assembly unit at ABB Control producing electrical push-buttons. Two years earlier the unit had productivity problems, but now they could look back on one and a half years of successful operation. The assembly was organized in teams responsible for everything, starting with the order reception and ending when the invoice is mailed to the customer.

The awareness meetings at ABB, Sweden, were repeated as half-day seminars on five occasions thus reaching two thousand managers and supervisors. Information activities were continued in a multi-dimensional matrix with functional orientation aiming at employees in purchasing, quality, personnel, information and market communication, sales and research and development focusing on each group's specific role in the T50-program.

The most striking objective of the program at the kick-off seminars was the average 50-percent cut of the cycle time by the end of 1993. Each company was to assign one member of its senior management team as coordinator for T50. Apart from being in charge of the company's program this person also acts as the liason officer between the company and the central T50-team. Every three months the T50-team arranges a one-day seminar for the people in charge of the T50-program to facilitate exchange of experience. In addition, it was recommended that the strategic plans should reflect the potential of the T50-program, and the budget for the coming year, i.e. 1991, was to include costs and revenues related to the program.

A milestone set in June 1990 on the road to the objectives of 1993 was that one T50-project should be initiated by at least half of the ABB companies before the end of that year and that they all should have a project in progress by the summer of 1991. Since the T50-program involves all ABB-companies, the program spans from assembling and manufacturing companies with short order cycles and fairly standardized products, via engineering and project related business to service oriented companies, e.g. financial services companies.

356

In the summer of 1990 a decision was taken to go public with the visions presented without having achieved ambitious objectives. One reason for this was that communication with ABB's employees through the media was more effective and the message of the Group Management was considered more committing by the recipients compared with the same message presented through internal channels. Another reason was that external media reach customers, suppliers, potential employees and the general public. In that way ABB should become widely recognised as a vital organization leading the development of industrial enterprise.

Cornerstones for the success of the T50-program are massive information on both corporate and company level, appropriate training programs and company-run projects in pilot or full-scale. Based on the experience from the first three months of training a set of training courses was launched in early 1991:

- 3 days including T50-training, customer and supplier relation, TBM and management of change
- 2 days training focused on TBM
- 2 days management of change
- 1 day awareness seminar

The training was to a large extent arranged and performed by teams combining consultants from different Swedish ABB companies.

The Swedish ABB Corporate Management is convinced that the average 50% time reduction in 1993 will in most cases be achieved. One basis for this conviction is that the first years of the T50-program raised high expectations amongst the employees. It is not necessary to push the program through. Incentives have been given which have raised the demand for training and resulted in an urge to participate. It has also been demonstrated that delegating responsibility is probably the fastest way to realize the potential of an organization.

The main reason behind the incentives for change in the organization is that the individual employee can see direct personal advantages in the program at the same time as the advantages to the company are transparently visible. The program has led to large improvements in productivity, quality, delivery punctuality and decreased absence due to illness. Some results from the program are illustrated in Figure 20.4. An important reason for the success of the T50-program is, according to some officers of ABB, that national media like TV, radio and newspapers have been successfully used to spread the message. More about the T50-program can be read in Peters (1992).

Time reductions in the order cycle

	Before	After
Tap changers	86	38 days
Standard AC motors	47	12
Standard DC motors	30	15
Robots	20	15
Standard ABB Master	60	30
Instrument transformers	75	18
Surge arrestors	43	24
HVDC contracted for delivery	3	2 years

Figure 20.4   Some improvement results from the T50-program in ABB Sweden.

20.6.2 Development of TQM at Ericsson

Ericsson has a more than 100-year history in the telecommunication industry. Today, the Ericsson group has about 70,000 employees in about 100 countries. The development of TQM in the Ericsson group can be divided into three phases:

1. "Ericsson Quality" – an awareness drive
2. Quality system focus
3. Total Quality Management.

The first phase was called "Ericsson Quality" (EQ), see Gummesson (1998). It started in 1983 as a three-year project and focused on customer-defined quality, not only in production but in the whole company. The new quality philosophy was based on the following strategies:

- focus on customers
- prevention
- zero defects
- long-term thinking
- everyone's full participation.

The vehicle to spread the new philosophy was a corporate education program that was run top-down. That program had three parts, one about awareness, one about tools and techniques, and one about planning. For managers the focus was on awareness and planning, while further down in the organization the emphasis was more on tools and techniques. The lasting benefits of this phase were important. The awareness and the philosophy were there. The measurements and follow-up systems were in place and the habit of running annual quality programs was created, although some people were still critical of "quality programs".

During the EQ-program much of the discussion was concentrated on "who are the internal customers, what are their requirements, and how do we live up to those requirements". During the next phase, the quality system phase, the focus was on what the routines for quality control look like, and how they were documented and put together to form a consistent quality assurance system. As a consequence of the expanding market requirements, it was natural for Ericsson to go for a third-party-certification according to ISO 9000. The company that spearheaded the process was

Ericsson Telecom in Stockholm. It was not the very first unit to get a third-party-certificate in the Ericsson group, but since Ericsson Telecom is by far the largest company in the group with about 14,000 employees, its impact has been decisive.

The decision to go for a certificate was taken in the middle of 1989 and already on December 14, 1990, the certificating body, British Standards Institute (BSI), announced that Ericsson Telecom was qualified. In the process of that successful accomplishment the following things turned out to be critical:

- It was a president decision that was never compromised.
- The top management of the company was engaged in a steering committee that met frequently.
- A decentralized approach was chosen.
- An organization with "ISO-consultants" was set up to support the effort.
- A lot of training was given.
- Early third party pre-assessment demonstrated to the organisation what it was all about.

Another important factor was that the certificate as such represented a very clear target, and although the contents of the standard are complex the label "ISO 9001" was easy to communicate. Inspired by the positive experience from Ericsson Telecom, other Ericsson companies set up similar efforts and with just one year's hard work several of them managed to organize their quality system and get a certificate.

The third phase is intended to make Ericsson a TQM-company. The emphasis is on improvements, not only in quality but in the total company performance. TQM is not seen as something separated from, or added to, other activities in the company but as an integrated tool that is needed to reach the business objectives. The development towards TQM, however, started already in the first phase. The basic strategy of the EQ drive is still the basis for the TQM approach.

The need for a third phase became clear when a new corporate Quality Follow-up was introduced during 1991. This Quality Follow-up was designed as a set of five questions focusing on business oriented quality performance improvements. A selection of managerial aspects are covered.

The follow-up is done at one company at a time. It is conducted by the group's vice president together with the corporate quality director, Sture Ögren. Usually a follow-up meeting is started with an outline by the president of the reviewed company followed by a presentation by the division managers covering the following five questions:

- *Measurements* (max 5 points): Which measurements are used to follow up quality and how are they selected to cover customer satisfaction and internal efficiency?

- *Reports and control* (max 7 points): How are the measurements used to control the business?

- *Planning for improvement* (max 7 points): How are improvement goals set and broken down into action programs?

- *Rate of improvement* (max 12 points): How large and widespread are improvements?

- *Level of quality* (max 12 points): What is the performance level compared to others?

Each division at the reviewed company is given a feed-back report with scores, "strengths", and "areas to improve". One important benefit from the follow-up is that a good understanding of how quality is handled in the different parts of the group has been created.

During the follow-ups, examples of excellent improvements in a broad range of areas from software design to hardware reliability were found. But also mechanically selected performance indicators, sloppy follow-up, inefficient improvement planning were observed. The Ericsson group also realized that the overall rate of improvement was too slow.

Bringing the quality system up to the standard of ISO 9001 had created a sound basis but it had not developed the company's improvement skills. The standard was not enough. The quality system had to be developed further with a strong emphasis on improvements. Therefore a corporate TQM initiative was launched.

In this phase the basic improvement skills are reinforced. They are based on the Deming cycle "Plan-Do-Study-Act" (see Figures 10.3 and 18.2) and the use of problem solving tools such as the seven QC-tools and the seven management tools, which have proven very useful also in non-manufacturing areas.

To make improvements happen, that is to manage improvements, three mechanisms are used:

- Day-to-day Management
- Process Management
- Management by Policy.

Day-to-day Management is a bottom-up approach, where the focus is on the improvements that take place in the small organizational unit or the team.

Process Management is used primarily for cross-functional processes where there is a need to coordinate the efforts from several linked activities in different departments.

Management by Policy has a top-down approach and is used to coordinate the efforts of several units to reach company-wide targets of highest priority.

These methods and systems are used to reach highly focused improvement targets that are usually numeric in nature. There is also an approach aiming at enhancing the quality system at such. The tools used here are the models laid out in the national and international quality awards. They are used for self-assessment but also as a target to focus the organization in the same way as the ISO 9000 certification was a target for the whole organization. In the early stages the self-assessment is the important part.

The strategy for introducing TQM at Ericsson is based on the experience of the EQ-program and the ISO-certification. A decentralized approach has been chosen. Common factors are

- the basic quality system
- corporate goals
- follow-up system
- education, especially for top management
- communication program
- recognition.

The rest, including specific approaches, selection of focused areas, pace, plans, and even the name of the program differ from company to company in order to fit the local company culture and the specific market needs.

20.6.3 TQM at Xerox

A successful quality improvement process is the one at Xerox, which produces and sells copiers. Xerox, founded in 1956, operates in over 80 countries, including Eastern Europe and the former Soviet Union. It has four European manufacturing plants, two research laboratories and a development centre. Xerox has over 28,000 employees and over 500,000 customers. Revenues for 1992 were more than USD 2 billion. Xerox became the first American company to regain market share from Japanese competitors, without the aid of tariff protection or other government help. The Xerox process, which has a large emphasis on identifying customer needs and doing everything possible to safisfy these needs, is described, for instance, in Gitlow & Loredo (1993) from which this summary is inspired.

In 1959 Xerox introduced the world's first plain-paper copier and thereby created quite a new industry. The absence of strong competitors resulted in Xerox losing sight of its customers' needs. By the late 1970s competitors were able to successfully beat Xerox prices and product features. Unit manufacturing cost was the same as the selling price of its nearest competitor. This caused Xerox's market share to drop to less than 50% in 1980. In the words of Bernard Fournier, CEO of Rank Xerox Limited: "We weren't looking at a market share issue: this was a question of survival".

At Xerox, initial reaction to its crisis focused on the following three priority areas:

- *Product development and delivery.* Xerox changed its processes for developing products by putting more emphasis on customer requirements.

- *Customer satisfaction.* Xerox began to focus on customer satisfaction as a priority issue and a "Customer Satisfaction Measurement System" was created.

- *Reduction of costs.* Executive management decided to launch a concerted effort to improve return on net assets.

In 1983 top management began to work on creating a process which would fundamentally change all work and management at Xerox, called *Leadership Through Quality (LTQ)*. LTQ is a process aimed at meeting customer requirements by continuously improving all processes. "Meeting customer satisfaction" is in fact the quality definition at Xerox.

Leadership Through Quality is the vehicle used to deploy goals into the processes. The four main goals are:

Customer Goal. To become an organization with whom customer are eager to do business.

Employee Goal. To create an environment where everyone can take pride in the organization and feel responsible for its success.

Business Goal. To increase profits and presence at a rate faster than the markets in which Xerox competes.

Process Goal. To use Leadership Through Quality principles in all Xerox does.

Leadership Through Quality consists of nine inter-related sub-processes. The sub-processes fall into the three caterories: tools, teams and management.

The tool processes are:

Quality Improvement Process. A tool to identify customer needs and design methods to satisfy these. It is built on the premise that all employees are suppliers of products or services to customers, either external or internal. Each employee must therefore be able to identify and respond to customer requirements.

Problem-Solving Process. A tool to improve and innovate the methods needed to satisfy customer satisfaction. This process is very similar to the Deming cycle: "Plan-Do-Study-Act". The six steps in this problem-solving process are illustrated in Figure 20.5.

Benchmarking. A tool to develop "best-in-class" methods to satisfy customer requirements. Benchmarking focuses the search for improved methods and encourages employees to seek solutions and improvements also outside the company. Benchmarking played an important role in closing the gap between Xerox and the Japanese competitors, see Section 18.4.

Customer Satisfaction Measurement System. A tool to collect feedback from customers on the performance of the methods used to satisfy customer requirements. The system gathers data from customers on their overall satisfaction with Xerox and their rating of key performance indicators. The survey consists of 25 questions structured in a five point satisfaction rating scale. Approximately 40,000 surveys are mailed to Xerox customers each month and the return rate is about 30%.

Statistical Tools. A set of statistical techniques for collecting and analysing data. Very important tools here are the seven QC-tools discussed in Chapter 11.

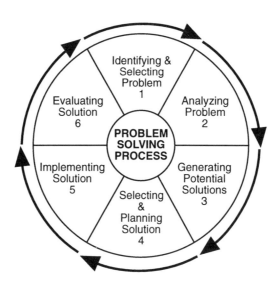

Figure 20.5   *The six steps in the Xerox Problem-Solving Process.*
            (From Gitlow & Loredo, 1993.)

The team processes are:

Product Delivery Process. A structure which organizes people into cross-functional teams to deal with product related issues. Xerox found in 1980 that its competitors were consistently delivering products in a more timely and less costly manner. This was due partly to the competitor's ability quickly to identify customer needs and to design products to meet these needs. The process provides organizational links among manufacturing, research and development, marketing, and business planning by allowing representatives from these key areas to participate as a part of the different teams.

Customer Delivery Process. A structure which organizes customers and suppliers into teams with customer-supplier issues. This process is used to ensure that Xerox products reach the end user with the quality, cost, timeliness, features and capabilities needed to meet customer requirements. It provides a method to create interaction between suppliers and the end users.

Partnerships and Empowerment. An organizational structure for dropping decision making to the lowest practical level to allow faster and better decisions regarding customer needs. Xerox's management recognised that employees at the district level are in the best position to identify the unmet needs and wants of the customers. This led to the formation of "district partnership" which consists of teams of Xerox employees from sales, service and administration. The teams are empowered to make decisions and implement policies that meet customer requirements. These partnerships decentralized decision-making power and increased the ability of Xerox employees to identify areas of opportunity and react quickly.

The management process, called *Management Inspection Process,* is a system designed to focus managerial attention to satisfy customer needs and wants. The idea is to assure continuous participation of management by creating a system in which managers are responsible for constantly monitoring all processes to determine opportunities for improvement and innovation. Xerox's managers are expected to act as tutors and coaches, not as judges.

Xerox realizes that quality is a never-ending process that depends on the proper training and motivating of all employees. Leadership Through Quality has unified Xerox management in their policy-making efforts.

As a result of the improvement process, customer dissatisfaction levels had fallen to 3% by 1992. This gave Xerox the confidence to introduce what they call a *Total Satisfaction Guarantee.* The principle is simple. If a customer is unhappy with a machine during the first three years of ownership, the company will replace it free of charge, without question. This powerful marketing tool not only reassures customers, it also serves to drive the internal goal of 100% customer satisfaction. In 1992, less than one-half percent of customers exercised their right to exchange equipment.

Xerox has also received several quality awards. Among these are Fuji Xerox, Japan (The Deming Prize in 1980), Rank Xerox U.K. (British Quality award in 1984), Xerox Canada Inc. (National Quality Award in 1989), Xerox Corp. U.S. (Malcolm Baldrige National Quality Award in 1989), Rank Xerox Netherlands (Netherlands Quality Award in 1990), Rank Xerox Australia (Australian Quality Award in 1990), Rank Xerox Mexico (Mexican Quality Award in 1990), Rank Xerox Ireland (Irish Quality Association Quality Mark in 1992), Rank Xerox Hong Kong (The Hong Kong Management Association Quality Award in 1992) and Rank Xerox Limited (The European Quality Award in 1992).

Xerox was able to achieve the following improvements (1981-1986) as a result of the Leadership Through Quality process:

• Product cost reduced by 10% per year

• Design cost reduced by 33%

• Materials cost reduced by 12% per year

• Prototype cost reduced by 50%

• Inbound logistics reduced by 13% per year

• Production lead time reduced by 65%

• New product development reduced by 50%

• Market share increased by 20%

Figure 20.6   Some of the results achieved by Xerox as a result of the Leadership Through Quality process. During that process Xerox was systematically reducing the number of suppliers (from about 5,000 to about 400) and teaming up with the suppliers in both training and design efforts. (From Spitzer, 1993. © American Society for Quality Control. Reprinted with Permission.)

20.7 Notes and References

Books dealing with QC-circle activities are Barra (1983) and Lillrank & Kano (1989). The history of QC-circles is also described in Nonaka (1993).

The development of Toyota's suggestion system is described in Yasuda (1991).

More about the "kaizen" philosophy and its significance to Japanese industry can be read in Imai (1986). See also Hannam (1993).

The very prestigious Deming Application Prize for Overseas Companies was obtained in 1989 by Florida Power & Light (FPL), a large American company in the energy supply business. Their quality improvement program, called QIP ("Quality Improvement Program"), is strongly influenced by quality work at the Japanese company Kansai, the first service company to get the Deming Prize. The program is described by Amon & Mogollon-Seemer (1990). John Hudiberg, former managing director and chairman of the board at Florida Power & Light, has described the quality work at FPL in his book Hudiberg (1991).

The large electronics company Motorola, which has obtained the Malcolm Baldrige National Award, has a quality improvement program under the name of "Six Sigma". The name refers to the fact that each process in the company has six standard deviations from process target value to any tolerance limit. This requirement, in other words, implies that the capability index for all processes shall be at least 2.0, see Figure 13.7. More about this improvement program can be read in Motorola (1989). IBM also has a quality program with the same heading and with corresponding targets.

Interest in quality improvements within the public sector is increasing. In the USA, for instance, many communities have started networks in order to support quality improvement programs and education for progressive quality control. Box et al. (1989) describe such a network and a quality improvement program, called MAQIN (Madison Area Quality Improvement Network).

Quality improvement programs for different American companies are sometimes described in the magazines mentioned in Chapter 1. David Kearns, former CEO at Xerox, for example, is interviewed in the April 1989 issue of Quality Progress and Colby Chandler, CEO at Kodak, in the April 1988 issue of the same journal. In Gitlow & Loredo (1992) in Quality Engineering and Gitlow & Loredo (1993) in the same journal the TQM work at Xerox and Florida Power & Light is described. The improvement process at Xerox is also described in Fournier (1993).

21 Company Assessments

A number of different quality awards have been created in order to stimulate companies and organizations, nationally and internationally, to work on quality improvements. The main purpose of these awards is to emphasize successful ventures and to stimulate companies and organizations to self-assessments. In this chapter we will study two important quality awards, the Japanese "Deming Prize" and the American "Malcolm Baldrige National Quality Award". These awards have been of decisive importance to the quality success in the two countries. Additionally, the recently instituted European Quality Award and Swedish Quality Award will be discussed.

In Section 21.5 we will discuss the ISO 9000 series of quality systems, which has had a great impact not least through the decision to make the series an EC-standard.

21.1 The Deming Prize

21.1.1 Background

The Deming Prize was instituted in 1951 to honour W. Edwards Deming's contribution to quality development in Japan. There are individual Deming Prizes and Deming Prizes to different kinds of companies. In 1984 the prize committee decided to open the Deming prize to companies outside Japan too and created "The Deming Application Prize for Oversea Companies" which was announced for the first time in 1987. Altogether the following prizes exist:

- The Deming Application Prize
- The Deming Application Prize for Small Enterprise
- The Deming Application Prize for Division
- The Deming Prize for Individual Person
- The Deming Application Prize for Oversea Companies

Among the 129 companies which have received a Deming prize between 1951 and 1993 there are many companies well-known in the West, i.e. Nippon Electric Co., Kawasaki Steel, Hitachi Ltd., Fuji Photo Film Ltd, Nissan Motor Co., Toyota Motor Co., Texas Instrument Japan Limited, Kansai Electric Power Company and Fuji Xerox Co.

Figure 21.1 A company that is awarded the Deming Application Prize receives this medal and a certificate.

So far (December 1993) only two companies have received the Deming Application Prize for Oversea Companies. One is Florida Power & Light in the US, which received the prize in 1989 after a quality program starting in 1981 under the name of QIP

(Quality Improvement Process). It is described as "a never-ending journey based on the principles of customer satisfaction, plan-do-study-act, management by fact and respect for people"; see Hudiberg (1991). The second award was given in 1991 to Philips Taiwan, an all-round electronic product manufacturer headquartered in Taipei with about 8,200 workers. Philips Taiwan introduced Total Quality Control from Japan in 1985 (see Williams & Bertsch, 1992).

The assessment of a company is done from an overall picture where the Japanese CWQC (Company Wide Quality Control) concept is focused, see Figure 21.2.

1. Policy
2. Organization and its management
3. Education and dissemination
4. Collection, dissemination and use of information on quality
5. Analysis
6. Standardization
7. Control
8. Quality assurance
9. Results
10. Planning for the future

Figure 21.2   Checklist for the Deming Application Prize.

21.1.2 Effects of the Prize

The Deming Prize has been of great importance to quality development in Japan. The mere fact that the prize has been applied for is regarded as an excellent means of further increasing the quality level of a company which is already working on quality improvements. The application works as an accelerator of the improvement effort. Every company applying for the prize receives judgements and recommendations from the jury. These are of course also an important part of the subsequent quality work. The effect that the examination in itself has on the quality process is also emphasized by representatives of Florida Power & Light (Hudiberg, 1991). The experiences and improvement programs of the award-winning companies also have an impact on other companies.

21.2 Malcolm Baldrige National Quality Award

21.2.1 Aim and Application Procedure

This award was instituted and confirmed by law by president Ronald Reagan in August 1987 in the "Malcolm Baldrige National Quality Improvement Act (Public Law 100-107). The work started, however, already in 1982 on the initiative of president Reagan, who had strong support for his ideas from the American Society for Quality Control, ASQC (see Hart & Bogan, 1992).

The aim of the award is to increase quality awareness within American companies. As a part of the rules it is required that the companies that receive the award should in various ways inform other companies about their work with their successful ventures within the quality field through publication and lectures. In that way an increased awareness of quality and distribution of knowledge will result.

The award is named after Malcolm Baldrige, who was Secretary of Commerce from 1981 until his death in a rodeo accident in 1987. He is considered to have had a great influence on the improvement and productivity work in the government administration. He was also a strong proponent of the award idea.

The award is given in the three categories

- Manufacturing company
- Service company
- Small-business company, by which is meant a manufacturing or a service company with not more than 500 employees.

However, two more categories, educational institutions and health care, are supposed to be added during the next few years. No more than two companies in each category are awarded per year. The American award is inspired by the Deming Prize and therefore they have several similarities, for instance as regards the assessment criteria. The Malcolm Baldrige criteria are, however, much more detailed and the evaluation system is different.

Number of Applicants/Site Visits						
Category	1988	1989	1990	1991	1992	1993
Manufacturing	45/10	23/8	45/6	38/9	31/7	32/4
Service	9/2	6/2	18/3	21/5	15/5	13/5
Small Business	12/1	11/0	34/3	47/5	44/5	31/4
Total	66/13	40/10	97/12	106/19	90/17	76/13

Figure 21.3   *The number of applicants and site visits in Malcolm Baldrige National Quality Awards in the three different categories. (Information from Quality World, December 1992, Taylor & Adair, 1993, and NIST.)*

21.2.2 The Analysis Process

The applications from the applicant companies are scrutinized by a group of people from the examiners board consisting of about 150 quality experts with different backgrounds such as industry, government and universities. The procedure is illustrated in

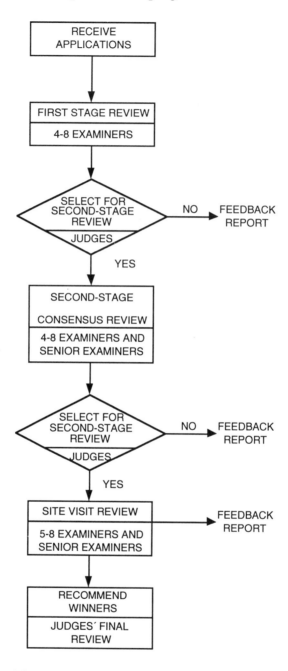

Figure 21.4   The assessment procedure for the Malcolm Baldrige National Quality Award. (From Steeples, 1993.)

Figure 21.4. The analysis is carried out according to the following seven criteria. The relative weights of the criteria in the Application Guide for 1994 are shown in brackets.

Leadership (9.5%). Here is assessed how the top management has succeeded in creating a good quality culture within the company.

Information and analysis (7.5%). Here is assessed how the company has succeeded in collecting and analysing information and how this information has been utilized for quality improvements and in planning of the quality work.

Strategic quality planning (6%). Here is assessed how the company has succeeded in integrating the customer's demands in the company's development work.

Human resources, development and management (15%). Here is studied how well the company has succeeded in engaging its employees in the quality improvement work and how the knowledge and experience of the employees are taken care of.

Management of process quality (14%). Here is assessed the company's activities to achieve good quality in all operations and aim at constant improvements.

Quality and operational results (18%). Here is studied how the company has succeeded in quality and improvement work measured by appropriate quantitative measures.

Customer focus and satisfaction (30%). Here is analysed how well the company measures the customers' demands and how well these demands are satisfied.

Figure 21.5   The assessments criteria for the Malcolm Baldrige National Quality Award for 1994 with the relative weights shown in brackets.

The last item, customer satisfaction, is ascribed the greatest importance with a maximum of 300 out of a total of 1,000 possible points. Together these seven items constitute important parts of a quality venture with emphasis on preventive action and continuous improvement.

21.2.3 Award Winners and the Effect of the Award

The first awards were made in 1988. In the group of manufacturing companies, Motorola Inc. and the Commercial Nuclear Fuel Division of Westinghouse Electric Corporationand among small companies Globe Metallurgical Inc. received awards. For Motorola, with about 99,000 employees at some 50 major facilities worldwide, communication systems and semiconductors each account for about one third of the annual sales. The company has had very strong leadership by the founder Paul Galvin and not least his son Robert. They were both strongly convinced of the neccessity of quality and also had an extremely strong commitment in the improvement work. The company's goal is simple: "Zero defects in everything we do" said Robert Galvin at the prize ceremony. To accomplish its quality goal and total customer satisfaction goals, Motorola concentrates on several key operational initiatives. At the top of the list is Motorola's improvemnet program with the name "Six Sigma" which means that the percent defectives in every process, customer services included, should be at most 3.4 parts per million (see also Figure 13.8). To achieve company objectives Motorola has set up its own training centre and spent more than USD 170 million on worker education during 1983-1987. About 40% of the education is devoted to quality matters. Westinghouse Electric Corporation is one of about 25 units in the Westinghouse Nuclear Fuel Business Unit, and has about 2,000 people at three sites. Some years ago the company supplied about 40% of the US market for fuel rod assemblies and about 20% of the world market. The drive for quality at Globe Metallurgical began in 1985, when the managerial staff were trained in Statistical Process Control. By the end of the year, the foundations of a company-wide quality improvement system, called Quality, Efficiency and Cost (QEC), were laid. Goals for quality improvement are integrated into strategic planning and research and development activities. Rapid communication closes the distance between top officials, who make up Globe's QEC steering committe, and workers, who participate in quality circles that meet weekly. Globe employs about 200 people at plants annually producing about 100,000 tons of ferro-alloys and silicon metal for more than 300 customers.

Year	Manufacturing	Small Business	Service
1988	• Motorola Inc. • Commercial Nuclear Fuel Division of Westinghouse Electric Corporation	• Globe Metallurgical, Inc.	• (None)
1989	• Milliken & Company • Xerox Business Products and Systems	• (None)	• (None)
1990	• Cadillac Motor Car Company • IBM Rochester	• Wallace Co., Inc.	• Federal Express Corporation
1991	• Solectron Corp. • Zytec Corp.	• Marlowe Industries	• (None)
1992	• Transmission Systems Business Unit • Texas Instruments Defense Systems & Electronics Group	• Granite Rock Company	• AT&T Universal Card Services • Ritz-Carlton Hotel Group
1993	• Eastman Chemical Company	• Ames Rubber Corporation	• (None)

Figure 21.6   The winners of Malcolm Baldrige National Quality Award.

In 1989 Milliken & Co. and Xerox Business Products and Systems received the award among manufacturing companies. No award was made to the other groups. In 1982, Xerox introduced its Leadership Through Quality (LTQ) program with the goal of stopping a decline of a company that in the early 1970s had held a near-monopoly in the copier business but in ten years had dropped its share to less than 50% (LTQ is discussed in Section 20.6.). When Xerox Business Products and Systems won the award the company had about 50,000 employees at 83 locations in the USA who made about 250 types of document-processing machines. Milliken had about 14,000 employees, or "associates", at 47 manufacturing facilities in the US producing more than 48,000 different textile and chemical products when they received the award. Like Xerox, Milliken has made inroads into the Japanese and Korean auto manufacturing markets. Important parts of the improvement process at Milliken are top management commitment, teamwork and education.

The award winners of 1990 were, among the manufacturing companies, Cadillac Motor Car Division, with about 10,000 employees, and IBM Rochester, with about 8,100 employees. Among small companies a prize was awarded to the family-owned company Wallace Express Co., a transport company, which has about 280 employees. The Federal Express Corporation, with about 89,000 employees received the first prize ever distributed in the service companies group. Federal Express has over 1.3 million transportation assignments per day.

The winners of 1991 were Zytec Corporation, Marlowe Industries and Solectron Corporation. Zytec Corporation is a supplier of electronic power-supply units to original-equipment manufacturers and received the award in the manufacturing category. The company's efforts to improve quality date back to 1984 when it first began implementing the "14 points" of Edwards Deming (see Chapter 22). All activities are charted at Zytec, including how long a phone rings before it is answered. Marlowe Industries employed 160 people in 1991 and are the market leader in the production of customised thermo-electric coolers. Over the past ten years Marlowe has not lost a single major customer according to Hart & Bogan (1992), and the company's top ten customers rated the quality of Marlowe coolers at 100%. Solectron Corporation specializes in custom-made printed circuit boards and sub-systems for producers of computers, work stations, tape drives and telecommunication equipment.

In 1992 the award winners were the Transmission Systems Business Unit within the AT&T Network Systems Group and Texas Instruments Defense Systems & Electronic Group in the group of manufacturing companies. The AT&T Universal Card Services and the Ritz-Carlton hotel group received the award in the group of service producing companies and the California company Granite Rock Company in the group of small companies. The aim of the Transmission Systems Business Unit is to become the world's largest supplier of systems and equipment for switches within the field of telecommunication by 1997. Today they are the second largest. About 80% of the 10,000 employees take part in 800 different improvement projects. Texas Instruments Defense Systems & Electronic Groups have about 15,000 employees and manufacture precision guided weapons, airborne radar systems and electro-optical systems. A very evident leadership is exerted by the fact that fourteen of the top managers are part of a particular Quality Improvement Team. From its start in 1990, AT&T Universal Card Services has been built up entirely around the motto "Delight the Customer". They have an extensive information and analysis system which is used very effectively in the improvement work. The company has in thirty months grown from zero to be the second largest credit card company in the US with 16 million card holders. The Ritz-Carlton hotel group runs 25 luxury hotels, 23 in the USA and 2 in Australia. Through massive education the 11,500 employees can live up to the device "ladies and gentlemen serving ladies and gentlemen". The Granite Rock Company is the third small company that has succeeded in winning a Baldrige award. They supply coating and filling to road constructions.

During 1993 only two award winners were announced. In the group of manufacturing companies Eastman Chemical Company won an award. Eastman Chemical Company, a division of Eastman Kodak company, has 17,750 employees and manufactures and markets over 400 chemicals, fibres and plastics. Eastman has adopted a no-fault return policy on its plastic products stating that a customer may return any product for any reason. This policy is believed to be the only one of its kind in the chemical industry. Like other Baldrige winners such as Xerox and Motorola, Eastman Chemical based its quality management program on the teaching of Edwards Deming and Joseph Juran. Deming helped jump-start Eastman Chemical's efforts when he held a four-days seminar for 400 of its managers in 1988. In the small business class Ames Rubber Corporation was a winner. Based in Hamburg, New Jersey, Ames Rubber Corporation's primarily products are rubber rollers used in office machines such as copiers, printers and typewriters to feed paper, transfer toner and fuse toner to paper. Ames Rubber Corporation employs 445 "Teammates" (the company's name on employees) at four New Jersey sites and has Xerox as a major customer. No service company was award was made in 1993.

Through a deliberate concentration on quality, the award-winners have had great success in productivity as well as in decreasing their non-quality costs. Milliken and Xerox, the 1989 award-winners, are said to have doubled their productivity in five years and have at the same time halved the costs of quality deficiencies. During 1987-1990 Wallace Express has increased its market share from 10% to 18% and their profits have increased by over 700%. Ames, one of the winners in 1993, has increased productivity, as measured by sales per employee, by 48% from 1989 to 1992 and the percentage of defective parts reaching customers has been reduced since 1989 from over 30,000 parts per million to 11.

The winning companies have the fact in common that they concentrate very much on education and problem preventive activities. At Xerox for instance, all employees have had at least 28 hours of education and training in solving quality improvement problems and the company has invested more than 4 million man-hours and USD 125 million in education. Xerox has invested very substantially in co-operation and problem solving groups. The concept of "Team Xerox" has been created and built up. About 75% of the employees now participate in at least one of the company's 7,000 quality improvement teams. In 1988 ideas and suggestions from these teams are said to have saved the company USD 115 million. Through better co-operation with their suppliers the number of deficiencies reaching production has decreased by about 75%. At Eastman Chemical, one of the 1993 winners, each employee spends about 40 to 60 hours each year learning about improvement methods, including process evaluation, control and improvement. At Ames Rubber Corporation the quality program started in 1987 with the help of Xerox. "We delivered 24 hours of training that year to everyone from janitor to me" says the CEO Joel Marvil. "Now we have about 40 hours of training per employee per year." Over the last five years Teammate ideas have saved Ames Rubber Corporation and its customers more than USD 3 million and will average over USD 2,700 per Teammate in 1993.

Milliken's successes also emanate to a large extent from the fact that the associates are devoted and their knowledge and experience are used in the improvement work, i.e. through improvement teams and problem solving groups. They do not talk about their "employees" but about their "associates". Likewise, Milliken invests very heavily in education. In 1988, for instance, education and training cost 1,300 USD per associate. The idea of using the concept "associate" instead of "employee" has also been used by Wallace Express. Since 1985, Wallace Express has invested about 19,000 man-hours in education in continuous improvement work. Everybody in the company's managerial group, consisting of five persons, has had more than 200 hours of education.

More about the awarded companies and their improvement processes can be read in Hart & Bogan (1992) and a number of articles in Quality Progress.

It should also be mentioned that in all companies that have received the Baldrige award, the top management has very strongly shown that quality is important and they themselves actively participate in the improvement process. David Kearns, former chairman and CEO of Xerox for example, took a very active part in the quality work and has personally led the work by introducing new methods regarding problem solving and improvement.

It should also be noted that every company that has applied for the award, not only the winners, can afterwards study the assessment and the comments of the examiners in the same way as for the Deming Prize. The feedback that these views gives is naturally very important in the continuous improvement work.

Figure 21.6   The prize for the Malcolm Baldrige National Quality Award. A 14-inch-high, solid crystal pillar, created by Steuben Glass, with an 18-carat gold plate on which is inscribed "Malcolm Baldrige National Quality Award" and "The Quest for Excellence" on one side and with the President's seal on the other.

The most important effect of the award is probably the guiding effect the assessment will have on quality work in other companies. Many companies in the US, and in other countries as well, use the criteria for the Malcolm Baldrige National Quality Award to build their own quality systems. This is illustrated by the great interest in the assessment criteria. In 1990 and 1991 about 180,000 copies of these criteria were distributed while only about 100 companies applied for the award, see Figure 21.3.

21.3 The European Quality Award

In 1992 the European Foundation for Quality Management, EFQM, with support from the European Organisation for Quality (EOQ) and the European Commission, introduced the "European Quality Award". The first award was made in Madrid in 1992 to Rank Xerox Limited who have over 28,000 employees, with manufacturing operations in France, the Netherlands, Spain and Great Britain. Another division of the American mother company won the Malcolm Baldrige National Quality Award in 1989. In 1993 the award was given to Milliken European Division with about 1,200 employees at eight different places in Great Britain, France, Denmark and Belgium. The company produces material for tires. Michelin, Goodyear, Bridgestone and Pirelli are among the largest customers. The mother company won the Malcolm Baldrige National Quality Award in 1989.

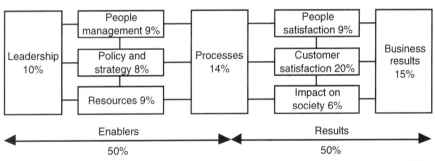

Figure 21.7   The award assessment model for the European Quality Award.

Leadership (10%). The behaviour of all managers in moving the company towards Total Quality.

People management (8%). People's feelings about the company, and the management of the company's people.

Policy and strategy (8%). The company's vision, values and direction, and the ways in which to achieve them.

Resources (9%). The management, utilization and preservation of financial resources, information resources and technological resources.

Processes (14%). The management of all the value-adding activities within the company.

People satisfaction (9%). What the people's feelings are about the organization.

Customer satisfaction (20%). The perceptions of external customers, direct and indirect, of the company and of its products and services.

Impact on society (6%). The perception of the community at large, of the company. Views on the company's approach to quality of life, to the environment and to the need for preservation of global resources are included.

Business results (15%). The company's achievement in relation to its planned business performance.

Figure 21.8   *Assessment criteria for "the European Quality Award" in 1993. These differ from those in the Deming Prize and the Malcolm Baldrige National Quality Award for instance through the point "impact on society", i.e. society's feedback from the company, how environmental problems are dealt with and economy with natural resources. Furthermore, greater importance is attached to business results compared to the other two awards. (From the 1993 Application Criteria.)*

Key words in the assessment criteria are leadership, quality strategy and improvement work referring to all processes of the company, how the knowledge of the employees is taken care of and developed, employee satisfaction and customer satisfaction; see Figure 21.8. Thus, the assessment criteria are rather similar to those of the Deming Prize and the Malcolm Baldrige National Quality Award.

21.4 The Swedish Quality Award

In Sweden, a national quality award was instituted in 1992 by SIQ, the Swedish Institute for Quality. The assessment criteria are similar to those of the Malcolm Baldrige National Quality Award. One major change is that examination items on environment protection aspects have been added. Another difference is that the award program is also open to public agencies. The award only has two application categories, namely organizations with more or less than 200 employees.

The first award was given in 1992 to the Manufacturing Division of IBM Sweden AB, IBM Järfälla (see below). In 1993, no award at all was distributed.

Figure 21.9   The logotype of the Swedish Quality Award.

More than 20,000 copies of the guidelines were requested and shipped out during the first year (that may be compared with

12,000 copies for the Malcolm Baldrige National Quality Award during its first year, 1988).

The Swedish Institute for Quality

The Swedish Institute for Quality, SIQ, was established in 1990. SIQ will stimulate and contribute actively to the positive development of quality in all sections of the Swedish community and has given high priority to the founding of the Swedish Quality Award.

Besides the Quality Award, the Institute's activities are conducted in the following main programs:

> *Information.* Information and opinion moulding in respect of the quality concept and its implementation. The work comprises periodicals, newsletters, seminars and conferences, and also information-based systems of different kinds. Co-operation with the International Benchmarking Clearinghouse in Houston has been established for the exchange of opinions and the promotion of benchmarking.

> *Training and education.* The Institute's work is aimed at increasing the opportunities for training and education in Total Quality Management. Encouragement of the establishment of teaching facilities and the practical implementation of the results of research and development work are some examples of activities.

> *Research and development.* The task of the Institute is to be a coordinating, activating and resource-creating body for research and development in the TQM area. Measures for an increase in international exchanges and the awarding of research scholarships are sectors where the Institute will be active.

The Swedish Institute for Quality is organized in the form of a so-called *"Industrial Research Institute"*. This set-up means that a sponsoring association, comprising companies, organizations and public agencies, has reached an agreement with the government on joint financing of the Institute. Members of the sponsoring association pay an annual sum of money. Thanks to grants from the government, the Institute has about SEK 8 million (about USD 1 million) per year at its disposal during the first three years. In May 1993 some sixty companies, trade unions and public agencies from different sectors of Swedish society had become members of the sponsoring association.

Quality Management at IBM Järfälla in Sweden

Quality efforts at IBM have evolved over the last decade or more, from an emphasis on product and manufacturing quality to one on process, time-saving and competitive analysis. Over the years the company has realized that quality is needed in all areas of business and that customers' requirements have to drive everything.

IBM has a fundamental value system - "Our Basic Beliefs". These are

- respect for the individual
- best customer service in the world
- the pursuit of excellence in everything we do.

They also have the following vision:

- be the best at creating value for our customers and all those with a stake in our business

- key to effective empowerment is a clear communication of a strong vision and mission statement

- IBM's family of businesses will be measured on customer satisfaction, six-sigma quality, revenue, profit, cost and returns.

Their business strategy shows how they will achieve the company vision, and the implementation plan for the strategy is called *Market-Driven Quality*. The creation of the vision is primarily the leader's responsibility and the process of communicating and sharing it as a team can be its most powerful aspect. Shared visions create a common sense of purpose for all.

The Manufacturing Division of IBM Sweden, IBM Järfälla (now Jarfalla Industry Competence Center), which received the first Swedish Quality Award in 1992, has gone through a significant transformation during the last few years in order to attain the leading position on the market. The company has 750 employees and manufactures advanced computer printers, 95% of which are exported. The statement of the award judges included these remarks: "The company is a model for quality work in Sweden. The management has bold aims and a broad engagement in quality work and the employees have high competence." About SEK 25 million (about USD 3 million) have been invested in education on quality. Since 1989 the time between order and delivery has decreased by two thirds and the stock value has been reduced by SEK 150-200 million (about USD 19-25 million).

A series of actions over the last few years have been taken by the plant management to create a complete IBM site in serving the customers.

- A business process management structure was implemented in the late 1980s when the plant operations were transformed into five main and four support processes, each with an identified owner responsible for process quality and efficiency.

- A Customer Briefing Center was established in 1990 with the objective of supporting the customers with the best printing solutions.

- In 1991 a Printer Development Laboratory was created with more than 50 experienced engineers in hardware and software development working in close partnership with the Customer Briefing Center.

- ISO 9001 certified in 1991.

- The education program provides more than 5 days of extensive training and education to all plant employees annually.

- The plant's suggestion program has been improved and the number of suggestions in 1992 was up four times compared with previous years.

- To improve policy deployment and communication the plant structure was enhanced and one level of management was eliminated during 1991/92.

- Printer marketing for the Nordic countries was transferred to the IBM Järfälla plant in 1992.

Some of the results achieved in 1993 compared to 1989 are

- Defects at customer installation reduced to zero.
- Defects during warranty period reduced 7 times.
- Make-to-Market time reduced from 32 days to 6.2 days.
- The use of freon in production eliminated in 1990.
- Recycling of solid waste increased to 70% or 1,200 tons.

21.5 The ISO 9000 Quality System

In recent years it has become common to talk about a company´s quality system. Many companies demand from their suppliers that they should have a documented quality system. Such a system has been defined as follows:

A quality system is the organizational structure, respon-sibilities, procedures, processes and resources for imple-menting quality management.

A quality system is a tool for steering and improving the quality of the company's products. In other words, it comprises most of the methods and routines as well as organization and distribution of responsibility. It is required that the system is well documented. The documentation is both a support and a basis for the quality audit of the company.

The International Organization for Standardization, which is responsible for ISO 9000, is a standardization organization with its administrative centre in Geneva. More than 90 countries are affiliated through their national standardization organizations. Great Britain, for instance, is affiliated through the BSI (British Standards Institute) and the US through the ANSI (American National Standards Institute).

The ISO 9000 series was established as an ISO-standard in 1987. Since then, it has been translated into national standards in more than 50 countries. The ISO 9000 series has different names in different countries. For instance, the term ANSI/ASQC Q90 is used in the US, JIS Z 9900 in Japan, BS 5750 in Great Britain, DS/EN 29000 in Denmark, DIN/ISO 9000 in Germany and NF X 50-121 in France. In all cases the contents are almost identical.

What is usually called ISO 9000 is in fact a series of five standards with the numbers 9000-9004. ISO 9000 contains some basic definitions and concepts describing how the other standards should be used. ISO 9004 is intended to give guidelines for the internal work in building a quality system. On the other hand, ISO 9001-9003 are intended to be of help when claims are set on a quality system in different contract situations. ISO 9001 is the most comprehensive one in this series and includes ISO 9002 which in turn comprises ISO 9003. The scope of the different standards of the series is shown in Figure 21.10.

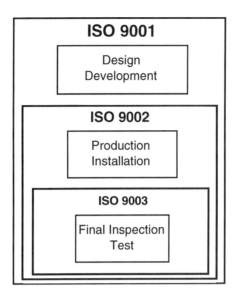

Figure 21.10 *Illustration of the connections between the three diffe-rent standards of quality systems in the ISO 9000 series. The three are:*
ISO 9001 Quality Systems - Model for Quality Assurance in Design/Development, Production, Installation and Servicing
ISO 9002 Quality Systems - Model for Quality Assurance in Production and Installation
ISO 9003 Quality Systems - Model for Assurance in Final Inspection and Test
The two standards which provide general guidelines are
ISO 9000 Quality Management and Quality Assurance Standards. Guidelines for Selection and Use.
ISO 9004 Quality Management and Quality System Elements - Guidelines

Third party certification according to ISO 9000, or its EC version EN 29000, is intended to be a requirement for doing public business with the EC countries. *Third party certification* means that a third independent party will evaluate the company's quality system according to the ISO 9000 series. This type of certification is expected by many people to decrease the number of customer appraisals of the company's quality system, but it also proves that the quality system has been built according to the standard series. A third party audit system exists in more than 30 countries today.

The wish to join the EC market will lead to the fact that many companies want to be certified according to ISO 9000/EN 29000. The EC market contains about 350 million people, to be compared with about 250 million in the US and about 120 million in Japan.

At the end of 1993 there are about 25,000 companies in Europe with a third party certification. Different countries in Europe have attained different levels in their work on certification of companies according to ISO 9000. Great Britain, which has come furthest, has about 20,000 companies certified by the BSI (British Standards Institution) or other certification institute. One reason for the large number of certified companies in Great Britain is that the Department of Trade and Industry has a "Grant Aid Program" financing a large proportion of the costs for the implementation of an ISO 9000 quality system. Interest has also increased in countries like Switzerland, Germany and the Netherlands. In Sweden, at the end of 1993, a little more than 300 companies were certified by a third party. Also in the US the interest in certification has increased rapidly during the last few years.

21.5.1 ISO 9001 in More Detail

As mentioned, ISO 9001 is the most comprehensive of the three systems of the series. It comprises twenty different points. Below, some short comments are made on these points.

(1) Management responsibilities

The management has to define a policy and determine the aim of the company's quality work. Furthermore, through its actions the management must show that questions concerning quality are in focus all the time. The management is also responsible for creating a suitable organization. The responsibilities and authorities of all employees should be defined and documented. In addition, the management shall continuously audit the quality system to guarantee its suitability and effectiveness. This audit must also be documented.

(2)   Quality system

A quality system must be established and maintained to ensure that the products fulfil the specified requirements. For instance, work descriptions, criteria concerning quality control, acceptance criteria in product control and routines for inspections and audits of the system shall be included. Sometimes there is a quality manual that clearly describes the quality system and a quality handbook containing detailed documentation. On top of this, the handbook must be supplemented by detailed work instructions in different divisions.

(3)   Contract review

Contract proposals shall be checked in special reviews. In these, requirements are made clear and it is decided whether the company is able to fulfil them. Current routines ought to be followed when appraising whether the customer's requirements are well enough defined and documented. The company must also be sure that it is possible to produce what the customer asks for. The documentation from such contract reviews shall be preserved. No orders are accepted and no contracts are signed if requirements and guarantee commitments are not made fully clear.

(4)   Design control

The supplier should have written routines to control the design of the products. There must be a plan to define the responsibility for every activity in design and development work. Planned design reviews and verification of design results shall be carried out and documented.

(5)   Document control

The introduction of a quality system involves an increasing amount of documents in the company. Therefore, routines are needed for control of all the documents with reference to the system. These documents must be scrutinized and approved by authorised personnel before publication. This control will certify that all documents are of the right edition and that they are in the right place at the right time. Routines for invalid documents and changes of current documents have to be included. This requires document registration.

(6)   Purchasing

The company shall choose suppliers on the basis of their ability to fulfil different requirements, including quality requirements. The company shall make sure that purchased products correspond to the specified requirements. This can be arranged by inspections on arrival from the suppliers. The buyer shall draw up a written routine for assessment and choice of supplier and a list of acceptable suppliers that must be up to date.

(7)   Purchaser supplied products

The supplier shall have routines for verification, storage and maintenance of products which are supplied by the buyer to form part of the delivery.

(8)   Product identification and traceability

By traceability is meant that it should be possible through identification of the product to gain access to the documents that controlled the product's creation. This applies, for instance, to specifications, drawings and documents from the production process and to any final inspection that may have been undertaken. Traceability is a condition for finding the causes of deviations from the requirements.

(9)   Process control

The company shall identify and plan the processes that affect quality. It shall also be certified that the processes are carried out under controlled conditions, i.e. through documented work and control instructions.

(10) Inspection and testing

It is to be checked in accordance with written instructions that everything that is bought or produced fulfil the requirements. Examples of inspection activities are acceptance sampling, production inspection and final inspection.

(11) Inspection, measuring and test equipment

All equipment for inspection shall be registered, calibrated and maintained according to documented instructions. The calibration results shall be documented.

(12) Inspection and test status

During production it should be possible through marking to see if parts or products are approved or not.

(13) Control of non-conforming products

The company shall have routines that certify that products which do not correspond to the specified requirements are not used or installed. The routines shall comprise identification, documentation, evaluation, and decisions on measures applicable to non-conforming products.

(14) Corrective action

The company shall have routines to analyse the reasons for the non-conformity of the product. Corrective steps are to be taken and changes of the routines as a result of these corrections shall be documented.

(15) Handling, storage, packaging and delivery

Damage and deterioration may occur in handling, storage, packaging and delivery. The company shall therefore have routines for these operations.

(16) Quality records

The company shall have routines for identification, collection, registration, filing, sorting out and maintenance of quality documents. The documents shall be maintained in order to be able to show that the required quality has been achieved and that the quality system works effectively. There shall also be routines for registration and filing of documents that show the quality status of manufactured products.

(17) Internal quality audits

The company shall undertake comprehensive, planned and documented internal audits. The aim is to verify that the quality activities correspond to what has been planned and to establish the effectiveness of the quality system. The modifications and associated follow-up shall be executed according to the documented routines.

(18) Training

There shall be routines to certify that all personnel have the right competence and education appropriate to the assignment.

(19) Servicing

In certain cases the supplier shall be responsible for the documentation of the quality of service and that service is executed in the right manner.

398

(20)   Statistical techniques

The company shall institute routines for the use of appropriate statistical methods in quality work, i.e. methods to verify the capability of the processes and to control the processes by means of control charts. Methods to ascertain the product properties through design of experiments also belong here.

21.5.2   Some Comments on ISO 9000

Naturally, systematic work on quality improvements needs well-planned routines. In this respect the ISO 9000/EN29000 series serves an important purpose. The introduction of a quality system according to ISO 9000 could be an alarm clock in a company's quality work. Despite this, there are some deficiencies in today's version of the system. Some of these are as follows:

- The system is defensive and product oriented instead of progressive and process oriented.

- The system encourages a conservative approach and does not emphasize the enormously important work on continuous improvements.

- The system involves rather comprehensive documentation work and, at least for small companies, it entails substantial effort when introduced. This can easily result in the paper-work being in the forefront and the improvement work itself being forgotten.

- The system represents a minimum of efforts to ensure good product quality. For instance, the system requirements for the Malcolm Baldrige National Quality Award, the Deming Prize and the European Quality Award are much more extensive.

- The system hardly mentions quality work in administrative support functions.

Figure 21.11 illustrates a comparison between the requirements according to ISO 9001 and the different criteria in the Malcolm Baldrige National Quality Award. A company certified according to ISO 9001 will only get about 250 points in an assessment according to the Malcolm Baldrige National Quality Award.

ISO 9001 Requirements	ISO 9001 Requirements	Baldrige Categories
Management Responsibility	1	1.4.5
Quality System	2	3.5
Contract Review	3	5.7
Design Control	4	5
Document Control	5	5
Purchasing	6	5
Purchaser Supplied Product	7	5.7
Product Identification and Traceability	8	5
Process Control	9	5
Inspection and Testing	10	5
Inspection, Measuring and Test Equipment	11	5
Inspection and Test Status	12	5
Control of Nonconforming Product	13	5
Corrective Action	14	5
Handling, Storage, Packaging and Delivery	15	5
Quality Records	16	5
Internal Quality Audits	17	5
Training	18	4
Servicing	19	5.7
Statistical Techniques	20	2.5
	ISO 9001 Certified	200-300 Points

Figure 21.11   *A comparison between the requirements according to ISO 9001 and the different criteria in the Malcolm Baldrige National Quality Award. A company certified according to ISO 9001 will get about 250 points in an assessment according to the criteria in the Malcolm Baldrige National Quality Award.*

At present, a modification of the ISO 9000 series is in progress. Hopefully, this will eliminate some of the above mentioned disadvantages. Guidelines for hardware (ISO 9000-4, Application for Dependability Management) and software (ISO 9000-3, Guidelines for the Applications of ISO 9001 to the Development, Supply and Maintenance of Software) are available. Moreover, ISO 9004-2 Guidelines for Services, ISO 9004-3 Guidelines for Processed Material, ISO 9004-4 Guidelines for Quality Improvement, ISO 9004-5, Guidelines for Quality Planning, ISO 9004-6 Quality Management in Projects and ISO 9004-7 Configuration Management will also be published.

We want to conclude the discussion on ISO 9000 with two quotations from Joseph Juran. The article "A few words about the last word" in Quality Progress, October 1993, pp. 63-65, describes Joseph Juran's final tour as a quality expert, a tour starting in Dallas in March 1993 and ending in Atlanta in December 1994. In that article Dr Juran says: "There's nothing in ISO 9000 about continuous quality improvement, customer satisfaction or employee participation. If I look into my cloudy cristal ball I think our European friends are in for a big letdown. The propaganda is that your quality problems is over when the organization is registered to ISO 9000. But registration doesn't mean you are going to have world-class quality. My opinion is not popular among standard organizations." The other quotation is from an interview in "Kundorienterat", a Swedish magazine dealing with quality where Dr Juran said: "Fulfil the requirements of ISO 9000 if necessary, but do not let it disturb the quality work."

21.6 The New Approach and the Global Approach

Included in the EC-activity plans for the 1980s there are two milestones usually called "the New Approach" and "the Global Approach".

The first of these, "the New Approach", is created in order to harmonize the product requirements within the EC countries. The basic intention is that the different countries should regularize safety requirements only and leave it to the market to decide about the technical solutions that fulfil these requirements. This means that legal and technical solutions are separated.

The second one "the Global Approach", or more fully "the Global Approach to Conformity Assessment", gives the legislation within the EC countries different possibilities for producers and importers to prove that the basic requirements are fulfilled. "The Global Approach" also introduces the product sign, the CE sign in Figure 21.12, which shall enable EC members in their market inspection to check that only goods which fulfil the common requirements exist on the market. The manufacturer has the right to mark the product with this sign and thus show that basic and common EC requirements are fulfilled. The responsibility is accordingly up to the manufacturer.

Figure 21.12 The CE-sign included in "the Global Approach".

21.7 Notes and References

Books discussing the Malcolm Baldrige National Quality Award, what it is, how to apply and how to work with the criteria within the company are Steeples (1992), Hart & Bogan (1992) and Brown (1993). In Hart & Bogan (1992) a number of other local American quality awards are also briefly discussed. In Fisher (1993) a simplified assessment model is presented, mainly intended for small and mid-sized companies. In Quality Progress, a journal published by ASQC, the American Society for Quality Control, a series of seven articles were published from May to December 1992, each one dealing with one of the seven criteria of the Malcolm Baldrige National Quality Award. It is also worth mentioning that a discussion about good and bad aspects of this award has been published in Harvard Business Review, November-December 1991, pp. 80-93 and January-February 1992, pp 126-147. Another debate by Curt Reiman, one of the organizers of the award, and the American quality consultant Philip Crosby, was published in Quality Progress, May 1991, pp 41-44. Descriptions of the award-winning companies' quality work can be found in several articles in Quality Progress, often in the December issues. A recent one is Axland (1992). Steeples (1992) and Hart & Bogan (1992) also describes the improvement processes of award-winning companies.

There is less information in the West about the Deming Prize. The best way to get information is to contact JUSE (Union of Japanese Scientist and Engineers) and order their 40th anniversary publication about the prize or the annual prize guide. Other papers dealing in part with the Deming Prize are Bush & Dooley (1989) and Cole (1991).

Information about the European Quality Award can be found in the annual application booklet which can be obtained from EFQM, Avenue des Plèiades 19, B-1200 Brussels, Belgium. Information about the Swedish Quality Award can be obtained from the Swedish Institute of Quality, Gårdatorget 1, S-412 50 Gothenburg, Sweden. A number of other countries have also instituted national quality awards, i.e. Argentina, Canada, Denmark, France, India, Israel, Mexico and Norway. Some information about these can be found in Hart & Bogan (1992).

The ISO 9000 series finds its roots in US military standards. Although it is true that the immediate inspiration to ISO 9000 came from the British standard BS 5750, that standard in turn is inspired by MIL Q 9858, first published in 1959. MIL Q 9858 was itself derived from Air Force Standards (in the 1930s) and the NATO standard AQAP-1, written in the 1940s.

A number of books have recently been published dealing with the process of creating a quality system in a company in accordance with the ISO 9000 series. Some of these are Lamprecht (1992), Johnson (1993), McLean (1993) and Cottman (1993). Sayle (1991) tries to explain how ISO 9000 can be interpreted in the TQM environment. In a British Association booklet, BDA (1992), there is also a discussion of how to go beyond ISO 9000.

The International Organization for Standardization, responsible for the ISO 9000 series, is a worldwide federation of national standards bodies from some 90 countries. It is a non-governmental organization established in 1947 with the mission of promoting the development of standardization and related activities in the world with a view to facilitating the international exchange of goods and services. The first ISO standard was published in 1951 with the title "Standard reference temperature for industrial length measurement". Many people incorrectly believe that ISO is an acronym for the International Organization for Standardization. In fact "ISO" is a word derived from the Greek "isos" meaning "equal", which is the root of the prefix "iso-" that occurs in terms such as isobar, isometric and isoterm. The line of thinking from "equal" to "standard" that led to the choice of "ISO" as the name of the organization is easy to follow. (From "ISO - Compatible Technology Worldwide".)

22 Leadership

Already in Chapter 1 we emphasized the role of top management for quality improvement. Top managements have to commit themselves to striving for continuously improved quality, not only by support but also by active participation. This is, as we have already seen, what business leaders in several successful companies are doing today. One example is Robert Galvin, former CEO at Motorola, who decided that quality issues should be the first items on the agenda at board meetings. If he had to leave the meeting before it was over, he had still been able to take part in the most important part of the meeting. Another example is Roger Milliken, Milliken & Co, who states that "if the man at the top isn't leading quality, what is he there for?". Milliken & Co, a family-owned textile company in the USA with more than 14,000 employees, received the Malcolm Baldrige National Quality Award in 1989. Other examples are David Kearns, formerly chairman and CEO of Xerox, and John Young at Hewlett-Packard (see also Section 21.2.3).

If top managements are unable to handle the problems of external and internal quality, they will not be able to solve the resulting non-quality problems. Such problems can be diminishing market shares, heavy expenses and too much tied-up capital.

In this chapter we will deal with some thoughts about leadership. First and foremost we will discuss Deming's approach to leadership as described in his books "Out of the Crisis" from 1986 and "The New Economics" from 1993. According to Deming, that approach was the basis of the management seminars he conducted in

Japan at the beginning of the 1950s. Some other recent contributions to the development of leadarship will also briefly be discussed.

22.1 Deming's 14 Points

We have chosen here to give an account of Deming's approach to management for quality since we find it interesting from several points of view. Above all, it is based on a human ideal, which ought to be attractive in today's democratic society. Many people also emphasize its significance for the development in Japan. At least, many of Deming's 14 points reflect what we today interpret as a Japanese leadership ideal.

Statistical process control and the process view presented in Chapter 18 have also been strongly emphasized by Deming. There is a strong connection between this process approach and several of the 14 points. Deming also states that the 14 points have a general applicability. He offers illustrations not only from the manufacturing industry but also from nursing institutions, banks and other fields.

The 14 points follow below together with a few brief comments, see also Figure 3.5. For a more detailed discussion we refer to Deming (1986, 1993), Scherkenbach (1986) and Neave (1990).

(1)   Create constancy of purpose for improvement of product and service

Short-term requirements for profitability and too much concentration on day-to-day problems are some of the biggest obstacles to success concerning quality, profitability and long-term survival. If we do not invest for the future in product and process development, we might perhaps meet short-term requirements for profitability, but we are heading for severe problems in the long run.

(2)   Adopt the new philosohy

We can no longer hold on to the previously accepted interpretation of quality problems. We have to think of quality in a new way and change from a "fix/remedy"-mentality to a concept built on systematic planning, problem prevention and continuous improvement of all processes. The remaining twelve points indicate, according to Deming, a way for this change.

(3)   Cease dependence on inspection to achieve quality

By establishing inspection organizations in companies we are heading for quality problems. If all signals indicate that errors are expected to occur, it is no wonder that they actually do occur. By inspecting and focusing our interest on whether individual parts fulfil the requirements, we distract interest from the development process itself and from the important improvement process.

On the whole, we should stop organizing for failures and errors. In the specification of a development process, for example, a phase called "problem solving and redesign" is often included. If we are explicitly expecting that the result of a process is to be faulty, how could we then expect it to be flawless?

(4)   End the practice of awarding business on the basis of price tag alone. Instead, minimize total cost by working with a single supplier.

Earlier, purchasing functions of a company have allowed the suppliers to compete with respect to price. The supplier selected was the one who matched the specification and had quoted the lowest price. This technique does not meet today's requirements on quality and reliability. The total costs for inferior quality from a supplier who gives a low purchase price can far exceed the actual purchasing cost. Therefore it is vital to take the overall cost picture into account. The Life Cycle Cost (LCC), briefly discussed in Chapter 5, can be a better criterion for making decisions.

It is also essential to realize that the supplier is part of the development process. To secure an efficient feedback to the suppliers' improvement work, it is required that strong and good relations are established between supplier and buyer. We should, therefore, look to having only one supplier for each article and, on the whole, having as few suppliers as possible. Only then can a close co-operation between customer and supplier be developed. Development at present is heading strongly towards that goal, as we have discussed in Chapter 14. Sometimes the advantage of one supplier delivering the same article to several industrial buyers can be noted. In that way the foundation for improvement work and improved quality can be achieved at a lower cost. This has been illustrated in the car industry.

(5)   Improve constantly and forever every process for planning, production and service

Continuous improvement is a topic that appears in every modern description within the quality field. We have emphasized this subject on several occasions throughout this book and hope that we have succeeded in convincing the reader that this topic is extremely important.

(6)   Institute training on the job

Many problems arise because people are ignorant of what is right. If we do not know what the outcome will be and what is to be expected, it is hard to avoid making mistakes. Often a new member of the staff has to look over the shoulder of a colleague and then try to do the same. After a short period of time she or he then has to take over the job. With an instruction technique like that, how can we know how to react in all situations that did not occur during the period of acclimatization? How are we to understand the way to control a process?

In many cases quality defects can consist of deviations in appearance. Then it is important to clarify what is acceptable and what is not. Otherwise, we will have a constant source of variation with continuing quality problems as a result.

In order to grow as an individual we also need the right facilities. In earlier years it was not unusual that operators had access to measuring instruments with poorer precision than the inspection department or that the inspection department had other requirements than the production department.

(7)   Adopt and institute leadership

Deming emphasizes very strongly the significance of management, or rather leadership, as opposed to supervision and administration of the processes' final results. The process and the people who work in it are thus what management should focus on.

Today, the most important task for the leader is to identify needs for personal education and development and to support others in their development to become good leaders.

(8)   Drive out fear

Deming claims, probably very rightly, that a person who feels unsafe, who is afraid to ask questions or who is too shy to point out a misunderstanding, will never do a good job.

A lot of people are afraid of innovations and changes. They feel safe in the familiar surrounding, in everything that remains as it has always been. This, however, is a deceptive safety. Unless we constantly work on improvements and development, we will in time be driven out of competition and the jobs will vanish. Another and deeper sort of safety is required to be able to accept changes. We have to know that management care about all their employees and that no one is running the risk of being made redundant due to the achievement of improvements and increasing productivity.

Today, there also is another kind of fear than the one Deming talks about, namely the fear of and discontent with a bad working environment. It is the task of management to continuously improve the working environment. A bad working environment does not lay a good foundation for a well-done job, and above all it may create fear of future health problems.

(9)   Break down barriers between staff areas

Many of today's quality defects are due to lack of communication between different departments of the company and to people not having identified their internal customers well enough. When a product is designed which satisfies the needs of the final customer but is impossible to manufacture, then we are heading for real trouble. People have often tried to solve this kind of problem by afterwards adapting their products to the manufacturing process through redesign. Such a procedure is seldom successful. Already at the design stage we must have produceability as a goal. The ideal is to work concurrently with product design and process development. Today this is referrred to as *Concurrent Engineering* or *Simultaneous Engineering.*

Different departments often strive to do their best, optimizing their own work. This is, however, rarely optimal from a total quality and cost point of view. We have to support an overall view and an orientation not only towards the final external customer, but also towards the internal customers.

(10)   Eliminate slogans, exhortations and targets for the work force.

General pep-talk and slogans can perhaps have a certain effect for a short period of time. Soon, however, everything will be back in the same old rut. The only thing that is different is the disappointment that follows after the failure of an ambitiously planned campaign.

Most quality defects appear, not because of the operator's or the employee's lack of will to do a good job, but because of shortcomings in the processes. These have to be remedied, if there is to be any real change. Juran claims that usually about 80% of quality problems are dependent on the system. Deming states that this figure may be as high as 94%.

(11)   Eliminate numerical quotas for the work force and numerical goals for the management.

Deming states that it is wrong to set up a target and to have piecework. When piecework is time-set, this is done according to some kind of average performance. About half of the operators are then over the average and the rest below. Those who are over are being kept back, whereas those below are fighting a losing battle. Deming claims that piecework decreases productivity. Far too many are busy doing work studies, time-setting piecework and measuring. These persons could be more usefully put to work in actual production. Piecework is also an obstacle to improvements and creates bad morale among the workers. Deming argues that wherever the piecework system has been thrown out and replaced by leadership, quality and productivity have increased and the staff have enjoyed their work more. Measure and control the various processes within the company, not the employees.

(12)   Remove barriers that rob people of pride of workmanship. Eliminate the annual rating or merit system.

It is difficult to feel pride of work if you do not know what a good job is, if you cannot influence your work situation or if your improvement suggestions are not met with sympathy. The same thing applies if you are not given the confidence to check whether your own job was well done or if the quantity of articles manufactured is more important than the final outcome.

It is the management's task to remove all these obstacles. It is the management's role to create a work situation which is positive and encourages people's own initiatives for continuous improvement and development.

(13)   Institute a vigorous program of education and self-improvement for everyone.

Every organization and company need staff people who are not only skilled in their professional field but who constantly go on developing, improving and broadening their knowledge. It is essential that management not only support the initiative in further development from individual staff members, but also initiate and stimulate education and personal development. The possibility of development and the feeling of adding something essential to the business and to society, is based on the feeling of satisfaction with one's work. This possibility and feeling are more worth than money.

(14)   Put everybody in the company to work to accomplish the transformation.

Management have to take vigorous steps to encourage and implement work on breaking old traditions and old ways of thinking. All those in leading positions have to be convinced through seminars, guidance and education that a change is essential. Everyone has to realize the importance of the improvement process and everyone has to understand the implication of the other thirteen points. One prerequisite for a successful job is that all those in leading positions involve themselves in improvement work, that they all speak the same language and that they all pull in the same direction.

Then an organization has to be created in the company that is favourable to work on quality improvements - an organization where all people involved feel responsible and motivated in their work on continuous improvement of all processes in the company.

22.2 Profound Knowledge

Deming (1993) explains how the fourteen points for management transformation are based on what he calls *profound knowledge*. System thinking plays an important role in profound knowledge. A system is a network of interdependent components trying to fulfil an aim. Deming emphasizes that without an aim there is no system.

Systems thinking is also discussed by Senge (1990), who gives a set of system archetypes, i.e. a number of common behaviours of systems.

Deming (1993) emphasizes that management is very much about prediction. In order to plan we must have a comprehension of what will be the consequence of different actions. We have to predict. To make a prediction it is neccessary to know the present and the past history and to have a theory from which past behaviour may be coupled to future behaviour. Therefore it is important to understand the formation of theories and how theories relate to the course of the real world and how they can be used for prediction. Popper (1956) has provided a great deal of insight into these matters. The archetypes of Senge (1990) gives building blocks for the creation of the necessary theories.

Psychology is important since in human systems human behaviour will determine the future. But both nature and human behaviour cannot be understood if we neglect variation. The world is full of variation and to understand the world we must take variation into account. Therefore, statistical theory is also an important element of profound knowledge.

Deming (1993) emphasizes that to be a good leader it is not neccessary to have a deep knowledge of all the elements of profound knowledge. It is, however, important to have an understanding of how all these elements interact.

22.3 Learning Organizations

Continuous improvement, an important theme in this book, has a firm link to learning. For continuous improvement to become a natural feature of an organization, the whole organization must always be learning. Garvin (1993) defines a *learning organization* as

> *an organization skilled at creating, acquiring, and transferring knowledge, and at modifying its behavior to reflect new knowledge and insights.*

Learning organizations have been discussed by Senge (1990). He describes five elements or disciplines, as being important to a learning organization: personal mastery, mental models, team learning, shared visions and systems thinking. Learning organizations are also described by Nonaka (1991). How to become a learning organization is discussed by Garvin (1993). He emphasizes that learning organizations are skilled at five main activities:

- systematic problem solving
- experimentation with new approaches
- learning from their own experience and past history
- learning from the experiences and best practice of others
- transferring knowledge throughout the organization.

Each of these is accompanied by a distinctive mind-set, tool-kit, and pattern of behavior. Here we recognize many ideas and tools already discussed in this book.

22.4 Successful Organizations

Since Peters & Waterman (1982) was published it has been realized that strong cultures are vital for corporate success. During the 1980s it became clear that strong cultures are not enough. Among the 43 companies studied by Peters & Waterman (1982), selected on the basis of 20 years of uninterrupted success, two thirds had lost their position only five years later, see Pascale (1991). It was realized that companies had to focus on the needs and expectations of their customers, employees, and other interested parties. Also, as noted by Kotter & Heskett (1992) based on their research findings, they have to be flexible enough to respond quickly to changing needs and expectations of their environment.

It is commonly believed that to be customer responsive it is necessary to have a strongly decentralised organization. To use a common organizational metaphor it is necessary to turn the organizational pyramid upside down. The operational knowledge in the organization is on the operational level. It is there the knowledge about the customers accumulates and it is the people at the operational level who can respond most quickly to the shifting requirements of their customers.

22.5 Total Quality Society

Today's world is becoming increasingly complex. Our political leaders have to understand a global system, the future of which is endangered by forces of immense power.

We hope that, in the future, political leaders will study and practice profound knowledge to create a learning society, where in all its processes, customer needs and expectations are focused upon, where only win-win solutions are considered and where continuous improvement is considered a natural way of life. We hope for a *Total Quality Society*.

22.6 Notes and References

Books that deal with Deming's 14 points more exhaustively are, apart from Deming (1986), also Walton (1986), Gitlow & Gitlow

(1986), Scherkenbach (1986), Neave (1990) and Kilian (1993). An appealing book describing Deming more as a person is Mann (1989). Recently, Deming has published a new book, Deming (1993).

Deming's philosophy has been studied and deepened by many Deming study groups in the US and by the British Deming Association (BDA) in England. Deming's ideas are discussed, applied and advanced in a series of booklets. In an interesting BDA publication from 1993 Ian Lambert has put together Deming's ideas with those of two now forgotten economists. In that way new economic principles are created.

Kotter & Heskett (1992) have developed what they call Theory 3. Theory 1 corresponds to findings from the early 1980s that strong company cultures lead to success (see e.g. Peters & Waterman, 1982). Theory 2 restricts these successes to companies responding to needs and expectations of their environment. Finally, Theory 3 predicts that strong corporate cultures lead to long lasting success if they respond to the needs and expectations of their environments but also are flexible enough to respond to new requirements from the environment. Kotter & Heskett also support their theory with a number of empirical findings. Companies fulfilling Theory 3 conditions have had much better development than those that do not.

Other interesting recent books on leadership, more or less pointing in the same direction as Deming (1986), are Argyris (1990) on leadership, Schein (1985) on corporate culture and Senge (1990) on learning organizations. Kotter (1990) discusses the diffence between leadership and management.

Appendix

This appendix consists of four parts. In Appendix A some basic statistical definitions, terms and concepts are discussed. Appendix B contains a few different tables and the appendix then concludes with references and index.

Appendix A
Basic Concepts in Statistics

A.1 Random Variations

Suppose that we have a number of units produced in the same manufacturing process. When measuring a certain dimension we will experience a variation among the measurements. Correspondingly, we would observe different times to failure when testing a number of units to failure, even if the units are manufactured under the same conditions.

In many situations we experience variations whose causes we cannot identify. The Japanese quality expert Kaoru Ishikawa argued that we "live in a world of dispersions". In a manufacturing process these variations can be due to dispersion in material characteristics or play in a bearing. Part of the dispersion can also be due to measurement errors. These in turn can be due to play in the testing equipment or to reading errors. In general there are many causes that individually contribute to the variations we experience in the manufacturing process. Since, as a rule, we neither know the separate causes nor their contributions, we blame variations on chance. We state that the variations are *random.*

The easiest way to illustrate variation is by using a diagram of the type in Figure A.1.

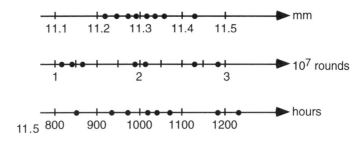

Figure A.1   *A simple diagram illustrating variations of test data of the same type. Each test value is represented by a dot in the diagram.*

Such a diagram, however, will be difficult to interpret and even confusing when we have too many observations. Instead we can then illustrate the variation of the values using a *frequency histogram*. Here the measurement axis is divided into separate *classes*. The proportion of observations within a class is then illustrated by using a rectangle as in Figure A.2. The area of the rectangle is proportional to the relative frequency of observations in the corresponding class. Note that the sum of the rectangles' areas thus equals unity.

The relative frequence of observations that is less than a certain value b, corresponding to a class limit, equals the sum A of the areas of the rectangles that lie to the left of b. The value A is then an estimator of the chance that a unit selected at random will give a value that is equal to or less than b; see Figure A.3.

The more units we measure, the narrower we can make the width of the rectangles, *the class interval*. Let us imagine that we measure more and more units and gradually reduce the class interval when we draw the corresponding histogram. The smooth and continuous curve that the histogram then approaches describes the random variation of the current measurement. The frequency histogram has converged to a *probability density function* (compare Figure A.4).

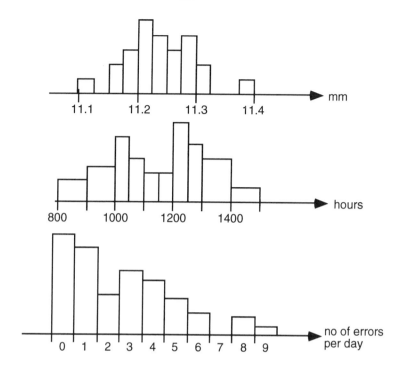

Figure A.2   *Illustration of frequency histograms.*
a) The histogram illustrates the outcome of measure-
ments of the diameter of 30 shaft pivots. Each class has
the same class width, i.e. the same distance between the
upper and lower limit in the class.
(b) The histogram illustrates times to failure from 50
light bulbs. Note that the classes are not equally wide.
(c) The histogram illustrates the number of errors per
day in a certain manufacturing stage over a total of 132
days. In this case each integer corresponds to one class.

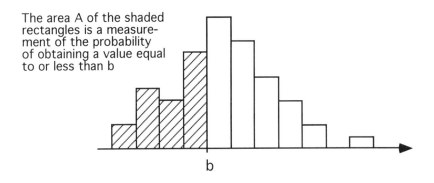

The area A of the shaded rectangles is a measurement of the probability of obtaining a value equal to or less than b

b

Figure A.3   *The total area A of the rectangles to the left of b is a mea-surement of the probability of obtaining a value which is equal to or less than b.*

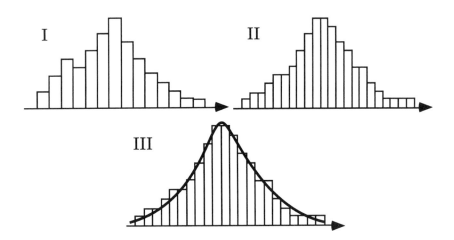

I   II   III

Figure A.4   *The more units we measure and the more we reduce the class width as we draw a corresponding histogram, the more the histogram will approach a smooth and conti-nuous curve.*

The area below the curve between the numbers b and c conse-quently corresponds to the number of units with measurements between b and c, drawn from a very large lot; see Figure A.5. The area corresponds to the chance of obtaining a test value between b and c if we select at random a unit from the lot and measure it. In particular the area to the left of b corresponds to the chance of obtaining a value equal to or less than b, or to the fraction of units in the population that have a value equal to or less than b.

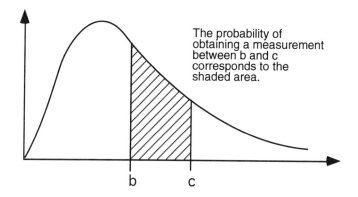

The probability of obtaining a measurement between b and c corresponds to the shaded area.

b   c

Figure A.5   The probability of obtaining a measurement between b and c corresponds to the area below the probability density function between the numbers.

Note that since the sum of the rectangle areas always is equal to unity, the area below the probability density function between the numbers also equals unity.

In general we only have a small number of observations at our disposal. Then it can be difficult to guess directly from the histogram what probability density function is appropriate. Still we can often on the basis of theoretical reasoning suggest a plausible probability density function. If, for example, each value originates as a sum of small independent disturbances, a normal distribution may be appropriate. Other arguments can sometimes lead to an exponential distribution. These distributions are described in Section A.4.

A number of units, selected at random from a manufacturing process, are called a *sample* or *a random sample*. The individual values we obtain when we measure the units are called *observa-*

tions. Due to the random variation, histograms based on two different samples from the same population will differ. If the number of units in the samples is small the difference can become very large. The difference, however, becomes smaller when the *sample size*, that is the number of units per sample, increases.

A.2 Probabilities

If we toss a symmetric coin, "head" as "tail" are equally likely. Since we certainly will obtain either "head" or "tail", the chance of obtaining "head" is 50%. We state that the *probability* of obtaining "head" is 50% or 0.50. The same thing holds for the outcome "tail". We write

P(head) = P(tail) = 0.50

Here P stands for probability. For corresponding symmetric reasons we claim that the probability of obtaining "one" when we toss a symmetric die is 1/6, since there are 6 possibilities which all have the same chance of occurring. The probability of obtaining "two", "three", "four", "five" or "six" is the same. We write

P(one) = P(two) = P(three) = P(four) = P(five) = P(six) = 3/6

The probability of obtaining "not higher than four" when tossing a symmetric die is 4/6 since

P(not more than three) = P(one) + P(two) + P(three) = 4/6

If we study an experiment in which all the outcomes have the same probability of occurring, for reasons of symmetry for example, we get

$$P(\text{certain event}) = \frac{\text{number of favourable outcomes}}{\text{total number of outcomes}}$$

This rule is sometimes called *the classical probability definition*.

We can also say that the probability of obtaining "head" when tossing a symmetric coin is 0.50 for another reason. If we toss a coin several times, we will obtain "head" in approximately half the tosses. The more we toss, the closer to 50% the relative number of tosses resulting in "head" will be. The relative number of tosses resulting in "head", *the relative frequency* for "head", approaches 0.50 with a growing number of tosses. This is called *the stability of the relative frequency*. That the probability of obtaining "one" is 1/6 when tossing a symmetric die can also be justified by the stability of the relative frequency.

Sometimes we use the stability of the relative frequency to get an estimator of a probability. When we say, for example, that the probability is 10% that a piece of bent sheet-iron has a crack, this can be based on the fact that we have bent many pieces of sheet-iron and we have observed that cracks have occurred in about 10% of these.

The probability concept discussed so far is only valid for situations where the experiment we are performing has a finite number of outcomes. A coin can only give two outcomes and a die six. A sheet-iron bending process gives units that are flawless or have at least one crack.

If we study an experiment which can have an infinite number of results, for instance a measurement that can result in any value in an interval, then we can define the probability concept using the concepts "frequency histogram" and "probability density function", which we studied in Section A.1.

Suppose that we are studying a measurement of a certain type of unit. If we measure many units of this type and draw a histogram, we will be able to approximate this histogram by a smooth and continuous curve to a function that is called *the probability density function*, and is denoted f(x). The probability of obtaining a measurement between b and c is then put equal to the area under the probability density function between the values b and c, i.e. the integral of f(x) over the interval from b to c; see Figure A.6.

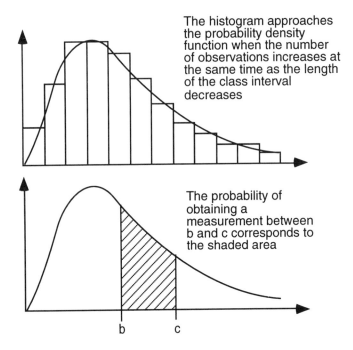

The histogram approaches the probability density function when the number of observations increases at the same time as the length of the class interval decreases

The probability of obtaining a measurement between b and c corresponds to the shaded area

b   c

Figure A.6   *The probability of obtaining a value between b and c cor-*
responds to the area under the probability density func-
tion f(x) over the interval.

The probability density function, therefore, can be interpreted as a density function showing how the probability mass, which is equal to unity, is distributed over the possible observation interval.

Using probabilities we can describe the variation that we have to take into account in quality work. Using histograms and probability density functions we can *predict* the outcome of a new unit produced according to the same manufacturing process. The probability density function reflects our uncertainty concerning the new unit. As long as the manufacturing process is subjected to the same disturbances, we can use the same probability density function. We state that the process is *statistically stable* or that the process is *in statistical control*. An important task for quality control during the manufacturing stage is to find the disturbing factors that to a large extent contribute to variation and try to eliminate these sources of variation.

Before we close the discussions on probabilities we would like to point to a type of probabilities that is becoming more common in everyday life, namely *subjective probabilities*. It is hard to make frequency interpretations of comments like "with a probability of 20% Charles XII was killed by his own soldiers", "with a probability of 80% the supplier will manage to meet the delivery requirements" or "there will be rain tomorrow with a 40% probability".

These statements must instead be understood as a means of quantifying the uncertainty that the person who makes the statement feels, with respect to his knowledge and experience concerning the problem. The probability is thus subjective in the sense that it varies from person to person depending on what information that person has in this matter. We all sometimes use subjective probabilities. If we estimate the probability of rain as more than 50%, then we probably take an umbrella or a rain-coat with us when we go for a walk.

A.3 Random Variables

A quantity which varies randomly is called a *random variable* (or a *stochastic variable*). The number of dots when tossing a die, the outcome when tossing a coin or the relative number of defective units in a sample from a certain manufacturing process are examples of random variables. The same thing applies for the diameter of shaft pivots produced in a certain manufacturing process. When we randomly select a shaft from the manufacturing process and measure the diameter of its pivot we say that we obtain an *observation* of the random variable. An observation is described by a single value. The random variable, however, is described by its probability density function. We say that we illustrate the *distribution of the random variable.*

When we select a sample of shafts and measure the diameter of their shaft pivots, the different shafts are supposed to be selected at random from the manufacturing process. The same uncertainty shall be valid for all observations. This uncertainty is described by the probability density function. If we know the probability density function, the measurement result from a shaft shall not give any information as to the measurement of the next shaft. We say that we have *independent observations.*

In general this is a simplified picture of reality. The system of disturbances can for instance change with time, which in turn can produce dependence between successive measurements. On the one hand we can say that small deviations from the simplified picture of reality are of no importance. Practically all descriptions of reality are simplifications. Not even Newton's theory of mechanics or Einstein's theory of relativity describe reality to perfection. Despite this, these simplifications, usually called *models*, are very useful. On the other hand we can say that these deviations from the theoretical picture of a statistically stable process can be used in quality work because of their ability to detect disturbing factors. The influence from these factors can then be eliminated or at least reduced.

A.3.1 Measures of Location and Dispersion

In many cases we only summarize the distribution of a random variable using a *measure of location*, describing where the probability mass is located, and a measure of dispersion, illustrating how spread the probability mass is.

A measure of location often used is the *mean* of the distribution or, equivalently, the *expectation* of the corresponding random variable. This value is usually denoted by μ and is the mass centre of the probability mass; see Figure A.7. If we have many observations and calculate the arithmetic mean of these, this mean will approach the expectation. That is why we often refer to the expectation as the *average value of the population*.

Another commonly used measure of location is the *median*, which in general is denoted by m or L_{50}. The probability of obtaining a value larger than m and the probability of obtaining a value smaller than m are both 50%. For symmetric distributions the expectation and the median coincide, but for distributions that are unsymmetric the concepts differ. For unsymmetric distributions the median may be a better measure of location than the expectation. Sometimes the *nominal life* L_{10} is also used, the time a unit will survive with the probability 0.90.

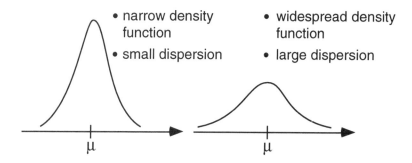

- narrow density function
- small dispersion

- widespread density function
- large dispersion

Figure A.7   *The mean μ of the distribution is a measure of where the mass centre of the probability mass is situated. The standard deviation σ is a measure of how spread the probability mass is.*

The dispersion of the distribution is often defined using the *standard deviation*, denoted by σ. Standard deviation is the square root of the moment of inertia of the probability mass with respect to the mass centre. Sometimes we say just *dispersion* when referring to the standard deviation of the distribution. The probability density function of a distribution with small standard deviation is thus more concentrated around the expectation of the distribution than if the distribution has a large value of the standard deviation; see Figure A.7.

When we have a number of observations from a distribution its expectation μ can be estimated using the arithmetic mean $\bar{x}$ which is given by

$$\bar{x} = \frac{x_1 + x_2 + \ldots + x_n}{n}$$

The standard deviation of the distribution σ can be estimated using the *standard deviation s of the sample* which is defined as

$$s = \sqrt{\frac{1}{n-1} \sum_{j=1}^{n} (x_j - \bar{x})^2}$$

Since the "average value" of the population is μ, every measurement value will lie "close to" μ. How close is determined partly by chance (a combination of unknown factors) and partly by the standard deviation σ of the distribution. If we calculate successive arithmetic means $\bar{x}$ these will vary in size. Since x_1, x_2, ..., x_n are outcomes of chance, their mean $\bar{x}$ will also be due to chance. On average the different test values of $\bar{x}$ will lie closer to μ than the individual observations. If the standard deviation of the distribution for the separate observations is σ then the standard deviation of the distribution for $\bar{x}$ equals $\sigma/\sqrt{n}$.

Figure A.8 illustrates how the standard deviation for $\bar{x}$ rapidly decreases with the sample size n. We observe that the standard deviation rapidly decreases when n increases from 1 to 2 or from 2 to 3. The decrease is, however, only modest if n increases from 6 to 7 or from 7 to 8. If n is very large the standard deviation for $\bar{x}$ will be extremely small. Then $\bar{x}$ has a large probability of being close to μ. This result is called the *Law of Large Numbers*.

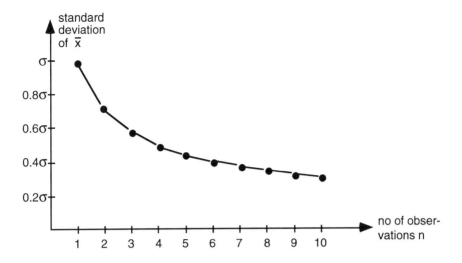

Figure A.8   The standard deviation to the distribution of x̄ as a function of the number of observations n.

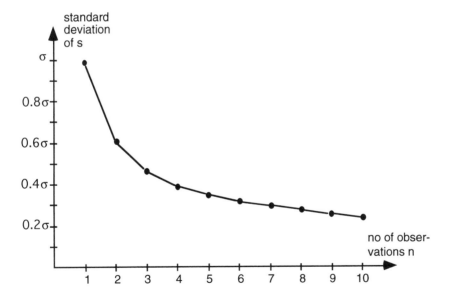

Figure A.9   The standard deviation of s as a function of the number of observations n when these observations are from a normal distribution (see Section A.4.2).

In the same way that x̄ varies between different samples, the standard deviation s of the sample also varies. In other words we get different approximations not only of the population's average value but also of its standard deviation depending on what test values we obtain in our sample. Also here holds that the standard deviation of the distribution, of which s is an observation, decreasies with increasing sample size n; see Figure A.9. This implies that the larger sample we have, the greater is the probability that s ends up close to the actual standard deviation σ. We can state that the larger the sample is, the more accurate our approximations of the population's average value and standard deviation will be.

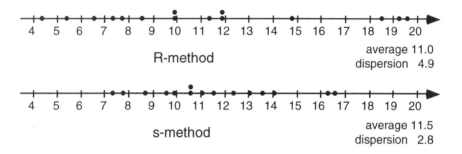

Figure A.10 Illustration of the variation between estimates of the standard deviation using the R-method and the s-method. The figures are based on estimators from 15 random samples of size n = 4 from a normal distribution with the standard deviation σ = 10.

When we have observations which can be considered to be derived from a normal distribution (see Section A.4.2), another technique is sometimes used for estimating the standard deviation of the distribution than computing the standard deviation s of the sample. We compute the *range of variation* R, which is the difference between the largest and the smallest observation, and then divide R by a constant (denoted by d_2 or α_n), which is dependent on the sample size n and is to be found in various tables.

This technique, which results in somewhat easier calculations than when using the s-method, provides a more uncertain result since the standard deviation between different estimates using the R-method is greater than if the estimates are made by using the s-method with the same sample size; see Figure A.10.

A.3.2 Sums of Random Variables

The deviations that we have in a manufacturing process can, as we have mentioned earlier, in many cases be understood as a sum of several independent random variables. If X_1 and X_2 are two independent random variables, then their sum $X = X_1 + X_2$ is also a random variable. If X_1 and X_2 are the number of dots when throwing two dice, then $X = X_1 + X_2$ is the sum of the dots. It is possible to prove that if X_1 and X_2 have the expectations μ_1 and μ_2, respectively, then $X = X_1 + X_2$ has the expectation μ, where

$$\mu = \mu_1 + \mu_2$$

If X_1 and X_2 have the standard deviations σ_1 and σ_2, respectively, then $X = X_1 + X_2$ has the standard deviation σ, where

$$\sigma = \sqrt{\sigma_1^2 + \sigma_2^2}$$

The dispersion of the distribution of X is thus greater than the dispersion of each of the separate terms. If X_1 and X_2 have the same dispersion, the dispersion of the sum is about 40% larger.

If we have a sum of several independent random variables X_1, X_2, ..., X_n, whose distribution is not too unsymmetric, the distribution of the sum $X = X_1 + X_2 + ... + X_n$ will be approximately normally distributed. This is what the *Central Limit Theorem* states. The Central Limit Theorem is one of the reasons why the normal distribution is so useful. If we have a sum of n independent random variables which all have the expectation μ and the standard deviation σ the sum is approximately normally distributed with expectation nμ and standard deviation σ√n̄.

A.4 Some Probability Distributions

A.4.1 Discrete Probability Distributions

A random variable is called *discrete* if the set of possible values is finite or enumerable. If a random variable counts the number of something then it is a discrete random variable.

If X is a random variable

- p(x) = P(X = x) is called the *probability function* of X

- F(x) = P(X ≤ x) is called the *cumulative distribution function* of X.

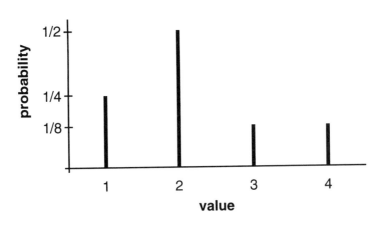

Figure A.11 The probability function of a random variable that takes the values 1, 2, 3, and 4 with the probability 1/4, 1/2, 1/8, and 1/8, respectively.

If we know the probability function or the cumulative distribution function of a random variable we say that we know the *distribution* of the random variable. The probability function is often illustrated by bars at the values that the random variable may attain. The height of a bar corresponds to the probability that the current value is attained. The sum of the heights of the bars thus equals unity, see Figure A.11.

Certain distributions are so common that they are assigned special names and tables are printed giving p(x) or F(x). We shall briefly have a look at some such distributions.

Binomial Distribution

Suppose that a manufacturing process produces defective units with the probability 0.20 (and correct units with the probability 0.80). If we randomly select three units from the process we may get 0, 1, 2 or 3 defective units. The probability of 0 defective units is 0.80·0.80·0.80, of one defective unit 3·0.20·0.80·0.80, of two defective units 3·0.20·0.20·0.80, and, finally, of three defective units 0.20·0.20·0.20.

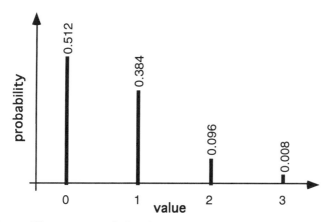

Figure A.12 Illustration of the distribution of the number of defective units out of three selected from a manufacturing process, where the probability of a unit being defective is 0.20.

435

If X denotes the number of defective units among the three we select from the process, then the probability function p(x) = P(X = x) is (compare Figure A.12)

P(X = 0) = 0.512   P(X = 1) = 0.384
P(X = 2) = 0.096   P(X = 3) = 0.008

Suppose that in this way we make independent repetitions of an experiment that at each repetition succeeds with the probability p (and fails with the probability 1–p). If we make n repetitions and let X denote the number of successful repetitions among those, then X is a random variable. We can show that

$$P(X = x) = \binom{n}{k} p^x (1-p)^{n-x} \quad \text{for } x = 0, 1, \ldots,$$

where

$$\binom{n}{k} = \frac{n!}{k! \cdot (n-k)!}$$

and k! = 1·2·3· ... ·k (and 0! = 1). We say that X is *binomially distributed with the parameters n and p* and we usually write that X is Bin(n, p).

To facilitate calculations concerning the binomial distribution there are several different types of tables. There also are different types of nomographs by whose aid we can calculate P(X ≤ x) for binomially distributed random variables X; see, for example, Duncan (1986).

In Table A.1 part of a table is reproduced that states P(X ≤ x), when X is Bin(n, p), that is the probability of succeeding at most x times when we make n repetitions of an experiment where each repetition is a success with the probability p. From that table we obtain, for instance, that if X is Bin(10, 0.20) then P(X ≤ 2) = 0.67780, P(X ≥ 3) = 1 – P(X ≤ 2) = 1 – 0.67780 = 0.32220. We also get that P(X = 3) = P(X ≤ 3) – P(X ≤ 2) = 0.87913 – 0.67780 = 0.20133.

n	x	0.05	0.10	0.15	p 0.20	0.25	0.30	0.40	0.50
10	0	0.59874	0.34868	0.19687	0.10737	0.05631	.02825	0.00605	0.00098
	1	0.91386	0.73610	0.54430	0.37581	0.24403	0.14931	0.04636	0.01074
	2	0.98850	0.92981	0.82020	0.67780	0.52559	0.38278	0.16729	0.05469
	3	0.99897	0.98720	0.95003	0.87913	0.77588	0.64961	0.38228	0.17188
	4	0.99994	0.99837	0.99013	0.96721	0.92187	0.84973	0.63310	0.37695
	5	1.00000	0.99985	0.99862	0.99363	0.98027	0.95265	0.83376	0.62305
	6	1.00000	0.99999	0.99987	0.99914	0.99649	0.98941	0.94524	0.82813
	7	1.00000	1.00000	0.99999	0.99992	0.99958	0.99841	0.98771	0.94531
	8	1.00000	1.00000	1.00000	1.00000	0.99997	0.99986	0.99832	0.98926
	9	1.00000	1.00000	1.00000	1.00000	1.00000	0.99999	0.99990	0.99902
11	0	0.56880	0.31381	0.16734	0.08590	0.04224	0.01977	0.00363	0.00049
	1	0.89811	0.69736	0.49219	0.32212	0.19710	0.11299	0.03023	0.00586
	2	0.98476	0.91044	0.77881	0.61740	0.45520	0.31274	0.11892	0.03271
	3	0.99845	0.98147	0.93056	0.83886	0.71330	0.56956	0.29628	0.11328
	4	0.99989	0.99725	0.98411	0.94959	0.88537	0.78970	0.53277	0.27441
	5	0.99999	0.99970	0.99734	0.98835	0.96567	0.92178	0.75350	0.50000
	6	1.00000	0.99998	0.99968	0.99803	0.99244	0.97838	0.90065	0.72559
	7	1.00000	1.00000	0.99997	0.99976	0.99881	0.99571	0.97072	0.88672
	8	1.00000	1.00000	1.00000	0.99998	0.99987	0.99942	0.99408	0.96729
	9	1.00000	1.00000	1.00000	1.00000	0.99999	0.99995	0.99927	0.99414
	10	1.00000	1.00000	1.00000	1.00000	1.00000	1.00000	0.99996	0.99951

Table A.1   *Extract from a table that gives P(X ≤ x), when X has a Bin(n, p)-distribution.*

Poisson Distribution

Suppose that events of some kind occur "randomly". They can be shocks in a mechanical system, units that arrive on a conveyor belt or the arrival of telephone calls at an exchange. Let X denote the number of events that have occurred in a time interval of a certain length. Then with a good approximation we have

$$P(X = x) = e^{-m} \frac{m^x}{x!} \quad \text{for } x = 0, 1, 2, \ldots$$

for some constant m. We say that X is *Poisson distributed with parameter m* and write that X is Po(m). The distribution is named after Simeon Denis Poisson (1781-1840), who was a French statistician.

Just as for the binomial distribution there are tables which give $P(X = x)$ or $P(X \leq x)$ for Poisson distributions with different values of m. In Table A.2 there is an extract from a table which gives $P(X \leq x)$ for some values of m. For instance, from that table we get that if X is Po(2.0) then $P(X \leq 2) = 0.67668$, $P(X \geq 3) = 1 - P(X \leq 2) = 1 - 0.67668 = 0.32332$ and $P(X = 3) = P(X \leq 3) - P(X \leq 2) = 0.85712 - 0.67668 = 0.18044$. Also for the Poisson distribution there are nomographs with whose aid we can calculate $P(X \leq x)$; see Duncan (1986).

					m				
x	1.0	1.2	1.4	1.6	1.8	2.0	2.2	2.4	2.6
0	0.36788	0.30119	0.24660	0.20190	0.16530	0.13534	0.11080	0.09072	0.07427
1	0.73576	0.66263	0.59183	0.52493	0.46284	0.40601	0.35457	0.30844	0.26738
2	0.91970	0.87949	0.83350	0.78336	0.73062	0.67668	0.62271	0.56971	0.51843
3	0.98101	0.96623	0.94627	0.92119	0.89129	0.85712	0.81935	0.77872	0.73600
4	0.99634	0.99225	0.98575	0.97632	0.96359	0.94735	0.92750	0.90413	0.87742
5	0.99941	0.99850	0.99680	0.99396	0.98962	0.98344	0.97509	0.96433	0.95096
6	0.99992	0.99975	0.99938	0.99866	0.99743	0.99547	0.99254	0.98841	0.98283
7	0.99999	0.99996	0.99989	0.99974	0.99944	0.99890	0.99802	0.99666	0.99467
8	1.00000	1.00000	0.99998	0.99995	0.99989	0.99976	0.99953	0.99914	0.99851
9	1.00000	1.00000	1.00000	0.99999	0.99998	0.99995	0.99990	0.99980	0.99962
10	1.00000	1.00000	1.00000	1.00000	1.00000	0.99999	0.99998	0.99996	0.99991
11	1.00000	1.00000	1.00000	1.00000	1.00000	1.00000	1.00000	0.99999	0.99998
12	1.00000	1.00000	1.00000	1.00000	1.00000	1.00000	1.00000	1.00000	1.00000

Table A.2   Extract from a table giving $P(X \leq x)$, when X is Po(m)-distributed.

Hypergeometric Distribution

A lot contains bolts, of which some are defective and the rest correct. There are a total of N bolts, of which the fraction p are defective. This implies that there are Np defective bolts and

N–Np correct bolts in the lot. If we select n bolts randomly from the lot and let X denote the number of defective bolts we obtain, then

$$P(X = x) = \frac{\binom{Np}{x}\binom{N-Np}{n-x}}{\binom{N}{n}} \quad \text{for certain values of x}$$

We say that X is *hypergeometrically distributed with parameters N, n and p*. Sometimes we write that X is Hypgeo(N,n,p).

The hypergeometric distribution is cumbersome to use since the expression above for P(X = x) is hard to compute. The access to tables is also limited since the distribution is dependent on three parameters. Under certain conditions we can, however, approximate a hypergeometric distribution by a binomial distribution or a Poisson distribution. A few common approximations together with rules of thumb when these provide acceptable results are illustrated in Figure A.13.

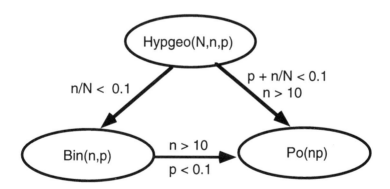

Figure A.13 Some common approximations of the hypergeometric distribution together with rules of thumb illustrating when the approximations provide acceptable results.

A.4.2 Continuous Distributions

A random variable which can attain values in an entire interval, for example all positive values, is called a *continuous random variable*. The probability that such a random variable X takes a value that lies between b and c is obtained as the area under its probability density funtion f(x) between b and c; see Figure A.14. Using mathematical symbols this means that

$$P(b < X < c) = \int_b^c f(x) \, dx$$

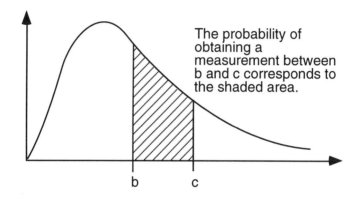

The probability of obtaining a measurement between b and c corresponds to the shaded area.

Figure A.14 The part of the area under the probability density function that lies between b and c corresponds to the probability of obtaining a value in that interval.

As for discrete random variables, there are certain continuous distributions that often appear in practice. We will briefly introduce some of these.

Normal Distribution

If X has the probability density function

$$f(x) = \frac{1}{\sigma\sqrt{2\pi}} \exp\left(-\frac{(x-\mu)^2}{2\sigma^2}\right) \quad \text{for} - \infty < x < \infty$$

where μ and $\sigma > 0$ are constants, X *is normally distributed with parameters μ and σ.* We write that X is N(μ,σ). If $\mu = 0$ and $\sigma = 1$ the density function is denoted $\varphi(x)$ and the distribution function $\Phi(x)$, that is

$$\varphi(x) = \frac{1}{\sqrt{2\pi}} \exp\left(-\frac{x^2}{2}\right) \quad \text{for} - \infty < x < \infty$$

and

$$\Phi(x) = \int_{-\infty}^{x} \varphi(t)\, dt$$

x	0.00	0.01	0.02	0.03	0.04	0.05	0.06	0.07	0.08	0.09
0.0	0.5000	0.5040	0.5080	0.5120	0.5160	0.5199	0.5239	0.5279	0.5319	0.5359
0.1	0.5398	0.5438	0.5478	0.5517	0.5557	0.5596	0.5636	0.5675	0.5714	0.5753
0.2	0.5793	0.5832	0.5871	0.5910	0.5948	0.5987	0.6026	0.6064	0.6103	0.6141
0.3	0.6179	0.6217	0.6255	0.6293	0.6331	0.6368	0.6406	0.6443	0.6480	0.6517
0.4	0.6554	0.6591	0.6628	0.6664	0.6700	0.6736	0.6772	0.6808	0.6844	0.6879
0.5	0.6915	0.6950	0.6985	0.7019	0.7054	0.7088	0.7123	0.7157	0.7190	0.7224
0.6	0.7257	0.7291	0.7324	0.7357	0.7389	0.7422	0.7454	0.7486	0.7517	0.7549
0.7	0.7580	0.7611	0.7642	0.7673	0.7704	0.7734	0.7764	0.7794	0.7823	0.7852
0.8	0.7881	0.7910	0.7939	0.7967	0.7995	0.8023	0.8051	0.8078	0.8106	0.8133
0.9	0.8159	0.8186	0.8212	0.8238	0.8264	0.8289	0.8315	0.8340	0.8365	0.8289
1.0	0.8413	0.8438	0.8461	0.8485	0.8508	0.8531	0.8554	0.8577	0.8599	0.8621
1.1	0.8643	0.8665	0.8686	0.8708	0.8729	0.8749	0.8770	0.8790	0.8810	0.8830
1.2	0.8849	0.8869	0.8888	0.8907	0.8925	0.8944	0.8962	0.8980	0.8997	0.9015
1.3	0.9032	0.9049	0.9066	0.9082	0.9099	0.9115	0.9131	0.9147	0.9162	0.9177
1.4	0.9192	0.9207	0.9222	0.9236	0.9251	0.9265	0.9279	0.9292	0.9306	0.9319

Table A.3 *Extract from a table that gives $\Phi(x)$, i.e. $P(X \le x)$, when X is N(0, 1)-distributed.*

The distribution function $\Phi(x)$ can be found in varioust tables. In Table A.3 an extract from such a table can be found. From this table it follows, for instance, that $P(X \le 0.5) = 0.6915$ and $P(X > 1.2) = 1 - P(X \le 1.2) = 1 - 0.8849 = 0.1151$.

If X is $N(\mu,\sigma)$ then

$$P(X \le x) = \Phi\left(\frac{x - \mu}{\sigma}\right)$$

If we have a binomial distribution or a Poisson distribution which is symmetric enough, it can be approximated by a normal distribution. The rules of thumb that one tends to use are

$$Bin(n,p) \approx N\left(np, \sqrt{np(1-p)}\right) \quad \text{for } np(1-p) \ge 10$$

$$Po(m) \approx N(m, \sqrt{m}) \quad \text{for } m \ge 10$$

Exponential Distribution

The exponential distribution is a frequently used distribution to describe times to failure for units that do not age, that is, have the constant failure rate λ.

If X only takes positive values and has the probability density function

$$f(x) = \lambda \exp(-\lambda x) \quad \text{for } x \ge 0$$

where λ is a constant, X is *exponentially distributed with parameter* λ. We sometimes write that X is $Exp(\lambda)$-distributed, see Figure A.15.

Note that an exponential distribution, in contrast to a normal distribution, is not symmetric. The distribution function

$$F(x) = 1 - \exp(-\lambda x) \quad \text{for } x \ge 0$$

states the probability that a unit fails before the time point x.

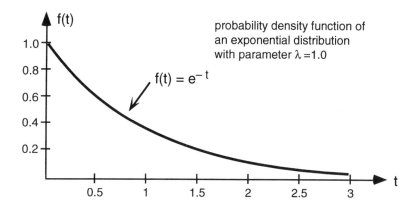

Figure A.15 Probability density function of the exponential distribution with λ= 1.0.

Corresponding *reliability function (survival function)*

$$R(x) = \exp(-\lambda x) \quad \text{for } x \geq 0$$

states the probability that a unit will survive x units of time.

For a unit whose time to failure is exponentially distributed the average time to failure (the expectation) is $1/\lambda$ and the median life L_{50} is equal to $(\ln 2)/\lambda$. Since $R(1/\lambda) = \exp(-1) = 0.37$ the unit has a chance of approximately 37% of surviving the average time to failure.

A.5 Probability Plotting

A practical and often used method when analysing statistical data is to use plotting on a probability paper. There are probability papers for a number of distributions such as exponential distribution, Weibull distribution, and lognormal distribution, but we will confine ourselves here to study plotting on a paper for normal distribution. For more about probability plotting, see for instance Nelson (1979), Martz & Waller (1982), King (1971) and Kececioglu (1991).

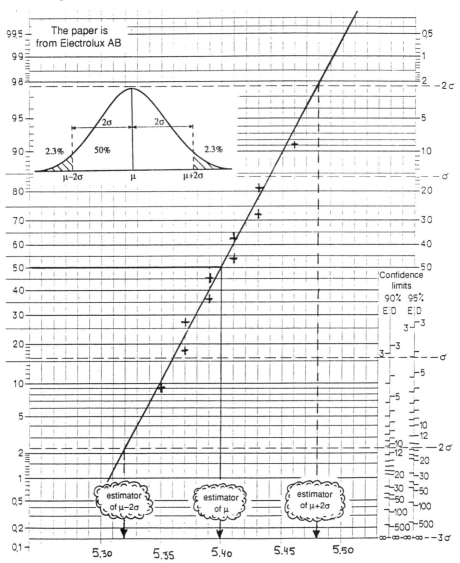

Figure A.16 Probability plotting paper for a normal distribution used in Examples A.1 and A.2.

The idea of probability plotting is the following. First we order the n observations, i.e. we get $t_1 \leq t_2 \leq \ldots \leq t_n$. Then we plot the j:th observation t_j on the horizontal scale against an estimate of the distribution function value at the time point t_j on the vertical. There are several different alternatives for this estimate, but here we will choose j/(n+1), which is called the *mean range*. If a normal distribution can be fitted to the observations the plotted points, except for random deviations, are expected to lie on a line.

Example A.1

When measuring the diameter of turned shafts the following ten values were obtained:

5.43   5.41   5.39   5.46   5.43   5.37   5.39   5.37   5.41   5.35.

What fraction of the produced units will have a diameter outside any of the tolerance limits, which are 5.35 and 5.50?

Solution: We start by arranging the observations according to size:

5.35   5.37   5.37   5.39   5.39   5.41   5.41   5.43   5.43   5.46.

Then we plot the smallest observation, that is 5.35, against 1/11 = 9%, the smallest but one, that is 5.37, against 2/11 = 18% and so on until the largest, that is 5.46, against 10/11 = 91%; see Figure A.16. Since the plotted points lie more or less on a line, there is nothing that contradicts an assumption that the observations are from a normal distribution.

Furthermore, we see that the probability of obtaining an observation under the lower tolerance limit 5.35 is 0.10. Approximately 10% of the shafts will have a diameter below 5.35. On the other hand, generally speaking no shafts have a diameter above the upper tolerance limit 5.50.

Example A.2

Estimate the expectation and the standard deviation of the distribution from which the observations in Example A.1 are taken.

Solution: The fitted straight line in Figure A.16 crosses the horizontal 50%-line for t = 5.40. This means that the expectation μ is about 5.40. (In this way we are actually estimating the median of the normal distribution but since the normal distribution is symmetric, the median and the expectation will coincide.) By starting at the values $\mu+2\sigma$ and $\mu-2\sigma$ to the right on the vertical axis and going down to the horizontal axis via the line, we see that $\mu+2\sigma$ is approximately 5.48 and $\mu-2\sigma$ is approximately 5.32. This implies that we can estimate σ by $(5.48 - 5.32)/4 = 0.04$.

A.6 Notes and References

In this appendix we have only superficially been trying to give an overview of some essential concepts and terms in connection with random variations. For deeper studies we refer to Hogg & Tanis (1988), Scheaffer & McClave (1990), Cryer & Miller (1991), Hogg & Ledolter (1992) and Evans (1992), for example.

$P(X \le x)$ when X is Bin(n,p)

n	x	0.05	0.10	0.15	0.20	0.25	0.30	0.40	0.50
2	0	0.90250	0.81000	0.72250	0.64000	0.56250	0.49000	0.36000	0.25000
	1	0.99750	0.99000	0.97750	0.96000	0.93750	0.91000	0.84000	0.75000
3	0	0.85738	0.72900	0.61413	0.51200	0.42188	0.34300	0.21600	0.12500
	1	0.99275	0.97200	0.93925	0.89600	0.84375	0.78400	0.64800	0.50000
	2	0.99988	0.99900	0.99663	0.99200	0.98438	0.97300	0.93600	0.87500
4	0	0.81451	0.65610	0.52201	0.40960	0.31641	0.24010	0.12960	0.06250
	1	0.98598	0.94770	0.89048	0.81920	0.73828	0.65170	0.47520	0.31250
	2	0.99952	0.99630	0.98802	0.97280	0.94922	0.91630	0.82080	0.68750
	3	0.99999	0.99990	0.99949	0.99840	0.99609	0.99190	0.97440	0.93750
5	0	0.77378	0.59049	0.44371	0.32768	0.23730	0.16807	0.07776	0.03125
	1	0.97741	0.91854	0.83521	0.73728	0.63281	0.52822	0.33696	0.18750
	2	0.99884	0.99144	0.97339	0.94208	0.89648	0.83692	0.68256	0.50000
	3	0.99997	0.99954	0.99777	0.99328	0.98438	0.96922	0.91296	0.81250
	4	1.00000	0.99999	0.99992	0.99968	0.99902	0.99757	0.98976	0.96875
6	0	0.73509	0.53144	0.37715	0.26214	0.17798	0.11765	0.04666	0.01563
	1	0.96723	0.88573	0.77648	0.65536	0.53394	0.42018	0.23328	0.10938
	2	0.99777	0.98415	0.95266	0.90112	0.83057	0.74431	0.54432	0.34375
	3	0.99991	0.99873	0.99411	0.98304	0.96240	0.92953	0.82080	0.65625
	4	1.00000	0.99994	0.99960	0.99840	0.99536	0.98907	0.95904	0.89063
	5	1.00000	1.00000	0.99999	0.99994	0.99976	0.99927	0.99590	0.98438
7	0	0.69834	0.47830	0.32058	0.20972	0.13348	0.08235	0.02799	0.00781
	1	0.95562	0.85031	0.71658	0.57672	0.44495	0.32942	0.15863	0.06250
	2	0.99624	0.97431	0.92623	0.85197	0.75641	0.64707	0.41990	0.22656
	3	0.99981	0.99727	0.98790	0.96666	0.92944	0.87396	0.71021	0.50000
	4	0.99999	0.99982	0.99878	0.99533	0.98712	0.97120	0.90374	0.77344
	5	1.00000	0.99999	0.99993	0.99963	0.99866	0.99621	0.98116	0.93750
	6	1.00000	1.00000	1.00000	0.99999	0.99994	0.99978	0.99836	0.99219
8	0	0.66342	0.43047	0.27249	0.16777	0.10011	0.05765	0.01680	0.00391
	1	0.94276	0.81310	0.65718	0.50332	0.36708	0.25530	0.10638	0.03516
	2	0.99421	0.96191	0.89479	0.79692	0.67854	0.55177	0.31539	0.14453
	3	0.99963	0.99498	0.97865	0.94372	0.88618	0.80590	0.59409	0.36328
	4	0.99998	0.99957	0.99715	0.98959	0.97270	0.94203	0.82633	0.63672
	5	1.00000	0.99998	0.99976	0.99877	0.99577	0.98871	0.95019	0.85547
	6	1.00000	1.00000	0.99999	0.99992	0.99962	0.99871	0.99148	0.96484
	7	1.00000	1.00000	1.00000	1.00000	0.99998	0.99993	0.99934	0.99609
9	0	0.63025	0.38742	0.23162	0.13422	0.07508	0.04035	0.01008	0.00195
	1	0.92879	0.77484	0.59948	0.43621	0.30034	0.19600	0.07054	0.01953
	2	0.99164	0.94703	0.85915	0.73820	0.60068	0.46283	0.23179	0.08984
	3	0.99936	0.99167	0.96607	0.91436	0.83427	0.72966	0.48261	0.25391
	4	0.99997	0.99911	0.99437	0.98042	0.95107	0.90119	0.73343	0.50000
	5	1.00000	0.99994	0.99937	0.99693	0.99001	0.97471	0.90065	0.74609
	6	1.00000	1.00000	0.99995	0.99969	0.99866	0.99571	0.97497	0.91016
	7	1.00000	1.00000	1.00000	0.99998	0.99989	0.99957	0.99620	0.98047
	8	1.00000	1.00000	1.00000	1.00000	1.00000	0.99998	0.99974	0.99805

n	x	0.05	0.10	0.15	0.20	0.25	0.30	0.40	0.50
10	0	0.59874	0.34868	0.19687	0.10737	0.05631	0.02825	0.00605	0.00098
	1	0.91386	0.73610	0.54430	0.37581	0.24403	0.14931	0.04636	0.01074
	2	0.98850	0.92981	0.82020	0.67780	0.52559	0.38278	0.16729	0.05469
	3	0.99897	0.98720	0.95003	0.87913	0.77588	0.64961	0.38228	0.17188
	4	0.99994	0.99837	0.99013	0.96721	0.92187	0.84973	0.63310	0.37695
	5	1.00000	0.99985	0.99862	0.99363	0.98027	0.95265	0.83376	0.62305
	6	1.00000	0.99999	0.99987	0.99914	0.99649	0.98941	0.94524	0.82813
	7	1.00000	1.00000	0.99999	0.99992	0.99958	0.99841	0.98771	0.94531
	8	1.00000	1.00000	1.00000	1.00000	0.99997	0.99986	0.99832	0.98926
	9	1.00000	1.00000	1.00000	1.00000	1.00000	0.99999	0.99990	0.99902
11	0	0.56880	0.31381	0.16734	0.08590	0.04224	0.01977	0.00363	0.00049
	1	0.89811	0.69736	0.49219	0.32212	0.19710	0.11299	0.03023	0.00586
	2	0.98476	0.91044	0.77881	0.61740	0.45520	0.31274	0.11892	0.03271
	3	0.99845	0.98147	0.93056	0.83886	0.71330	0.56956	0.29628	0.11328
	4	0.99989	0.99725	0.98411	0.94959	0.88537	0.78970	0.53277	0.27441
	5	0.99999	0.99970	0.99734	0.98835	0.96567	0.92178	0.75350	0.50000
	6	1.00000	0.99998	0.99968	0.99803	0.99244	0.97838	0.90065	0.72559
	7	1.00000	1.00000	0.99997	0.99976	0.99881	0.99571	0.97072	0.88672
	8	1.00000	1.00000	1.00000	0.99998	0.99987	0.99942	0.99408	0.96729
	9	1.00000	1.00000	1.00000	1.00000	0.99999	0.99995	0.99927	0.99414
	10	1.00000	1.00000	1.00000	1.00000	1.00000	1.00000	0.99996	0.99951
12	0	0.54036	0.28243	0.14224	0.06872	0.03168	0.01384	0.00218	0.00024
	1	0.88164	0.65900	0.44346	0.27488	0.15838	0.08503	0.01959	0.00317
	2	0.98043	0.88913	0.73582	0.55835	0.39068	0.25282	0.08344	0.01929
	3	0.99776	0.97436	0.90779	0.79457	0.64878	0.49252	0.22534	0.07300
	4	0.99982	0.99567	0.97608	0.92744	0.84236	0.72366	0.43818	0.19385
	5	0.99999	0.99946	0.99536	0.98059	0.94560	0.88215	0.66521	0.38721
	6	1.00000	0.99995	0.99933	0.99610	0.98575	0.96140	0.84179	0.61279
	7	1.00000	1.00000	0.99993	0.99942	0.99722	0.99051	0.94269	0.80615
	8	1.00000	1.00000	0.99999	0.99994	0.99961	0.99831	0.98473	0.92700
	9	1.00000	1.00000	1.00000	1.00000	0.99996	0.99979	0.99719	0.98071
	10	1.00000	1.00000	1.00000	1.00000	1.00000	0.99998	0.99968	0.99683
	11	1.00000	1.00000	1.00000	1.00000	1.00000	1.00000	0.99998	0.99976
13	0	0.51334	0.25419	0.12091	0.05498	0.02376	0.00969	0.00131	0.00012
	1	0.86458	0.62134	0.39828	0.23365	0.12671	0.06367	0.01263	0.00171
	2	0.97549	0.86612	0.69196	0.50165	0.33260	0.20248	0.05790	0.01123
	3	0.99690	0.96584	0.88200	0.74732	0.58425	0.42061	0.16858	0.04614
	4	0.99971	0.99354	0.96584	0.90087	0.79396	0.65431	0.35304	0.13342
	5	0.99998	0.99908	0.99247	0.96996	0.91979	0.83460	0.57440	0.29053
	6	1.00000	0.99990	0.99873	0.99300	0.97571	0.93762	0.77116	0.50000
	7	1.00000	0.99999	0.99984	0.99875	0.99435	0.98178	0.90233	0.70947
	8	1.00000	1.00000	0.99998	0.99983	0.99901	0.99597	0.96792	0.86658
	9	1.00000	1.00000	1.00000	0.99998	0.99987	0.99935	0.99221	0.95386
	10	1.00000	1.00000	1.00000	1.00000	0.99999	0.99993	0.99868	0.98877
	11	1.00000	1.00000	1.00000	1.00000	1.00000	1.00000	0.99986	0.99829
	12	1.00000	1.00000	1.00000	1.00000	1.00000	1.00000	0.99999	0.99988

For 0.5 < p < 1 use that
$P(X \leq x)$ when X is Bin(n,p)
is equal to
$1 - P(Y \leq n - x - 1)$ when Y is Bin(n,1-p)

P(X ≤ x) when X is Po(m)

x	0.1	0.2	0.3	0.4	m 0.5	0.6	0.7	0.8	0.9
0	0.90484	0.81873	0.74082	0.67032	0.60653	0.54881	0.49659	0.44933	0.40657
1	0.99532	0.98248	0.96306	0.93845	0.90980	0.87810	0.84420	0.80879	0.77248
2	0.99985	0.99885	0.99640	0.99207	0.98561	0.97688	0.96586	0.95258	0.93714
3	1.00000	0.99994	0.99973	0.99922	0.99825	0.99664	0.99425	0.99092	0.98654
4		1.00000	0.99998	0.99994	0.99983	0.99961	0.99921	0.99859	0.99766
5			1.00000	1.00000	0.99999	0.99996	0.99991	0.99982	0.99966
6					1.00000	1.00000	0.99999	0.99998	0.99996
7							1.00000	1.00000	1.00000

x	1.0	1.2	1.4	1.6	1.8	2.0	2.2	2.4	2.6
0	0.36788	0.30119	0.24660	0.20190	0.16530	0.13534	0.11080	0.09072	0.07427
1	0.73576	0.66263	0.59183	0.52493	0.46284	0.40601	0.35457	0.30844	0.26738
2	0.91970	0.87949	0.83350	0.78336	0.73062	0.67668	0.62271	0.56971	0.51843
3	0.98101	0.96623	0.94627	0.92119	0.89129	0.85712	0.81935	0.77872	0.73600
4	0.99634	0.99225	0.98575	0.97632	0.96359	0.94735	0.92750	0.90413	0.87742
5	0.99941	0.99850	0.99680	0.99396	0.98962	0.98344	0.97509	0.96433	0.95096
6	0.99992	0.99975	0.99938	0.99866	0.99743	0.99547	0.99254	0.98841	0.98283
7	0.99999	0.99996	0.99989	0.99974	0.99944	0.99890	0.99802	0.99666	0.99467
8	1.00000	1.00000	0.99998	0.99995	0.99989	0.99976	0.99953	0.99914	0.99851
9			1.00000	0.99999	0.99998	0.99995	0.99990	0.99980	0.99962
10				1.00000	1.00000	0.99999	0.99998	0.99996	0.99991
11						1.00000	1.00000	0.99999	0.99998
12								1.00000	1.00000

x	2.8	3.0	3.2	3.4	3.6	3.8	4.0	4.2	4.4
0	0.06081	0.04979	0.04076	0.03337	0.02732	0.02237	0.01832	0.01500	0.01228
1	0.23108	0.19915	0.17120	0.14684	0.12569	0.10738	0.09158	0.07798	0.06630
2	0.46945	0.42319	0.37990	0.33974	0.30275	0.26890	0.23810	0.21024	0.18514
3	0.69194	0.64723	0.60252	0.55836	0.51522	0.47348	0.43347	0.39540	0.35945
4	0.84768	0.81526	0.78061	0.74418	0.70644	0.66784	0.62884	0.58983	0.55118
5	0.93489	0.91608	0.89459	0.87054	0.84412	0.81556	0.78513	0.75314	0.71991
6	0.97559	0.96649	0.95538	0.94215	0.92673	0.90911	0.88933	0.86746	0.84365
7	0.99187	0.98810	0.98317	0.97693	0.96921	0.95989	0.94887	0.93606	0.92142
8	0.99757	0.99620	0.99429	0.99171	0.98833	0.98402	0.97864	0.97207	0.96420
9	0.99934	0.99890	0.99824	0.99729	0.99598	0.99420	0.99187	0.98887	0.98511
10	0.99984	0.99971	0.99950	0.99919	0.99873	0.99807	0.99716	0.99593	0.99431
11	0.99996	0.99993	0.99987	0.99978	0.99963	0.99941	0.99908	0.99863	0.99799
12	0.99999	0.99998	0.99997	0.99994	0.99990	0.99983	0.99973	0.99957	0.99934
13	1.00000	1.00000	0.99999	0.99999	0.99997	0.99996	0.99992	0.99987	0.99980
14		1.00000	1.00000	0.99999	0.99999	0.99998	0.99997	0.99994	0.99994
15				1.00000	1.00000	1.00000	0.99999	0.99998	0.99998
16							1.00000	1.00000	1.00000

x	4.6	4.8	5.0	5.5	6.0	6.5	7.0	7.5	8.0
0	0.01005	0.00823	0.00674	0.00409	0.00248	0.00150	0.00091	0.00055	0.00034
1	0.05629	0.04773	0.04043	0.02656	0.01735	0.01128	0.00730	0.00470	0.00302
2	0.16264	0.14254	0.12465	0.08838	0.06197	0.04304	0.02964	0.02026	0.01375
3	0.32571	0.29423	0.26503	0.20170	0.15120	0.11185	0.08177	0.05915	0.04238
4	0.51323	0.47626	0.44049	0.35752	0.28506	0.22367	0.17299	0.13206	0.09963
5	0.68576	0.65101	0.61596	0.52892	0.44568	0.36904	0.30071	0.24144	0.19124
6	0.81803	0.79080	0.76218	0.68604	0.60630	0.52652	0.44971	0.37815	0.31337
7	0.90495	0.88667	0.86663	0.80949	0.74398	0.67276	0.59871	0.52464	0.45296
8	0.95493	0.94418	0.93191	0.89436	0.84724	0.79157	0.72909	0.66197	0.59255
9	0.98047	0.97486	0.96817	0.94622	0.91608	0.87738	0.83050	0.77641	0.71662
10	0.99222	0.98958	0.98630	0.97475	0.95738	0.93316	0.90148	0.86224	0.81589
11	0.99714	0.99601	0.99455	0.98901	0.97991	0.96612	0.94665	0.92076	0.88808
12	0.99902	0.99858	0.99798	0.99555	0.99117	0.98397	0.97300	0.95733	0.93620
13	0.99969	0.99953	0.99930	0.99831	0.99637	0.99290	0.98719	0.97844	0.96582
14	0.99991	0.99985	0.99977	0.99940	0.99860	0.99704	0.99428	0.98974	0.98274
15	0.99997	0.99996	0.99993	0.99980	0.99949	0.99884	0.99759	0.99539	0.99177
16	0.99999	0.99999	0.99998	0.99994	0.99983	0.99957	0.99904	0.99804	0.99628
17	1.00000	1.00000	0.99999	0.99998	0.99994	0.99985	0.99964	0.99921	0.99841
18		1.00000	0.99999	0.99998	0.99995	0.99987	0.99970	0.99935	0.99935
19 0.			1.00000	0.99999	0.99998	0.99996	0.99989	0.99975	0.99975
20				1.00000	1.00000	0.99999	0.99996	0.99991	0.99991
21						1.00000	0.99999	0.99997	0.99997
22							1.00000	0.99999	0.99999
23								1.00000	1.00000

P(X ≤ x) when X is N(0,1)

x	0.00	0.01	0.02	0.03	0.04	0.05	0.06	0.07	0.08	0.09
0.0	0.5000	0.5040	0.5080	0.5120	0.5160	0.5199	0.5239	0.5279	0.5319	0.5359
0.1	0.5398	0.5438	0.5478	0.5517	0.5557	0.5596	0.5636	0.5675	0.5714	0.5753
0.2	0.5793	0.5832	0.5871	0.5910	0.5948	0.5987	0.6026	0.6064	0.6103	0.6141
0.3	0.6179	0.6217	0.6255	0.6293	0.6331	0.6368	0.6406	0.6443	0.6480	0.6517
0.4	0.6554	0.6591	0.6628	0.6664	0.6700	0.6736	0.6772	0.6808	0.6844	0.6879
0.5	0.6915	0.6950	0.6985	0.7019	0.7054	0.7088	0.7123	0.7157	0.7190	0.7224
0.6	0.7257	0.7291	0.7324	0.7357	0.7389	0.7422	0.7454	0.7486	0.7517	0.7549
0.7	0.7580	0.7611	0.7642	0.7673	0.7704	0.7734	0.7764	0.7794	0.7823	0.7852
0.8	0.7881	0.7910	0.7939	0.7967	0.7995	0.8023	0.8051	0.8078	0.8106	0.8133
0.9	0.8159	0.8186	0.8212	0.8238	0.8264	0.8289	0.8315	0.8340	0.8365	0.8389
1.0	0.8413	0.8438	0.8461	0.8485	0.8508	0.8531	0.8554	0.8577	0.8599	0.8621
1.1	0.8643	0.8665	0.8686	0.8708	0.8729	0.8749	0.8770	0.8790	0.8810	0.8830
1.2	0.8849	0.8869	0.8888	0.8907	0.8925	0.8944	0.8962	0.8980	0.8997	0.9015
1.3	0.9032	0.9049	0.9066	0.9082	0.9099	0.9115	0.9131	0.9147	0.9162	0.9177
1.4	0.9192	0.9207	0.9222	0.9236	0.9251	0.9265	0.9279	0.9292	0.9306	0.9319
1.5	0.9332	0.9345	0.9357	0.9370	0.9382	0.9394	0.9406	0.9418	0.9429	0.9441
1.6	0.9452	0.9463	0.9474	0.9484	0.9495	0.9505	0.9515	0.9525	0.9535	0.9545
1.7	0.9554	0.9564	0.9573	0.9582	0.9591	0.9599	0.9608	0.9616	0.9625	0.9633
1.8	0.9641	0.9649	0.9656	0.9664	0.9671	0.9678	0.9686	0.9693	0.9699	0.9706
1.9	0.9713	0.9719	0.9726	0.9732	0.9738	0.9744	0.9750	0.9756	0.9761	0.9767
2.0	0.97725	0.97778	0.97831	0.97882	0.97932	0.97982	0.98030	0.98077	0.98124	0.98169
2.1	0.98214	0.98257	0.98300	0.98341	0.98382	0.98422	0.98461	0.98500	0.98537	0.98574
2.2	0.98610	0.98645	0.98679	0.98713	0.98745	0.98778	0.98809	0.98840	0.98870	0.98899
2.3	0.98928	0.98956	0.98983	0.99010	0.99036	0.99061	0.99086	0.99111	0.99134	0.99158
2.4	0.99180	0.99202	0.99224	0.99245	0.99266	0.99286	0.99305	0.99324	0.99343	0.99361
2.5	0.99379	0.99396	0.99413	0.99430	0.99446	0.99461	0.99477	0.99492	0.99506	0.99520
2.6	0.99534	0.99547	0.99560	0.99573	0.99585	0.99598	0.99609	0.99621	0.99632	0.99643
2.7	0.99653	0.99664	0.99674	0.99683	0.99693	0.99702	0.99711	0.99720	0.99728	0.99736
2.8	0.99744	0.99752	0.99760	0.99767	0.99774	0.99781	0.99788	0.99795	0.99801	0.99807
2.9	0.99813	0.99819	0.99825	0.99831	0.99836	0.99841	0.99846	0.99851	0.99856	0.99861
3.0	0.99865	0.99869	0.99874	0.99878	0.99882	0.99886	0.99889	0.99893	0.99897	0.99900
3.1	0.99903	0.99907	0.99910	0.99913	0.99916	0.99918	0.99921	0.99924	0.99926	0.99929
3.2	0.99931	0.99934	0.99936	0.99938	0.99940	0.99942	0.99944	0.99946	0.99948	0.99950
3.3	0.99952	0.99953	0.99955	0.99957	0.99958	0.99960	0.99961	0.99962	0.99964	0.99965
3.4	0.99966	0.99968	0.99969	0.99970	0.99971	0.99972	0.99973	0.99974	0.99975	0.99976
3.5	0.99977	0.99978	0.99978	0.99979	0.99980	0.99981	0.99982	0.99982	0.99983	0.99984
3.6	0.99984	0.99985	0.99985	0.99986	0.99986	0.99987	0.99987	0.99988	0.99988	0.99989
3.7	0.99989	0.99990	0.99990	0.99990	0.99991	0.99991	0.99992	0.99992	0.99992	0.99993
3.8	0.99993	0.99993	0.99993	0.99994	0.99994	0.99994	0.99994	0.99995	0.99995	0.99995
3.9	0.99995	0.99995	0.99996	0.99996	0.99996	0.99996	0.99996	0.99996	0.99997	0.99997

Constants for control charts

sample size n	A	A_2	A_3	c_4	B_3	B_4	B_5	B_6	d_2	d_3	D_1	D_2	D_3	D_4
2	2.121	1.880	2.659	0.7979	0	3.267	0	2.606	1.128	0.853	0	3.686	0	3.267
3	1.732	1.023	1.954	0.8862	0	2.568	0	2.776	1.693	0.888	0	4.358	0	2.575
4	1.500	0.729	1.628	0.9213	0	2.266	0	2.088	2.059	0.880	0	4.698	0	2.282
5	1.342	0.577	1.427	0.9400	0	2.089	0	1.964	2.326	0.864	0	4.918	0	2.115
6	1.225	0.483	1.287	0.9515	0.030	1.970	0.029	1.874	2.534	0.848	0	5.078	0	2.004
7	1.134	0.419	1.182	0.9594	0.118	1.882	0.113	1.806	2.704	0.833	0.205	5.203	0.076	1.924
8	1.061	0.373	1.099	0.9650	0.185	1.815	0.179	1.751	2.847	0.820	0.387	5.307	0.136	1.864
9	1.000	0.337	1.032	0.9693	0.239	1.761	0.232	1.707	2.970	0.808	0.546	5.394	0.184	1.816
10	0.949	0.308	0.975	0.9727	0.284	1.716	0.276	1.669	3.078	0.797	0.687	5.469	0.223	1.777
11	0.905	0.285	0.927	0.9754	0.321	1.679	0.313	1.637	3.173	0.787	0.812	5.534	0.256	1.744
12	0.866	0.266	0.886	0.9776	0.354	1.646	0.346	1.610	3.258	0.778	0.924	5.592	0.284	1.716
13	0.832	0.249	0.850	0.9794	0.382	1.618	0.374	1.585	3.336	0.770	1.026	5.646	0.308	1.692
14	0.802	0.235	0.817	0.9810	0.406	1.594	0.399	1.563	3.407	0.762	1.121	5.693	0.329	1.671
15	0.775	0.223	0.789	0.9823	0.428	1.572	0.421	1.544	3.472	0.755	1.207	5.737	0.348	1.652
16	0.750	0.212	0.763	0.9835	0.448	1.552	0.440	1.526	3.532	0.749	1.285	5.779	0.364	1.636
17	0.728	0.203	0.739	0.9845	0.466	1.534	0.458	1.511	3.588	0.743	1.359	5.817	0.379	1.621
18	0.707	0.194	0.718	0.9854	0.482	1.518	0.475	1.496	3.640	0.738	1.426	5.854	0.392	1.608
19	0.688	0.187	0.698	0.9862	0.497	1.503	0.490	1.483	3.689	0.733	1.490	5.888	0.404	1.596
20	0.671	0.180	0.680	0.9869	0.510	1.490	0.504	1.470	3.735	0.729	1.548	5.922	0.414	1.586
21	0.655	0.173	0.663	0.9876	0.523	1.477	0.516	1.459	3.778	0.724	1.606	5.950	0.425	1.575
22	0.640	0.167	0.647	0.9882	0.534	1.466	0.528	1.448	3.819	0.720	1.659	5.979	0.434	1.566
23	0.626	0.162	0.633	0.9887	0.545	1.455	0.539	1.438	3.858	0.716	1.710	6.006	0.443	1.557
24	0.612	0.157	0.619	0.9892	0.555	1.445	0.549	1.429	3.895	0.712	1.759	6.031	0.452	1.548
25	0.600	0.153	0.606	0.9886	0.565	1.435	0.559	1.420	3.931	0.709	1.804	6.058	0.459	1.541

$\bar{x}$-diagram

$\mu \pm A\sigma$

$\bar{\bar{x}} \pm A_2\bar{R}$

$\bar{x} \pm A_3\bar{s}$

R-diagram

$D_1\sigma$ and $D_2\sigma$

$D_3\bar{R}$ and $D_4\bar{R}$

s-diagram

$B_5\sigma$ and $B_6\sigma$

$B_3\bar{s}$ and $B_4\bar{s}$

References

Ackerman, R.B., Coleman, R.J., Leger, E. & MacDorman, J.C. (1988). Process quality management and improvement guidelines. AT & T, October, LCS 340.90.500.

Ahlmann, H. (1989). Quality strategies for survival and increased prosperity. The Quality Meeting at Linköping University, January 1989. (In Swedish.)

Akao, Y. (editor). (1990). *Quality Function Deployment: Integration Customer Requirements into Product Design*. Productivity Press, Cambridge, Massachusetts.

Akao, Y. (editor). (1991). *Hoshin Kanri. Policy Deployment for Successful TQM*. Productivity Press, Cambridge, Massachusetts.

Akao, Y. & Ono, M. (1993). Recent development in cost deployment and QFD in Japan. *Proceedings EOQ Conference, Helsinki, 1993*, vol. 2, 250-256.

American Productivity & Quality Center (1993). *Benchmarking the Best. A Look at the Finalists' Applications for the 1992 International Benchmarking Awards*. American Productivity & Quality Center, Houson, Texas.

Amon, V.N. & Mogollon-Seemer, M.T. (1990). The Deming prize process at FPL. *ASQC 44th Annual Quality Congress Transactions*, 10-15.

Andersson, R. (1991). *QFD – A System for Efficient Product Development*. Studentlitteratur, Lund. (In Swedish.)

Andreasen, M.M. & Hein, L. (1987). *Integrated Product Development*. IFS Publications/Springer Verlag, Kempston.

Application Guidelines for 1993 Malcolm Baldrige National Quality Award. (Can be ordered from the National Institute of Standards and Technology, Route 270 and Quince Orchard Road, Administration Building, Room A537, Gaithersburg, MD 20899, USA.)

Argyris, C. (1990). *Overcoming Organizational Defences*. Prenctice Hall, New York.

Arnerup, B. & Edvardsson, B. (1992). *Marketing of Services*. Studentlitteratur, Lund. (In Swedish.)

References

Asaka, T. & Ozeki, K. (1990). *Handbook of Quality Tools.* Productivity Press, Cambridge, Massachusetts.

Ascher, H. (1981). Weibull distribution vs Weibull process. *1981 Proceedings Annual Reliability and Maintainability Symposium,* 426-431.

Ascher, H. & Feingold, H. (1984). *Repairable Systems Reliability.* Marcel Dekker, Inc., New York.

Aven, T. (1992). *Reliability and Risk Analysis.* Elsevier Publishing Company, Barking, Essex.

Axland, S. (1992). Small wonders. *Quality Progress,* **25**, November, 29-34.

Bain, L.J. (1991). *Statistical Analysis of Reliability and Life Testing Models,* Second Edition. Marcel Dekker, Inc., New York.

Barlow, R.E. (1984). Mathematical theory of reliability: a historical perspective. *IEEE Transactions on Reliability,* **R-33**, 16-20.

Barlow, R.E. & Campo, (1975). Total time on test processes and applications to failure data analysis. *Reliability and Fault Tree Analysis,* R.E. Barlow, J. Fussell & N.D. Singpurwalla (ed.), SIAM, Philadelphia, 451-481.

Barlow, R.E. & Proschan, F. (1965). *Mathematical Theory of Reliability.* John Wiley & Sons, New York.

Barlow, R.E. & Proschan, F. (1981). *Statistical Theory of Reliability and Life Testing.* Second Edition. To Begin With, Silver Spring.

Barnard, G. (1990). Fisher: a retrospective. *Chance,* **3**, 22-28.

Barra, R. (1983). *Putting Quality Circles to Work: A Practical Strategy for Boosting Productivity and Profits.* McGrawHill, New York.

Becker, R., Plaut,H. & Runge, I. (1927). *Anwendungen der Mathematischen Statistik auf Problem der Massenfabrikaten.* Springer-Verlag, Berlin.

Bendell, T. & Mellor, P. (1986). *Software Reliability. State of the Art Report.* Pergamon Infotech Ltd, London.

Bendell, A., Disney, J. & Pridmore, W.A. (1989). *Taguchi Methods Applied in World Industry.* (Ed. Bendell, A., Disney, J. & Pridmore, W.A.). IFS Publication, Bedford.

Bergman, B. (1985). On reliability theory and its applications (with discussion). *Scandinavian Journal of Statistics,* **12**, 1-41.

Bergman, B., Gustafsson, A. & Gustafsson, N. (1991). Quality Function Deployment as a tool for the improvement of a course in Total Quality Management and Methodology. In *Proceedings from Deuxieme Symposium Renault-Volvo de la Qualité,* November 4-6, Paris.

Bergman, B. & Klefsjö, B. (1984). The total time on test concept and its use in reliability theory. *Operations Research,* **32,** 596-605.

Bergman, B. & Klefsjö, B. (1985). Burn-in models and TTT-transforms. *QRE International,* 1, 125-130.

Bertsch, B. & Williams, R. (1993). The Quality Paradox - quality and productivity improvement; does it always pays? Presented at The World Productivity Conference, Stockholm.

Birnbaum, Z.W., Esary, J.D. & Saunders, S.C. (1961). Multicomponent systems and structures and their reliability. *Technometrics,* 3, 55-77.

Bisgaard, S. (1989). Book Review. *Technometrics,* 31, 257-258.

Bitner, M.J. (1992). Managing the evidence of service. In *Proceedings from QUIS 3,* Karlstad, June 1992.

Blanchard, B.S. (1978). *Design and Manage Life Cycle Cost.* MA Press, New York.

Bossert, J.L. (1991). *Quality Function Deployment: A Practitioner's Approach.* ASQC Quality Press, Milwaukee.

Bowles, J. & Hammond, J. (1991). *Beyond Quality.* The Berkeley Publishing Group, New York.

Box, G.E.P., & Bisgaard, S. (1987). The scientific context of quality improvement. *Quality Progress,* **20,** June, 54-61.

Box, G.E.P., Bisgaard, S. & Fung, C.A. (1988). An explanation and criticism of Taguchi's contribution to quality engineering. *Quality and Reliability Engineering,* **4:2,** 123-132.

Box, G.E.P. & Draper, N.R. (1967). *Evolutionary Operation.* John Wiley & Sons, New York.

Box, G.E.P. & Draper, N.R. (1987). *Empirical Model Building and Response Surfaces.* John Wiley & Sons, New York.

Box, G.E.P., Hunter, W.G. & Hunter, J.S. (1978). *Statistics for Experimenters.* John Wiley & Sons, New York.

Box, G.E.P., Joiner, L.W., Rohan, S. & Sensenbrenner, F.J. (1989). Quality in the community; one city's experience. Research Report no 36, Center for Quality and Productivity Improvement, University of Wisconsin-Madison.

Brimson, J.A. (1991). *Activity Accounting – an ABC Approach.* John Wiley & Sons, New York.

Brimson, J.A. (1991). *Activity Based Investment Management.* American Management Association, New York.

Brinker, B.J. (editor) (1992). *Emerging Practices in Cost Management.* 1992 Edition. Waren, Gorham & Lamont, Boston, Massachusetts.

British Deming Association (1992). *Beyond ISO 9000.* Booklet No 123, British Deming Association, Salisbury.

British Deming Association (1992). *Elements of Successful Customer/Supplier Relationships.* Booklet, British Deming Association, Salisbury.

British Deming Association (1992). *A Perspective on Dr Deming's Theory of Profound Knowledge.* Booklet No W1, British Deming Association, Salisbury.

British Deming Association (1993). *Out of the Crisis with George, Mises and Deming.* Booklet No W3, British Deming Asociation, Salisbury.

Brown, M.G. (1993). *Baldrige Award Winning Quality.* Third Edition. ASQC Quality Press, Milwaukee.

Bush, D & Dooley, K. (1989). The Deming Award and Baldrige Award: how they compare. *Quality Progress,* 22, January, 28-30.

Buzzell, R.D. & Gale, B.T. (1987). *The PIMS Principles. Linking Strategy to Performance.* The Free Press, New York.

Cali, J.F. (1993). *TQM for Purchasing Management.* McGrawHill, New York,

Camp, R. (1989). Benchmarking. The search for industry best practices that lead to superior performance. *Quality Progress,* 22, January, 61-68, February, 70-75, March, 76-82, April, 62-69.

Camp, R. (1989). *Benchmarking. The Search for Industry Best Practices that Lead to Superior Performance.* ASQC Quality Press, Milwaukee

References

Carlzon, J. (1987). *Moments of Thruth.* Ballinger, Cambridge, Massachusetts.

Carter, D.E. & Baker, B.S. (1992). *Concurrent Engineering: The Product Development Environment for the 1990s.* Addison-Wesley Publishing Co Inc., New York.

Chambers, J.M., Cleveland, W.S., Beat, K. & Tukey, P.A. (1983). *Graphical Methods for Data Analysis.* Wadsworth International & Duxbury Press, Murray Hill.

Chan, L.K., Cheng, S.W. & Spiring, F.A. (1988). A new measure of process capability C_{pm}. *Journal of Quality Technology,* **20**, 162-175.

Chou, C.K. (1987). *Quality Programming. Developing and Testing Software with Statistical Quality Control.* John Wiley & Sons, New York.

Chou, Y.M., Owen, D.B. & Borrego, S.A. (1990). Lower confidence limits on process capability indices. *Journal of Quality Technology,* **22**, 223-229.

Cobb, R.H. & Mills, H.D. (1990). Engineering software under statistical quality control. *IEEE Software,* November, 44-54.

Cochran, W.G. & Cox, G.M. (1957). *Experimental Designs.* Second Edition, John Wiley & Sons, New York.

Cole, R.E. (1991). Comparing the Baldrige and the Deming. *Journal for Quality and Participation,* July/August, 94-104.

Cottman, R.J. (1993). *A Guidebook to ISO 9000 and ANSI/ASQC Q 90.* ASQC Quality Press, Milwaukee.

Cox, D.R. (1984). *Analysis of survival data.* Chapman and Hall Ltd, London.

Cox, D.R. & Oakes, D. (1984). *Failure time data analysis.* Chapman and Hall Ltd, London.

Crosby, P. (1979). *Quality is Free.* McGraw-Hill, New York.

Crosby, P. (1984). *Quality Without Tears - The Art of Hassle-Free Management.* McGraw-Hill, New York.

Crosby, P. (1986). *Running Things - The Art of Making Things Happen.* McGraw-Hill, New York.

Crow, L. (1972). Reliability growth modelling. US Army Material System Analysis Activity, Aberdeen Proving Ground, M.D., Technical Report No 55.

Crowder, M.J., Kimber, A.C., Smith, R.L. & Sweeting, T.J. (1991). *Statistical Analysis of Reliability Data*. Chapman and Hall Ltd, London.

Cryer, J.D. & Miller, R.B. (1991). *Statistics for Business: Data Analysis and Modelling*. PWS-KENT Publishing Company, New York.

Csíkszentmihályi, M. (1990). Flow. The psychology of optimal experience.

Daeves, K.H. (1924). The utilization of statistics. A new and valuable aid in industrial research and in the evaluation of test data. *Testing*. March, 173-189.

Dahlgaard, J.J., Kanji, G.K. & Kristensen, K. (1990). A comparative study of quality control methods and principles in Japan, Korea and Denmark. *Total Quality Management*, **1**, 115-132.

Dahlgaard, J.J., Kristensen, K. & Kanji, G. (1993). *The Quality Journey*. Carfax Publishing Co, London.

Dale, B.G. & Allan, D.G. (1993). Japan – myth or miracle. *The TQM Magazine*, **5**, June, 55-60.

Daniels, C. (1976). *Applications of Statisticals to Industrial Experimentation*. John Wiley & Sons, New York.

Davenport, T.H. (1992). *Process Innovations: Reengineering Work Through Information Technology*. Harvard Business Press, Boston, Massachusetts.

Day, R.G. (1993). *Quality Fuction Deployment: Linking a Company with Its Customers*. ASQC Quality Press, Milwaukee.

Deming, W.E. (1982). *Quality, Productivity and Competitive Position*. Massachusetts Institute of Technology, Massachusetts.

Deming, W.E. (1986). *Out of the Crisis*. Cambridge University Press, Cambridge, Massachusetts. Reprinted by permission of MIT and The W. Edwards Deming Institute. Published by MIT, Center for Advanced Engineering Study, Cambridge MA 02139. Copyright © 1986 by W. Edwards Deming.

Deming, W.E. (1993). *The New Economics for Industry, Government and Education*. MIT Center for Advanced Engineering Study, Massachusetts.

DeRosa, D., Ashley, K.M. & Bernstein, A.J. (1990). Process characterization: the key to quality planning. *ASQC 44th Annual Quality Congress Transactions*, 159-168.

Dertouzos, M.L., Lester, R.K. & Solow, R.M. (1989). *Made in America: Regaining the Productive Edge.* The MIT Press, Cambridge, Massachusetts.

Dodge, H.F & Romig, H.G. (1941). Single Sampling and Double Sampling Inspection Tables. *The Bell System Technical Journal,* 20, 1-61.

Draper, N.R. & Smith, H. (1981). *Applied Regression Analysis.* Second Edition. John Wiley & Sons, New York.

Drucker, P.F. (1954). *The Practice of Management.* Harper & Row, New York.

Duane, J.T. (1964). Learning curve to reliability monitoring. *IEEE Transactions on Aerospace,* 2, 563-566.

Duncan, A.J. (1986) *Quality Control and Industrial Statistics.* Fifth Edition. Irwin Inc., Homewood. (The first edition was published in 1951.)

Dyer, M. (1992). *The Cleanroom Approach to Quality Software Development.* John Wiley & Sons, New York.

Epstein, B. & Sobel, M. (1953). Life testing. *Journal of American Statistical Association,* 48, 486-502.

Evans, D.H. (1992). *Probability and Its Applications for Engineers.* Marcel Dekker, New York.

Feigenbaum, A.V. (1951). *Total Quality Control.* McGraw-Hill, New York. (Third edition was published in 1983.)

Feigenbaum, A.V. (1987). Total quality developement into the 1990's – an international perspectives. *EOQC-Conference Proceedings in Munich,* 1987.

Ferguson, I. (1991). The goal for the future. *Managing Service Quality,* 1, May, 233-235.

Fisher, D.C. (1993). *The Simplified Baldrige Award Organization Assessment.* Lincoln-Bradley Publishing Group, New York.

Fornell, C. (1992). A national customer satisfaction barometer: the Swedish experience. *Journal of Marketing,* 56, 6-21.

Fournier, F.F. (1993). The Rank Xerox quality journey. *European Quality,* Special Showcase Edition, June, 32-35.

Futami, R. (1986). The outline of seven management tools for QC. *Rep. of Statistical Application Research, JUSE,* **33:2,** 7-26.

Garvin, D.A. (1988). *Managing Quality.* The Free Press, New York.

Garvin, D.A. (1993). Building a learning organization. *Harvard Business Review,* **71,** July-August, 78-91.

Gitlow, H.S. & Gitlow, S.J. (1986). *The Deming Guide to Quality and Competitive Position.* ASQC Quality Press, Milwaukee.

Gitlow, H.S. & Gitlow, S.J. Oppenheim, A. & Oppenheim, R. (1989). *Tools and Metohods for the Improvement of Quality.* Irwin Inc., Boston, Massachusetts.

Gitlow, H.S. & Loredo, E.N. (1992). Total Quality Management at Florida Power & Light Company: a case study. *Quality Engineering,* **5(1),** 123-158.

Gitlow, H.S. & Loredo, E.N. (1993). Total Quality Management at Xerox: a case study. *Quality Engineering,* **5(3),** 402-432.

Godfrey, A.B. (1993). Ten areas for future research in Total Quality Management. *Quality Management Journal,* **1,** 47-70.

Green, P.E. & Rao, V.R. (1971). Conjoint measurement for quantifying judgement data. *Journal of Marketing Research,* **8,** 355-363.

Green, P.E. & Srinivasan, V. (1978). Conjoint analysis in consumer research: issues and outlook. *Journal of Consumer Research,* September, 103-123.

Grönroos, C. (1990). *Service Management and Marketing in the Service Sector.* Marketing Science Institute, Cambridge, Massachusetts and Chartwell-Bratt and Studentlitteratur, Lund.

Gummesson, E. (1988). *Quality – The Ericsson Approach.* Ericsson, HF/DHQC, Stockholm.

Gunnarsson, C. & Holmberg, C. (1993). TQM - a way to change attitudes to total quality and continuous improvement. Master Thesis, Division of Quality Technology, Linköping University, Linköping. (In Swedish.)

Gunnerhed, M. (1991). Assessment of safety-critical electronics and software. FOA Report C 30636-3.8, National Defense Research Establishment, Department of Information Technology, Linköping.

Gunter, B.H. (1989). The use and abuse of C_{pk}. *Quality Progress,* **22**, January 72-73, March 108-109, May 79-80, July 86-87.

Gustafsson, A. & Gustafsson, N. (1993). Exceeding customer expectations. In Gustafsson, A. (1993). QFD and Conjoint Analysis - the key to customer oriented products. Linköping Studies in Science and Technology, Thesis No. 393, LiU-Tek-Lic.1993:35, Linköping University, Linköping.

Gustafsson, A. (1993). QFD and Conjoint Analysis - the key to customer oriented products. Linköping Studies in Science and Technology, Thesis No. 393, LiU-Tek-Lic.1993:35, Linköping University, Linköping.

Hammer, M. & Champy, J. (1993). *Reengineering the Corporation. A Manifesto for Business Revolution.* Harper Business, New York.

Hannam, R.G. (1993). *Kaizen for Europe.* IFS Ltd, Bedford.

Harrington, H.J. (1991). *Business Process Improvement.* McGrawHill, New York.

Hart, C.W.L.& & Bogan, C.E. (1992). *The Baldrige.* McGrawHill, New York.

Helling, J. (1991). *The World Champions - a New Generation of Manufacturing Companies.* Sellin & Partner, Stockholm. (In Swedish.)

Henkoff, R. (1993). The hot new seal of quality. *Fortune,* June 28, 68-71.

Henley, E.J., & Kumamoto, H. (1981). *Reliability Engineering and Risk Assessment.* Prentice-Hall, London.

Herzberg, F. (1969). *The Motivation to Work.* John Wiley & Sons, New York.

Hoaglin, D.C., Mosteller, F. & Tukey, J.W. (1983). *Understanding Robust and Exploratory Data Analysis.* John Wiley & Sons, New York.

Hogg, R.V. & Ledolter, J. (1992). *Applied Statistics for Engineers and Physical Scientists.* Second Edition. Macmillan Publishing Company, Don Mills, Ontario

Hogg, R.V. & Tanis, E.A. (1988). *Probability and Statistical Inference.* Third Edition. Macmillan, New York.

Hollings, L. (1992). Clearing up the confusion. *The TQM Magazine,* **4**, June, 149-151.

Hubka, V. (1987). *Principles of Engineering Design.* Heürika, Zürich.

461

Hudiberg, J.J. (1991). *Winning with Quality. The FPL Story.* Quality Resources, New York.

Imai, M. (1986). *Kaizen. The Key to Japan's Competitive Success.* Random House, Inc., New York.

IEC Standard 812. Analysis Techniques for System Reliability. Procedure for Failure Mode and Effect Analysis (FMEA). Bureau Central de la Commission Electrotechnique Internationale, 3 Rue de Varembé, Geneve.

IEC Standard 1025. Analysis Techniques for System Reliability. Fault Tree Analysis (FTA). Bureau Central de la Commission Electrotechnique Internationale, 3 Rue de Varembé, Geneve.

IPA Software Technology (ed.). (1989). High Quality Software Development by QFD. Computer Age Inc.

Isaacson, D.N. (1990). *Life Cycle Cost Analysis.* SAE RMS Guidebook, Warrendale, PA.

Ishikawa, K. (1982). *Guide to Quality Control.* Asian Productivity Press, Tokyo.

Ishikawa, K. (1985). *What is Total Quality Control? The Japanese Way.* Prentice Hall, Engelwood Cliffs, N.J.

Ishikawa, K. (1989). How to apply company-wide quality control in foreign countries. *Quality Progress,* **22**, September, 70-74.

Jaehn, A.H. (1991). The zone control chart. *Quality Progress,* **24**, July, 65-68.

Jaehn, A.H. (1989). Zone control charts find new application. *1989 ASQC Quality Congress Transactions,* 890-893.

Jaehn, A.H. (1987). Zone control charts – SPC made easy. *Quality,* October, 51-54.

Jelinski, Z & Moranda, P.B. (1972). Software Reliability Research. (W. Freiberger, ed.) *Statistical Computer Performance Evaluation.* Academic Press, New York, 465-484.

Johansson, H.J., McHugh, P., Pendlebury, A.J. & Wheeler III, W.A. (1993). *Business Process Reengineering.* John Wiley & Sons, New York.

Johnson, H.T. & Kaplan, R.S. (1987). *Relevance Lost – the Rise and Fall of Management Accounting.* Harvard Business School Press, London.

Johnson, P.L. (1993). ISO 9000. *Meeting the New International Standards.* McGraw-Hill, New York.

Jolliffe, I.T. (1986). *Principal Component Analysis.* Springer Verlag, Berlin.

Juran, J.M. (ed.) (1951). *Quality Control Handbook.* McGraw-Hill, New York. (Third edition was published in 1988.)

Juran, J.M. (1964). *Managerial Breakthrough.* McGraw-Hill, New York.

Juran, J.M. (1986). The Quality Trilogy. *Quality Progress,* **19**, August, 19-24.

Juran, J.M. (1989). *Juran on Leadership for Quality.* McGraw-Hill, New York

Juran, J.M. (1992). *Juran on Quality by Design.* McGraw-Hill, New York.

Juran, J.M. & Gryna, F.M. (1980). *Quality Planning and Analysis.* Second Edition, McGraw-Hill, New York.

JUSE (1990). *Deming Prize 40, November 1990.* The 40th anniversary for the establishment of the Deming Prize. (Can be ordered from JUSE, 5-10-11 Sendagaya, Shibuya-ku, Tokyo, Japan.)

Kackar, R.N. & Shoemaker, A.C. (1986). A cost-effective method for improving manufacturing processe. *AT&T Technical Journal,* **65**, 39-50.

Kackar, R.N. (1985). Off-line quality control, parameter design, and the Taguchi method. *Journal of Quality Technology,* **17**, 176-209.

Kane, V.E. (1986). Process capability indices. *Journal of Quality Control,* **18**, 41-52.

Kano, N., Seraku, N. & Takahashi, F. (1984). Attractive quality and must-be quality. *Quality,* **14**, No 2, 39-44. (In Japanese.)

Kapur, K.C. & Lamberson, L.R. (1977). *Reliability in Engineering Design,* John Wiley & Sons, New York.

Karatsu, H. (1988). *TQC Wisdom of Japan.* Productivity Press, Cambridge, MA.

Kececioglu, D. (1991). *Reliability Engineering Handbook.* Prenctice Hall, New Jersey

Kiesler, C.A. (1971). *The Psychology of Commitment.* Academic Press, New York.

Kilian, C.S. (1993). *The World of Edwards Deming.* Second Edition. SPC Press, Knoxville.

King, J.R. (1971). *Probability Charts for Decision Making.* Industrial Press, New York.

King, J.R. (1987). *Better Design in Half the Time – Implementing QFD in USA.* G.O.A.L./QPC.

Kondo, Y. (1991). *Human Motivation - A Key Factor for Management,* 3A Corporation. (Published in Japanese in 1989).

Kondo, Y. (1993). Quality and human motivation. *European Quality,* Special Showcase Edition, June, 44-50.

Kondo, Y. (1993). Quality education in Japan. *Total Quality Management,* **4**, 115-126.

Kopetz, H. (1979). *Software Reliability.* MacMillan Press, London.

Kotter, J.P. (1988). *The Leadership Factor.* The Free Press, New York.

Kotter, J.P. (1990). *A Force for Change. How Leadership Differs from Management.* The Free Press, New York.

Kotter, J.P. & Heskett, J.L. (1992). *Corporate Culture and Performance.* The Free Press, New York.

Kotz, S. & Johnson, N.L. (1993). *Process Capability Indices.* Chapman & Hall, London.

Krafcik, J.F. & MacDuffie, J.P. (1989). Explaining high performance manufacturing: the international automotive assembly plant study. *IMVP International Policy Forum.*

Kumar, U., Klefsjö, B.& Granholm, S. (1989). Reliability investigation for a fleet of Load Haul Dump Machines in a Swedish mine. *Reliability Engineering and Systems Saftey,* **26**, 341-361.

Labovitz, G.H. & Chang, Y.S. (1990). Learn from the best. *Quality Progress,* **23**, May, 81-85

Lamprecht, J.L. (1992). *ISO 9000. Preparing for Registration.* Marcel Dekker, New York.

Lawless, J.F. (1982). *Statistical Models and Methods for Lifetime Data.* John Wiley & Sons, New York.

Lawton, R. (1993). *Creating a Customer Centered Culture: Leadership in Quality, Innovation and Speed.* ASQC Quality Press, Milwaukee.

Lee, W.S., Grosh, D.L., Tillman, F.A. & Lie, C.H. (1985). Fault tree analysis methods and applications - a review. *IEEE Transactions on Reliability,* **R-34**, 194-203.

Lillrank, P. & Kano, N. (1989). *Continuous Improvement.* Center for Japanese Studies, University of Michigan, Ann Arbor, MI.

Littlewood, B. (1987). *Software Reliability, Achievement and Assessment.* Blackwell, London.

Lochner, R.H. & Matar, J.E. (1990). *Designing for Quality.* ASQC Quality Press, Milwaukee.

Lowe, T.A. & Mazzeo, J.M. (1986). Crosby, Deming, Juran – three preachers, one religion. *Quality,* **25**, September, 22-25.

Luce, R.D. & Tukey, J.W. (1964). Simultaneous conjoint measurement: a new type of fundamental measurement. *Journal of Mathematical Psychology,* **1**, 1-27.

McLean, G.E. (1993). *Documenting Quality for ISO 9000 and Other Industry Standards.* ASQC Quality Press, Milwaukee.

Mann, N.R. (1989). *The Keys to Excellence. The Story of the Deming Philosophy.* Third Edition. Prestwick Books, Los Angeles.

Mann, N.R., Schafer, R.E., & Singpurwalla, N.D. (1974). *Methods for Statistical Analysis of Reliability and Life Data.* John Wiley & Sons, New York.

Martz, H.F. & Waller, R.A. (1982). *Bayesian Reliability Analysis.* John Wiley & Sons, New York.

Maslow, A.H. (1943). A theory of human motivation. *Psychological Review,* **50**, 370-396.

McCabe, W.J. (1989). Examining processes improves operations. *Quality Progress,* **22**, July, 26-34.

Mekanresultat 84216 (1984). *LCC - a Technique to Reduce the Total Cost during a Product's Life.* Sveriges Mekanförbund, Stockholm. (In Swedish.)

Melan, E.H. (1993). *Process Management. Methods for Improving the Products and Services.* McGraw-Hill, New York.

Melan, E.M. (1986). Process management. *ASQC 40th Annual Quality Congress Transactions*, 329-342.

Milburn, I. (1992). A race against time. *Manufacturing Breakthrough*, 1, 15-20.

Mills, H.D., Dyer, M. & Linger, R. (1987). Cleanroom software engineering. *IEEE Software*, September, 19-24.

MIL-HDBK 217F Reliability Prediction for Electronic Systems. National Technical Information Service, Springfield, Virginia.

MIL-STD 1629 Failure Mode and Effects Analysis. National Technical Information Service, Springfield.

Mizuno, S. (1988). *Management for Quality Improvement. The Seven New QC Tools.* English translation copyright © 1988 by Productivity Press, Inc., PO Box 13390, Portland, OR 97213-0390, (800) 394-6868. Reprinted by permission.

Montgomery, D.C. (1991). *Introduction to Statistical Quality Control.* Second Edition. John Wiley & Sons, New York.

Montgomery, D.C. (1991). *Design and Analysis of Experiments* Third Edition. John Wiley & Sons, New York.

Motorola (1989). Six sigma quality - TQC, the American style. *Hinshitsu, Journal of the JSQC*, July.

Musa, J.D., Iannino, A. & Okumoto, K. (1987). *Software Reliability.* McGraw-Hill, New York.

Myers, G.J. (1976). *Software Reliability: Principles and Practices.* McGraw-Hill, New York.

Nayatani, Y. (1986). Seven management tools for QC. *Rep. of Statistical Application Research*, JUSE, **33**, June 1-6.

Neave, H.R. (1990). *The Deming Dimension.* SPC Press, Inc, Tennesee.

Nakajima, S. (1988). *TPM - An Introduction to Total Productive Maintenance.* Productivity Press, Cambridge, Massachusetts.

Nelson, W. (1979). How to analyse data with simple plots. ASQC Basic Reference in Quality Control: Statistical Techniques. ASQC Quality Press, Milwaukee.

Nelson, W. (1982). *Applied Life Data Analysis.* John Wiley & Sons, New York.

Nelson, W. (1990). *Accelerated Testing. Statistical Models, Test Plans and Data Analysis.* John Wiley & Sons, New York.

Nonaka, I, (1991). The knowledge-creating company. *Harvard Business Review,* November/December, 96-104.

Nonaka, I, (1993). The history of the Quality Circle. *Quality Progress,* **26,** September, 81-83.

Normann, R. (1984). *Service Management.* John Wiley & Sons, New York.

O'Conner, P.D.T. (1991). Practical Reliability Engineering. Third Edition. John Wiley & Sons, New York.

Oakland, J.S. & Followell, R. F. (1990). *Statistical Process Control. A Practical Guide.* Heinemann Professional Publishing Ltd., Oxford.

Oakland, J.S. (1991). *Total Quality Management.* Heinemann Professional Publishing Ltd., Oxford.

Ohmae, K. (1982). *The Mind of the Strategist.* McGraw-Hill, New York.

Oliver, N. (1990). Employee commitment and total quality control. *International Journal of Quality and Reliability Management,* **7,** 21-29.

ORLIGAME (1989). *Product Liability in Europe. A Practical Guide for Industry.*

O'Toole, J. (editor). (1974). *Work and Quality of Life. Resource Papers for Work in America.* MIT Press, Cambridge, Massachusetts.

Page, E.S. (1954). Continuous Inspection Schemes. *Biometrics,* **41,** 100-114.

Parasuraman, A., Zeithaml, V.A. & Berry, L.L. (1984). A conceptual model of service quality and its implications for future research. Report from Marketing Science Insitute.

Parasuraman, A., Zeithaml, V.A. & Berry, L.L. (1985). A conceptual model of service quality and its implications for future research. *Journal of Marketing,* **49,** 41-50.

Pascale, R. (1991). *Managing on the Edge.* Penguin.

Peters, T. (1992) *Liberation Management, Necessary Disorganization for the Nanosecond Nineties,* Macmillan, London.

Peters, T. & Waterman Jr., R. H. (1982). *In Search of Excellence.* Harper & Row, New York.

Peters, T. (1987). *Thriving on Chaos.* Harper Collins Publisher, New York.

Phadke, M.S. (1989). *Quality Engineering Using Robust Design.* Prentice-Hall, London.

Pignatiello, J.J. & Ramberg, J.S. (1993). Process capability indices: just say "no!". In *ASQC Quality Congress Transactions 1993*, Boston, 92-104.

Popper, K.R. (1956). *The Logic of Scientific Discovery.* Harper & Row, New York.

Powers, V.J. (1993). The Toyota customer satisfaction framework. *Continuous Journey,* 1, April/May, 42-44.

Pyzdek, T. (1992). *Pyzdek's guide to SPC. Vol. 2. Applications and special topics.* ASQC Quality Press, Milwaukee.

Randall, L. (1993). Perceptual blueprinting. *Managing Service Quality,* 1, 7-12.

Reichheld, F.F. (1993). Loyalty Based Management, *Harvard Business Review,* 71, 64-73.

ReVelle, J.B. (1989). *The New Quality Technology.* Hughes Aircraft Company.

Rigdon, S.E. & Basu, A.P. (1989). The power law process: a model for the reliability of repairable systems. *Journal of Quality Technology,* 21, 251-260.

Rigdon, S.E. & Basu, A.P. (1990). The effect of assuming a homogeneous Poisson process when the true process is a power law process. *Journal of Quality Technology,* 22, 111-117.

Roberts, S.W. (1959). Control charts tests based on geometric moving averages. *Technometrics,* 1, 239-250.

Roche, J.G. (1989). *Product Liability.* IFS Publications, Bedford.

Ross, P.J. (1988). *Taguchi Techniques for Quality Engineering.* McGraw-Hill, New York.

Ryan, T. P. (1989). *Statistical Methods for Quality Improvement.* John Wiley & Sons, New York.

Salancik, G.P. (1977). Commitment and control of organizational behaviour and belief. *New Directions in Organizational Behaviour,* Staw, B.M & Salancik, G.P. (red.), St. Clair Press.

Sayle, A.J. (1991). *Meeting ISO 9000 in a TQM World.* Allan J. Sayle Ltd., Hantshire.

Scharp, A. (1988). Electrolux, in statements of the 14 founding companies, *European Foundation for Quality Management.* 15 September 1988, Brussels, 23-24.

Scheaffer, R.L. & McClave, J.T. (1990). *Probability and Statistics for Engineers.* Third Edition. PWS-KENT Publishing Company, Boston, Massachusetts.

Schein, E.H. (1985). *Organizational Culture and Leadership.* Jossey-Bass.

Scherkenbach, W. W. (1986). *Deming Route to Quality and Productivity.* Ceepress Books, Washington.

Schonberger, R.J. (1984). *Japanese Manufacturing Techniques.* The Free Press, New York.

Schulmeyer, G.G. & McManus, J.I. (1987). *Handbook of Software Quality Assurance.* Schulmeyer, G.G. & McManus, J.I. (ed.), van Nostrand Reinhold Company, New York.

Selby, R.W., Basili, V.R. & Baker, F. T. (1985). Cleanroom software development: an empirical evaluation. University of Maryland, TR-1415.

Senge, P.M. (1990). *The Fifth Discipline; The Art and Practice of the Learning Organization,* Dubleday Currency, New York.

Senior, M. & Akehurst, G. (1990). The perceptual blueprinting paradigm. In *Proceedings from QUIS II, a Symposium on Quality in Service,* Norwalk, Connecticut, July 8-11, 1992.

Shewhart, W.A. (1931). *Economic Control of Quality of Manufactured Product.* Van Nostrand, New York.

Shewhart, W.A. (1939). *Statistical Method. From the Viewpoint of Quality Control.* Graduate Scool of the Department of Agriculture, Washington, D.C.

Sheridan, B. (1993). *Policy Deloymnet: the TQM Approach to Longe-Range Planning.* ASQC Quality Press, Milwaukee.

Shilling, E.G. (1982). *Acceptance Sampling in Quality Control.* Marcel Dekker, New York.

Shina, S.G. (1993). *Concurrent Engineering and Design of Manufacture of Electronic Products.* Van Nostrand Reinhold, New York.

Shores, A.R. (1988). *Survival for the Fittest. Total Quality and Management Evolution.* ASQC Quality Press, Milwaukee.

Shostack, G.L. (1984). Designing services that deliver. *Harvard Business Review,* January/February.

Slabey, W.R. (1990). QFD: A basic primer. Excerpts from the implementation manual for the three days QFD workshop. *The Second Symposium on Quality Function Deployment,* Novi, Michigan. GOAL/QPC, Automotive Division, ASQC, and the Arerican Supplier Institute.

Slater, R. (1991). *Integrated Process Management.* McGrawHill, New York.

Smith, S. (1989). Trends in TQM. *The TQM Magazine,* 1, 257-260.

Spendolini, M.J. (1992). *The Benchmarking Book.* Amacon.

Spitzer R.D. (1993). Valuing TQM through rigorous financial analysis. *Quality Progress,* **26**, July, 49-54.

Stangenberg, K. (1990). From a small start..., *Quality Link, European Foundation for Quality Management Newsletter,* 2:5, 5-6.

Steeples, M.M. (1993). *The Corporate Guide to Malcolm Baldrige National Quality Award.* Second edition. ASQC Press, Milwaukee, Wisconsin.

Stigler, S.M. (1977). Eight centuries of sampling inspection. The trial of the pyx. *Journal of Statistical Association of America,* **72**, 493-500.

Sullivan, L.P. (1984). Reducing variability: A new approach to quality. *Quality Progress,* **17**, 15-21.

Sullivan, L.P. (1986). The seven stages in company-wide quality control. *Quality Progress,* **19**, May, 77-83.

Suzuki, T. (1992). *New Directions for Total Productivity Maintenance.* Productivity Press, Cambridge, Massachusetts. (Published in Japanese in 1989 with the title "TPM No Shin Tenkai".)

Taguchi, G. & Wu, Y. (1979). *Introduction to Off-line Quality Control.* Central Japan Quality Control Assciation, Tokyo.

Taguchi, G. (1986). *Introduction to Quality Engineering.* Asian Productivity Center, Tokyo.

Taguchi,G., Elsayed, E.A. & Hsiang, T.C. (1989). *Quality Engineering in Production Systems.* McGraw-Hill, New York.

Tajiri, M. & Gotoh, F. (1992). *TPM Implementation. A Japanese Approach.* McGraw-Hill, New York.

Taylor, A. & Adair, R. (1993). Quality awards and quality models in the context of small organisations. *Proceedings from EFQM's Conference TQM - The Learning Edge,* Amsterdam 31 March - 2 April.

Tukey, J. (1977). *Exploratory Data Analysis.* Addison-Wesley, Reading, MA.

Vesely, W.E. Goldberg F. F., Roberts, N.H. & Hassl, D.F. (1981). *Fault Tree Handbook.* Systems and Reliability Research Office of Nuclear Regulatory Research. US Nuclear Regulatory Commission, Washington, DC.

Villemeur, A. (1992). *Reliability, Availability, Maintainability and Safety Assessment.* Vol. 1 and 2. John Wiley & Sons, New York.

deVries, J. & Rodgers, L. (1991). Bridging business boundaries. *The TQM Magazine,* **3**, 335-340.

Vännman, K. (1993). A unified approach to capability indices. Research Report 1993:3, Division of Quality Technology & Statistics, Luleå University, Sweden.

Wadsworth, H.M., Stephens, K.S. & Godfrey, A.B. (1986). *Modern Methods for Quality Control and Improvement.* John Wiley & Sons, New York.

Walton, M. (1986). *The Deming Management Method.* ASQC Quality Press, Milwaukee.

Watson, G.H. (1992). *The Benchmarking Workbook.* Copyright © 1992 by Productivity Press, Inc., PO Box 13390, Portland, OR 97213-0390, (800) 394-6868. Reprinted by permission.

Watson, G.H. (1993). *Strategic Benchmarking.* John Wiley & Sons, New York.

Weber, R.T. & Johnson, R.H. (1993). *Buying and Supplying Quality.* ASQC Quality Press, Milwaukee.

Weibull, W. (1951). A distribution of wide applicability. *Journal of Applied Mechanics,* **18,** 293-297.

Westberg, U. & Klefsjö, B. (1994). TTT-plotting for censored data based on the piecewise exponential estimator. *International Journal of Reliability, Quality & Safety Engineering,* **1,** 1–13.

Wetherill G.B.& Brown, D.W. (1991). *Sampling Inspection and Quality Control.* Second Edition, Chapman & Hall, London.

Wheeler, D.J. (1993). *Understanding Variation. The Key to Managing Chaos.* SPC Press, Knoxville, Tennessee.

Wheeler, D.J. & Chambers, D.S. (1992). *Understanding Statistical Process Control.* Second Edition. SPC Press, Knoxville, Tennessee.

Xie, M. (1991). *Software Reliability Modelling.* World Scientific Publishing Co, Singapore.

Xie, M. & Åkerlund, O. (1989). Applications of software models – possible problems and practical solutions. *Proceedings SRE Symposium 1989 in Stavanger,* Elsevier Applied Science, New York, 158-165.

Western Electric (1956). *Statistical Quality Control Handbook.* Western Electric Corporation, Indianapolis.

Williams, R. & Bertsch, B. (1992). Quality Leadership in Taiwan. Philips International Corporate Quality Bureau, Eindhoven.

Womack, J.P., Jones, D.T. & Roos, D. (1990). *The Machine that Changed the World.* Rawson Associates, Macmillan Publishing Company, New York.

Wöhler, A. (1860). Versuche über die Festigkiet der Eisenbahnwagenachsen. *Zeitschrift für Bauwesen,* **10.** (English summary in *Engineering,* 1867, **4,** 160-161.)

Yoshizawa, T, Akao, Y., Ono, M. & Shino, H. (1993). Recent aspects of QFD in the Japanese software industry. *Quality Engineering,* **5,** 495-504.

Yoshizawa, T. (1993). Quality strategy deployment by means of QFD. *Proceedings EOQ Conference in Helsinki,* vol. 1, 1993, 43-47

Yasuda, Y. (1991). *40 Years, 20 Million Ideas. The Toyota Suggestion System.* Productivity Press, Cambridge, MA.

Zeithaml, V.A., Parasuraman, A. & Berry, L.L. (1990). *Delivering Quality Service.* The Free Press, New York.

Index